ASSISTING CHILDREN WITH SPECIAL NEEDS: AN IRISH PERSPECTIVE

Second Edition

Eilis Flood

Gill Education
Hume Avenue
Park West
Dublin 12
www.gilleducation.ie
Gill Education is an imprint of M.H. Gill and Co.

978 07171 5624 5

Index compiled by Fionbar Lyons
Print origination in Ireland by Carole Lynch
Printed by Printer Trento Srl, Italy

For permission to reproduce photographs, the author and publisher
gratefully acknowledge the following:

© Alamy: 68, 101, 116, 124T, 154, 245, 247, 303, 306; © Corbis: 304; © Dorling
Kindersley/Andy Crawford and Steve Gorton: 50; © Getty Images: 54, 220L; © Jen
Patton: 63, 208; © Science Photo Library: 124B; Courtesy of Nuance Communications,
Inc.: 305; Courtesy of Ontex: 278; Courtesy of Shannon Blaeske: 220R.

The author and publisher have made every effort to trace all copyright holders,
but if any has been inadvertently overlooked we would be pleased to make the necessary
arrangement at the first opportunity.

Contents

Preface

Assisting Children with Special Needs provides a comprehensive yet uncomplicated guide to special needs assisting in Ireland. The book provides information on a range of special needs and associated issues, addressing key elements of good practice within various settings. The book begins by looking at special needs provision in Ireland from a historical and legislative perspective, listing key pieces of Irish legislation related to special needs and their implications. The book details the structures within Irish special needs provision and outlines the role of key personnel such as special needs teachers, assistants and health professionals. Up-to-date information is provided regarding resources, services and facilities available in Ireland to children with special needs.

Acknowledgments

I would like to express my sincere thanks to all who assisted in the production of this book. In particular, I would like to thank, as always, my husband John for his very practical support and my sons Luke and Mark for their understanding.

I would also like to thank my students at Drogheda Institute of Further Education who have used and commented on the first edition of this book and who are so genuinely interested in and passionate about working with children with special needs.

I would like to thank everyone at Gill & Macmillan, especially Marion O'Brien, Catherine Gough, Kristin Jensen and Jen Patton for their support, advice and efficiency.

chapter one

The Context of Special Needs in Ireland

> **CHAPTER OUTLINE**
>
> ▸ Definitions of special need
> ▸ Models of disability
> ▸ History of special needs service provision in Ireland

This book is aimed primarily at students working towards a special needs qualification that will make them more employable as special needs assistants (SNAs) in Irish schools and for those providing respite care for children with special needs in the children's own homes.

DEFINITIONS OF SPECIAL NEED

All children have needs, e.g. physical, safety and security, love and belonging, praise and encouragement. Children with special needs have these same needs together with some additional ones. Special needs can be defined or categorised in many different ways. They are often categorised according to how frequently they occur in the general population, or else according to the area of development affected by the special need.

Classification according to frequency of occurrence

▸ **High incidence special needs:** These are special needs that **occur relatively frequently** in the general population. They tend to be less severe in that the child's overall development is not usually as severely affected by the special need as children with low incidence special needs. Examples of high incidence special needs are borderline general learning disability and dyslexia. Usually children with high incidence special needs do not receive many additional resources, e.g. they are not usually eligible for an SNA, but instead receive additional learning support hours.

▶ **Low incidence special needs:** These are special needs that **occur infrequently** in the general population. They tend to be severe in nature in that the child's overall development is often highly affected by the special need. Examples of low incidence special needs are autism, moderate or severe learning disability, syndromes such as Down's syndrome and physical conditions such as cerebral palsy or muscular dystrophy. In general, children with low incidence special needs require considerable additional resources, such as a special needs assistant, resource teaching hours, speech therapy and physiotherapy and they may be educated outside the mainstream school system.

For the purpose of allocation of resources and services, the Department of Education and Science classifies special needs as follows.

Disability codes

No.	Category of special education need	Incidence
1	Physical disability	Low
2	Hearing impairment	Low
3	Visual impairment	Low
4	Emotional disturbance	Low
5	Severe emotional disturbance	Low
6	Borderline general learning disability	High
7	Mild general learning disability	High
8	Moderate general learning disability	Low
9	Severe/profound general learning disability	Low
10	Autism/autistic spectrum disorders	Low
11	Specific learning disability	High
12	Assessed syndrome	Low
13	Specific speech and language disorder	Low
14	Multiple disabilities	Low

Classification according to the area of development predominately affected by the special need

Physical health and development:

- Epilepsy
- Sickle cell anaemia
- Diabetes
- Asthma
- Dyspraxia (difficulty with motor co-ordination)
- Dysgraphia (difficulty with handwriting)
- Visual impairment
- Disability resulting from accidental injury
- Cystic fibrosis
- Spina bifida
- Hydrocephalus
- Muscular dystrophy
- Cerebral palsy
- HIV and AIDS

Intellectual or cognitive development:

- Borderline general learning disability
- Mild general learning disability
- Moderate general learning disability
- Severe or profound learning disability
- Specific learning disability, e.g. dyscalculia

Language and communication:

- Hearing impairment
- Specific speech and language disorder
- Dyslexia
- Newcomer children whose first language is not English

Emotional and social development:

▹ Emotional problems

▹ Oppositional defiant disorder

▹ Conduct disorder

▹ Attention deficit hyperactivity disorder

Complex conditions and syndromes (affect more than one area of development):

▹ Autistic spectrum disorders

▹ Down's syndrome

▹ Fragile X syndrome

Sometimes children will have multiple special needs, e.g. a child with ADHD may also have dyslexia and oppositional defiant disorder. In addition, children who are exceptionally able are also recognised under the Education Act 1988 as having special needs.

MODELS OF DISABILITY

There are two main models or ways of looking at disability: the **medical model** and the **social model.**

Medical model of disability

As the name suggests, with the medical model of disability, the focus is on the causes and symptoms of the disability and on its treatment. While this model does have its uses and advantages, the person is seen by this model as abnormal and remains so until the condition is cured. Many disabilities have no cure, so this model of disability can often have a negative effect on the person's self-image and self-esteem. With the medical model, the 'problem' is seen to lie with the person with the disability, so for example, a deaf person should learn to lip read because not many people know sign language.

Social model of disability

The social model of disability focuses on the environment in which the disabled person lives. With this model of disability, the environment should be adapted to meet the needs of the disabled person, not the other way around. For example, consider someone who uses a wheelchair. They are perfectly able to enter buildings, cross roads, travel along footpaths and drive if their environment facilitates them to do so with ramps, lifts and hand-operated cars. This model of disability does not label people as abnormal and is therefore much more respectful of people with disabilities.

HISTORY OF SPECIAL NEEDS SERVICE PROVISION IN IRELAND

Swan (2000) described the progression of special needs education in Ireland in three phases: the era of neglect and denial, the era of the special school and the era of integration or inclusion.

Under English rule, the National Education System was established in 1831, making school attendance compulsory for all children between the ages of six and 14. By 1892, children had to attend at least 150 days of school each year (today, the primary school year is 183 days). The government did not consider that the education of children with special needs was necessary in that their needs were seen as purely medical. Many children with special needs lived in hospitals, asylums and county homes. However, some religious-run special schools were established at this time. For example, St Mary's School for Deaf Girls in Cabra, Dublin, was established in 1846 by the Dominican order, St Joseph's School for Deaf Boys in Cabra was established in 1857 by the Christian Brothers and St Joseph's School for the Blind was established by the Carmelite order in 1884 in Drumcondra, Dublin. Children from all over the country boarded in these schools from young ages.

From the foundation of the state in 1919 to the early 1990s, practically all education and care, including the education and care of children with special needs, was carried out by the religious orders in Ireland. As a result, there was very little government policy or legislation regarding special needs provision in Ireland. The situation remained largely the same until the numbers of religious in Ireland began to decline rapidly and many of the schools and institutions formally run by them were taken over by the state. This, together with an increasing awareness among parents, teachers and other professionals of how our special needs provision had fallen badly behind that of other nations, resulted in a relatively rapid change in government policy and the introduction of a number of new important pieces of legislation.

In 1947, St Vincent's Home for Mentally Defective Children (founded in 1926) was recognised by the state as an official school. The establishment of this school, along with other similar schools that followed, reflected the belief at the time that children with special needs should not be educated alongside their peers, as this was considered to be detrimental to the education of 'normal' children and their teachers (Commission of Inquiry into the Reformatory and Industrial School System

1934–1936). Most children with special needs at this time were assessed in what were known as County Clinics. After assessment, options were generally limited to institutional care or some form of basic training. In 1959, the first inspector for special education was established, and throughout the 1960s, 1970s and until the mid-1980s, considerable numbers of new special schools were established throughout the state to cater for children with physical, mental and sensory impairments. This era represented the era of the special school, where it was recognised that children with special needs required education, but not within the mainstream setting. Today there are a total of 107 special schools in Ireland (some schools cater for more than one special need, hence when the numbers listed below are added together they total 129).

- Schools for students with mild general learning disability (30)
- Schools for students with moderate general learning disability (33)
- Schools for students with severe and profound general learning disability (6)
- Schools for students with emotional and behavioural disturbance (10)
- Schools for students with severe emotional and behavioural disturbance (9)
- Schools for students with physical disability (7)
- Hospital schools (6)
- Schools for students with hearing impairment (3)
- Schools for students of Traveller families (3)
- Schools for students with multiple disabilities (1)
- Schools for students with visual impairment (1)
- Schools for students with reading disability (4)
- Schools for students with autism (5)
- Schools for young offenders and disadvantaged students (11)

In the mid-1980s there was a worldwide lobby for the integration of children with special needs into mainstream schools. This lobby began to influence Irish educational policy and a number of classes for children with special needs began to be established within mainstream schools for children with mild learning disabilities or physical disabilities. Special education became part of teacher training courses in the state's teacher training colleges. By 1993, over 2,000 children were being educated in special classes within mainstream schools.

The Report of the Special Education Review Committee (SERC) (1993)

In 1991, the government commissioned a comprehensive review of all special needs provision in Ireland from preschool through to secondary. On foot of this review, the *Report of the Special Education Review Committee* (SERC) was published in 1993 (Department of Education and Science 1993). This report was important for a number of reasons.

- It provided a definition of special needs that included those with severe and profound difficulties through to those who were exceptionally able and it included both physical and mental disabilities.
- It recognised the desire of the majority of parents of children with special needs that they be educated in mainstream schools.
- It recommended that there be a school psychological service linked to the existing school health service. The school psychological service should deal with issues of assessment and assist with planning.
- Integration was to be the most desirable option, with as little segregation as possible for all children, not just those at the milder end of the spectrum.
- It found that segregated special education inhibits the realisation of one of the main goals of education for children with special needs – that of equipping them with the necessary skills to live, socialise and work in their own communities.
- It identified that teacher training was inadequate in the area of special needs provision and that there was a lack of contact between special education and mainstream systems.
- It recommended the establishment of a continuum of educational provision to meet various levels of special educational need. Depending on individual need, children could have:
  - Full-time placement in a mainstream school with additional support
  - Part-time or full-time placement in a special class or school
  - Full-time placement in a residential special school
  - Part-time placement in a Child Education and Development Centre or special school

The 1995 White Paper on education, *Charting our Educational Future* (Department of Education and Science 1995), reiterated the report's findings when it stated 'all students, regardless of their personal circumstances, have a right of access to and participation in the education system, according to their potential and ability'. Other important documents and reports included the 1996 report *A Strategy for Equality* (Commission on the Status of People with Disabilities 2006), which highlighted the lack of co-operation between special and mainstream schools, the lack of support services, transport, resources and equipment and the lack of flexibility within the mainstream curriculum for people with special needs. In 1999, the government published *Ready to Learn* (Department of Education and Science 1999), a White Paper on early childhood education. This report highlighted the importance of early intervention for children with special needs and called upon the government to improve this sector's provision by:

- Giving parents access to early childhood education experts
- Improving the training and skill of early childhood educators
- Increasing the level of provision for preschool children with special needs
- Increasing support for preschools already enrolling children with special needs
- Increasing resources with visiting teacher supports
- Extending the National Educational Psychological Service (NEPS) to the early years sector

There have been a number of legislative changes running alongside and as a result of these White Papers and reports. These will be outlined in chronological order in Chapter 2.

The National Educational Psychological Service was established in September 1999. NEPS was and still is responsible for all educational psychological services for children, with clinical psychological services provided by the Health Service Executive (HSE).

The National Council for Special Education was set up in December 2003. It has overall responsibility for special needs provision in Irish schools, assessing applications for and co-ordinating services throughout the country.

chapter two

Legislation, National and International Policy Relating to Special Needs

CHAPTER OUTLINE

- Current legislation relating to special needs provision in Ireland
- Current national policies relating to special needs provision and the main policy implications
- International policy in relation to children with special needs

CURRENT LEGISLATION RELATING TO SPECIAL NEEDS PROVISION IN IRELAND

The following pieces of legislation will be dealt with in this section because of their relevance to children with special needs. Full copies of any of the Acts below can be downloaded at www.irishstatutebook.ie.

- The Child Care Act 1991 and Children Act 2001
- The Education Act 1998
- The National Disabilities Authority Act 1999
- The Education Welfare Act 2000
- The Equal Status Act 2000 and Amended Equality Acts 2004 and 2011
- Data Protection Acts 1988, 1998 and 2003
- Freedom of Information Acts 1997 and 2003
- The Teaching Council Act 2001
- The Education for Persons with Special Education Needs (EPSEN) Act 2004
- The Disability Act 2005

The Child Care Act 1991 and Children Act 2001

Both these Acts deal with the issue of child protection and are dealt with in full as part of Chapter 13 on child protection (see p. 285–7).

The Education Act 1998

This was the first piece of legislation passed since the foundation of the state that directly outlined the government's rights and legal obligations regarding education. While the Act is a general one encompassing all aspects of education, many parts of it are relevant to special needs and special education.

Firstly, the Act provided the **first legal definition of disability**:

'Disability' means:
(a) the total or partial loss of a person's bodily or mental functions, including the loss of a part of the person's body, or
(b) the presence in the body of organisms causing, or likely to cause, chronic disease or illness, or
(c) the malfunction, malformation or disfigurement of a part of a person's body, or
(d) a condition or malfunction which results in a person learning differently from a person without the condition or malfunction, or
(e) a condition, illness or disease which affects a person's thought processes, perception of reality, emotions or judgement or which results in disturbed behaviour. (Part 1, section 2)

Secondly, the Act provides the **first legal definition of special educational needs**:

'Special educational needs' means the educational needs of students who have a disability and the educational needs of exceptionally able students … (Part 1, section 2)

Thirdly, the Act defines what it means by **support services**:

'Support services' means the services which the Minister provides to students or their parents, schools or centres for education in accordance with section 7 and shall include any or all of the following:
(a) assessment of students;
(b) psychological services;
(c) guidance and counselling services;
(d) technical aid and equipment, including means of access to schools, adaptations to buildings to facilitate access and transport for students with special needs and their families;

(e)   provision for students learning through Irish sign language or other sign language, including interpreting services;

(f)   speech therapy services;

(g)   provision for early childhood, primary, post-primary, adult or continuing education to students with special needs otherwise than in schools or centres for education;

(h)   teacher welfare services;

(i)   transport services;

(j)   library and media services;

(k)   school maintenance services;

(l)   examinations provided for in Part VIII;

(m) curriculum support and staff advisory services; and

(n)   such other services as are specified by this Act or considered appropriate by the Minister. (Part 1, section 2)

Under the Irish Constitution, children have a right to receive free primary education. This Education Act explicitly extends this right to children with special educational needs:

(a)   to give practical effect to the constitutional rights of children, including children who have a disability or who have other special educational needs, as they relate to education;

(c)   to promote equality of access to and participation in education and to promote the means whereby students may benefit from education … (Part 2, section 6, a and c)

The **functions of the Minister for Education** are also defined under the Act. One such function is:

… to ensure subject to provisions of this Act, that there is made available to each person resident in the state, including a person with a disability or who has other special education needs, support services and a level and quality of education appropriate to meeting the needs and abilities of that person. (Part 2, section 7 (1a))

In addition, under the Act, the minister has a responsibility to plan, co-ordinate and fund support services for students who have a disability or other special education needs (see Part 2, section 7 (1a, 2b, 2c)).

In the section dealing with the **functions of a school**, the Act states that a school will:

(a)   ensure that the educational needs of all students, including those with a disability or other special educational needs, are identified and provided for …

Part 3 (section 13 (4, a–e)) of the Act outlines the **role and responsibilities of the school inspectorate** in relation to children with special needs:

(a) in consultation with parents to assess the psychological needs of students in recognised schools and to advise as appropriate those students, their parents and the schools in relation to the educational and psychological development of such students;

(b) to advise recognised schools on policies and strategies for the education of children with special educational needs;

(c) to advise the Minister on any matter relating to the psychological needs of students in recognised schools;

(d) in collaboration with parents and the Principal and teachers in recognised schools, to assist in the creation of a school environment which prevents or limits obstacles to learning which students may experience; and

(e) to advise the Minister on any matter relating to the linguistic needs of deaf students in recognised schools. (Part 9, a)

Part 4, section 15 (2, d and g) of the Act outlines the role and responsibilities of school **boards of management** in relation to children with special needs:

(d) publish, in such manner as the board with the agreement of the patron considers appropriate, the policy of the school concerning admission to and participation in the school, including the policy of the school relating to the expulsion and suspension of students and **admission to and participation by students with disabilities or who have other special educational needs, and ensure that as regards that policy principles of equality and the right of parents to send their children to a school of the parents' choice are respected** and such directions as may be made from time to time by the Minister, having regard to the characteristic spirit of the school and the constitutional rights of all persons concerned, are complied with,

(g) use the resources provided to the school from monies provided by the Oireachtas to make reasonable provision and accommodation for students with a disability or other special educational needs, including, where necessary, alteration of buildings and provision of appropriate equipment.

Under the Education Act, all schools are required to have a **school plan**. School plans need to indicate how the school will deal with issues of equality of access and participation in the school by those with disabilities or other special needs. The plan needs to show how the school intends to deal with the situation if there are barriers to access or participation, e.g. if there are no wheelchair ramps, the school will install them.

The school plan shall state the objectives of the school relating to equality of access to and participation in the school and the measures which the school proposes to take to achieve those objectives, including equality of access to and participation in the school by students with disabilities or who have other special needs. (Part 4, section 21 (2))

The Act also introduces the process of **appeal** for the first time in Part 6, sections 28 and 29. If parents or students (if they are over 18) feel that they have a grievance against a school decision or members of staff within a school, they may appeal decisions against them. If the appeal is upheld, then remedial action must be taken by the school. Section 29 of the Act deals with cases where students are refused enrolment, suspended or expelled from a school. This part of the Act may apply to children with some special needs, e.g. conduct disorder or ADHD, in that they may be refused enrolment, suspended or expelled from schools because of their behaviour. Having a special need could form grounds for appeal. In addition, children with other special needs may be refused enrolment altogether.

Under the Act, the **National Council for Curriculum and Assessment** (NCCA) was established. The main function of the NCCA is curriculum development and review at all levels within the Irish education system. With regards to special needs, the NCCA must:

Advise the Minister on the requirements, as regards curriculum and syllabuses, of students with a disability or other special educational needs … (Part 7, section 41 (f))

Implications of the Act for children with special needs

This Act has wide-ranging implications for children with special needs. The Act recognises the right of children with special needs to participate fully in the life of the school and their right to supports and services to allow them to do so. However, the major limitation with this Act is that all the services for children with special needs mentioned in the Act need only be provided *if* there is sufficient money there to do so. This limits what the government is **legally** required to provide. This limitation is outlined in the section below.

… to provide that, as far as is practicable and having regard to the resources available, there is made available to people resident in the State a level and quality of education appropriate to meeting the needs and abilities of those people … (Part 2, section 6 (b))

In other words, services should be made available provided there are the resources (money) to do so.

The National Disabilities Authority Act 1999

The principal function of the National Disabilities Authority Act 1999 was to establish the National Disability Authority (NDA). Up until this, no one body had overall responsibility for the planning, delivery and inspection of services for people with disabilities in Ireland. The functions of the NDA are detailed in Part 2 of the Act and are as follows:

- Provide policy advice to government and public bodies.
- Undertake, commission and collaborate in disability research and assist in the development of statistical information.
- Advise on standards and guidelines in services to people with disabilities.
- Develop standards and education and promote awareness of universal design.

One major piece of work that has been undertaken by the NDA is the development of *Building for Everyone: A Universal Design Approach*. This series of 10 booklets provides comprehensive best practice guidance on how to design, build and manage buildings and spaces so that they can be readily accessed and used by everyone, regardless of age, size, ability or disability.

The Education Welfare Act 2000

The main purpose of this Act is to help ensure that all children in Ireland, including those with special needs, attend a recognised school or otherwise receive an appropriate education, e.g. home tuition. The Act also resulted in the creation of the **Education Welfare Board** to promote recognition of the importance of education in the lives of children. In reality, the Act has become synonymous with school attendance. Under the Act, the board must appoint Education Welfare Officers to investigate cases of poor and non-attendance at school.

Implications of the Act for children with special needs

The main implications of this Act are for children with special emotional or behavioural needs. Frequently these children are poor school attendees, either because they themselves resist the school environment or because the school restricts their attendance, such as through suspensions, etc.

The Education Welfare Act requires that reasons for poor or non-attendance are investigated and plans put in place to aid improvement. Parents who resist this process can be required to do so by the circuit courts. Some schools have responded to the requirements of the Act by putting very disruptive children on restricted timetables. This way, on the surface school attendance appears to be adequate.

School management often have little choice in this matter in that they have to consider the rights of all children in their care. If resources are not available, e.g. SNAs or small class sizes, to help work with children with special emotional or behavioural needs, these children may have to be removed from the classroom to allow work to continue with the other children present.

The Equal Status Act 2000 and Amended Equality Acts 2004 and 2011

The Equal Status Act 2000 promotes equality of opportunity for all citizens and legal residents of the state and prohibits discrimination on nine different grounds, one of which is disability. Part 2, section 7 deals with the obligations of educational establishments to, where possible, provide admission and access to all courses and facilities for people with disabilities. There are exceptions under the Act if the nature of the student's disability is such that their presence has a serious detrimental effect on the education of other students around them. The Act also requires educational establishments to have provisions in their rules for cases of harassment of students or staff on any of the nine grounds, e.g. a child with a disability being called names because of their disability. The amended Equality Act 2004 makes a number of additions and changes to the Equality Act 2000. Only one change relates to education though and it is in relation to grants. The Act states that the minister is not discriminating on the grounds of equality if an education grant (to a college, university or college of further education) is only paid to nationals who are members of the European Union.

Data Protection Acts 1988, 1998 and 2003 and Freedom of Information Acts 1997, 2003

Both of these Acts and their amended Acts concern personal data held on computer or manual file by organisations, including schools and preschools. In general, personal information must be:

- Obtained and processed fairly
- Kept for a specific purpose, e.g. applying for extra resources for a child with special educational needs (SEN)
- Used only for that specific purpose(s)
- Kept secure and safe
- Kept accurate and up to date
- That the level of information kept is adequate, relevant and not excessive
- Not retained longer than necessary

Generally, under this Act, organisations must give a copy of their personal data to an individual on request.

Under the Freedom of Information Acts 1997, 2003, the person on whom the data is kept is entitled to a copy of that data. At present, this Act does not relate to schools, but copies of data need to be made available on request under the Data Protection Act.

The Teaching Council Act 2001

Under this Act and when it is fully implemented, all practising teachers will eventually have to be members of the Teaching Council. To be a member of the Teaching Council, the person must be suitably qualified and also be considered fit to teach. In terms of special needs provision, in the future, cases may arise whereby parents believe a teacher to be unfit to teach a child with a particular special need. This could mean that there will be an ongoing requirement for practising teachers to keep up to date with best practice in all areas of teaching.

The Education for Persons with Special Educational Needs (EPSEN) Act 2004

This is the most significant piece of legislation relating to special needs in education. While it was meant to be fully implemented by January 2009, recent budgetary cutbacks have delayed this. The Act comes from the standpoint of inclusion. The Act is extensive and covers the following general areas:

- The issue of inclusion with regards to children with special needs in mainstream settings
- Preparation of individual education plans for children with special needs by educational establishments
- Assessment of special needs
- Service provision for children with special educational needs
- Appeals

In relation to inclusion, the Act states that:

> A child with special educational needs shall be educated in an inclusive environment with children who do not have such needs unless the nature or degree of those needs of the child is such that to do so would be inconsistent with:

(a)   the best interests of the child as determined in accordance with any assessment carried out under this Act,

or

(b)   the effective provision of education for children with whom the child is to be educated. (Section 2)

Under section 3 of the Act, if the principal of a school believes that a child with special needs is not making satisfactory progress in the school, they are required to make changes in an attempt to better address the child's needs. Should no progress still be made, then in consultation with the child's parents, the principal must arrange an assessment to be carried out with the child within one month through the National Council for Special Education (NCSE).

After assessment, the NCSE must prepare an **individual education plan (IEP)** for the child. An organiser called a **special educational needs organiser** (SENO) helps co-ordinate the formation of the plan and the school's implementation of it. Depending on the child and their needs, many people may be involved in the formation of the plan – parents, principal, psychologists, speech and language therapists, physiotherapists, child psychiatrists and occupational therapists. There is therefore a crossover between the Departments of Health and Education here.

Should the principal consider that the IEP compiled by the NCSE is unworkable, then through the SENO they can request that a revised plan be compiled. Parents can also appeal plans created for their child if, for example, they feel the plan does not adequately cater for their child's needs – perhaps they feel their child should have an SNA and this was not granted.

Parents of children younger than school-going age who suspect their child may have special needs can arrange for assessment through the Health Service Executive (HSE).

According to the Act (see section 9), an IEP must include information on the following:

(a)   the nature and degree of the child's abilities, skills and talents;

(b)   the nature and degree of the child's special educational needs and how those needs affect his or her educational development;

(c)   the present level of educational performance of the child;

(d)   the special educational needs of the child;

(e)   the special education and related support services to be provided to the child to enable the child to benefit from education and to participate in the life of the school;

(f)   where appropriate, the special education and related services to be provided to the child to enable the child to effectively make the transition from preschool education to primary school education;

(g) where appropriate, the special education and related support services to be provided to the child to enable the child to effectively make the transition from primary school education to post-primary school education; and

(h) the goals which the child is to achieve over a period not exceeding 12 months.

The principal of the school has overall responsibility for implementing the IEP. Under the Act, funds and supports are to be provided by the NCSE. Should a child transfer from one school to another, the principals of both schools should liaise with each other so that the plan is smoothly handed over.

Designation of school is an issue dealt with under section 10 of the Act. The NCSE is responsible for ensuring that a child is designated to a suitable school in consultation with their parents or guardians. Boards of management of a school can appeal a decision to send a particular child to their school if they feel they do not have adequate resources to cater for the needs of that child. Appeals are made to a special **Appeals Board**. The onus is on the school's board of management to prove lack of resources. Appeals must be dismissed or allowed within two months of being filed. If allowed, then the NCSE must find another, more suitable school for the child.

A child's IEP must be reviewed each year by the principal (with inputs from relevant staff members and parents) and the findings of the review reported to parents and the SENO connected with the child's case. The purpose of the review is to evaluate whether the resources and services recommended in the plan have been put in place and whether or not the plan is working, i.e. are the goals of the plan being achieved? On receiving the report, if the SENO believes that the plan is not working, he or she may call together the child's team or part of their team and amend the plan. Parents or guardians can request a review if they believe the goals of their child's plan are not being achieved. This can only be done if a review has not taken place in the previous six months and the request can be denied by the principal if they believe they have good reason. Parents or guardians can appeal this decision to the Appeals Board, where a decision will be made within one month.

This Act involves co-operation between three different government departments – Education and Science, Health and Children, and Finance. Each department has their own functions under the Act. In summary:

- **Education and Science:** Assess children with special needs and co-ordinate, compile and implement their IEPs. Liaise with parents or guardians and others involved in the child's case. Where applicable, provide SNAs, resource and learning support teachers and psychologists. Also, train class teachers in special needs education.

- **Health and Children:** Assess, co-ordinate, compile and implement plans for children under school-going age and provide services to children in schools, such as speech and language therapy, occupational therapy, physiotherapy and child psychiatry.
- **Finance:** Is responsible for providing funding for all of the above.

The Disability Act 2005

The Disability Act 2005 places a statutory obligation on public service providers to support access to services and facilities for people with disabilities. Under the Act, the following issues are dealt with in relation to people with disabilities:

- Assessment of health and educational needs
- Creation of individual service statements outlining the services they should have access to
- Independent complaints and appeals procedures
- Access to public buildings and public service employment
- Restrictions on genetic testing
- Broadcasting

Under the Act, the term 'disability' means 'a substantial restriction in the capacity of a person to carry out a profession, business or occupation in the State or to participate in social or cultural life in the State by reason of an enduring physical, sensory, mental health or intellectual impairment'. Substantial restriction means a restriction that is permanent (or likely to be permanent), which results in significant difficulty in communication, learning or mobility and which means that the person has a need for services to be provided on a continuous basis.

Assessment reports

A person can apply for an independent assessment of their needs if they think that they have a disability. The reason for the assessment is to establish the person's health and educational needs and to assess the services required to meet those needs. Assessment officers, appointed by the HSE, carry out the assessments.

Once this has been done, the person will receive an assessment report. This report will indicate:

- If the person has a disability
- The nature and extent of the disability

▶ The health and educational needs arising from the disability

▶ The services considered appropriate to meet those needs and the timescale ideally required for their delivery

▶ When a review of the assessment should be undertaken

It is important to note that the educational needs of a child can be assessed under the Disability Act 2005 or the Education for Persons with Special Educational Needs Act 2004. If, under the Disability Act, a special educational need is identified for a child, then that aspect of the assessment will be referred to the National Council for Special Education or to the principal of their school.

Service statements

If a person is found to have a need for disability-related services, they will then be given a service statement drawn up by an HSE liaison officer. The service statement will indicate the health and educational services that can be provided, taking account of:

▶ The assessment report

▶ Eligibility criteria for services

▶ Relevant standards and codes of practice

▶ The practicability of providing the service

▶ The financial resources available

Unlike the assessment report, the service statement takes cost into account. In addition, the service statement does not deal with the educational needs of children, as these are dealt with under the Education for Persons with Special Educational Needs Act 2004 (see above). Once the service statement is drawn up, the delivery of services is arranged for the individual.

A complaint and/or an appeal can be taken against findings and decisions made in relation to assessment and service reports.

Access to public buildings

From 31 December 2005, an obligation was placed by this Act on all pubic bodies to make their buildings and services accessible to people with disabilities. All buildings must be in compliance with part M of the Building Regulations by 31 December 2015. The exception lies in cases where adaptations or modifications to buildings would either change the nature of the business or constitute a risk to the health, safety or welfare of any person.

Access to public services

From 31 December 2005, an obligation was placed on all public bodies to ensure that services provided to them by third parties, including the supply of goods, are accessible to people with disabilities. The exception lies in cases where such access would not be practicable, would not be justified by the cost involved or would cause unreasonable delay in making goods and services available to other people.

Access to heritage sites

From 31 December 2007, an obligation was placed on public bodies to ensure that people with disabilities will be able to visit heritage sites easily and with dignity. The exception lies in cases where adaptations or modifications to sites would have an adverse effect on the site.

Complaints

A person may make a complaint to the public body if they consider that a public building or goods and services are not accessible.

Centre for Excellence in Universal Design

The Disability Act also deals with the extension of the NDA Act 1999 to set up an authority within the National Disability Authority (NDA), to be known as the Centre for Excellence in Universal Design. This centre will promote standards and principles of universal design in the education and training of designers and also promote public awareness of universal design principles.

Sectorial plans

A number of different government departments must produce sectorial plans. These plans basically outline how the department intends to further improve accessibility within their department.

Genetic testing restrictions

The Act states that people may not process genetic data in relation to employment, insurance policies (including life assurance), health insurance, occupational or other retirement annuities and mortgages.

Public service employment

An obligation will be placed on all public bodies to promote and support the employment of people with disabilities (with the exception of the gardaí, defence forces or prison officers). Public bodies must ensure that at least 3 per cent of their workforce are people with disabilities.

Broadcasting

The Broadcasting Commission of Ireland may require that broadcasters promote the enjoyment of programmes for people who are deaf, hearing impaired, blind or partially sighted, e.g. sign language, subtitles.

CURRENT NATIONAL POLICIES RELATING TO SPECIAL NEEDS PROVISION AND THE MAIN POLICY IMPLICATIONS

When legislation such as the EPSEN Act is passed into law, the Department of Education (like other departments) issues related **circulars** instructing staff on how to implement various parts of the Act. These circulars represent official department policy on particular issues. This section gives an account of the circulars related to special needs provision and which therefore highlight current national policy.

In general, government policy in relation to special education has changed over the years from denial and exclusion, to segregation, to finally one of inclusion. While this process is far from complete, good progress has certainly been made in the past 10 to 15 years.

One of the most important government initiatives in the area of special education services was announced by the then Minister of Education and Science, Micheál Martin, on 5 November 1998. For the first time, the Irish government recognised that children with special needs have an **automatic entitlement** to the special services and supports needed for them to be able to properly avail of an education.

While launching the report in 1998, Minister Martin said, 'For too long, the needs of many children with disabilities, particularly those in smaller groups or in isolated settings, have been supported in a reactive and entirely unsatisfactory manner. For too long parents have had to campaign tirelessly to give their children the chance to participate in and benefit from education.'

The key measures of this initiative included:

- The introduction of a formalised system of **special teaching support** for all children attending schools on a fully integrated basis who have been assessed as having special educational needs (**resource teaching hours**).

- The introduction of a formalised system of **child care support** for all children with special needs, including those in special schools, special classes and ordinary schools, who have been assessed as requiring such support (**special needs assistant**).

- Formal recognition of the distinct educational needs of all children with **autism** whose condition so requires the introduction of a **special pupil–teacher ratio of 6:1** for such children, together with an automatic entitlement to child care support.

- Children will be assessed and catered for on an individual basis. Resources and services provided will be **based on the needs of the child as an individual, rather on the ability of the system to provide for those needs**.

After the announcement of this initiative, a number of Department of Education circulars were issued to schools explaining how to implement the initiative on the ground. The main circulars related to this initiative are outlined below.

> A complete list of Department of Education circulars relating to special needs is available to download from the Special Education Support Service website (www.sess.ie; look under Documents and Publications). A list of them (without explanation) is also given in Appendix 1 on www.gillmacmillan.ie/assisting childrenwithspecialneeds.

All Department of Education circulars, including those relating to children with special needs, are available to download from www.education.ie (click on Circulars and Forms).

Circular M08/99

This circular deals with resource teaching in primary schools. It outlines the role of the resource teacher and how a school can apply for resource teaching hours for a student with special educational needs. The circular also lists the criteria used to determine whether or not a student has a particular education condition. See Appendix 2 on www.gillmacmillan.ie/assistingchildrenwithspecialneeds for a copy of the circular.

Circular SPED08/02

This was a second circular relating to resource teachers. This circular made some downward adjustments to the pupil–teacher ratios for special classes as well as some adjustments to the process of applying for resource teaching hours. This circular also outlined the number of resource hours allocated per pupil depending on the nature of their special need. This section of the circular is new and is therefore included in Appendix 3 on www.gillmacmillan.ie/assistingchildrenwithspecialneeds.

Circular SPED24/03

This circular deals with the allocation of resources for students with special educational needs. It outlines procedures for the application and appointment of **special needs assistants** and where their appointment fits in with the department's **three-staged approach to provision**. The circular points out that the department is considering taking a different approach to employing SNAs. Instead of SNAs being appointed to a particular pupil, there would be a weighted system of allocation for resource teachers and SNAs. In other words, resource teachers and SNAs would be employed to provide special needs support generally to children requiring it within the school as opposed to their employment being tied to specific pupils. It was believed that this system would cut down on the costs of administrating the scheme. However, as of 2013, this system is not currently operating and resource teachers and SNAs are still employed in accordance with the first system of allocation to individual pupils (see Appendix 7, circular SPED07/02, on www. gillmacmillan.ie/assistingchildrenwithspecialneeds).

Three-stage approach to special education provision

Stage one
If a class teacher or a parent or guardian has concerns regarding a child's academic, physical, social, behavioural or emotional development, the class teacher should first administer a screening test. Screening measures include checklists for younger children and standardised tests, e.g. Drumcondra (reading and mathematics), Micra-T (reading attainment) or Sigma-T (mathematic attainment) for older children. Behavioural and social checklists can be used for all age groups if these are the areas causing concern. The class teacher should then draw up a short, simple behaviour or learning plan (whatever is relevant) for extra help. This plan is worked through in the normal classroom setting. The plan is reviewed by the class teacher and the child's parents or guardians. If there is no progress after two terms, then the child progresses to stage two.

At stage one, the teacher has access to their local area psychologist for advice and guidance on formulating the plan and may also have access to a home/school liaison teacher.

Stage two

With parental permission, the child is referred by the class teacher to the learning support teacher for further diagnostic testing (in the past, these teachers were called remedial teachers). If these tests indicate that the child would benefit from extra tuition, then this will be arranged. A learning plan will then be drawn up for the child. If no progress is being made after one school term, the child may progress to stage three.

At stage two, learning support is the principal service offered to children experiencing difficulties in English and mathematics. Generally, learning support is offered to children from first class and up who score at or below the 12th percentile on standardised, norm-referenced tests. At this stage, class teachers and learning support teachers have access to their local area psychologist.

Stage three

At stage three, the school formally requests a consultation with and, where appropriate, an assessment of need from a specialist from outside the school in respect of a child with learning difficulties and mild/moderate behavioural problems who has failed to make progress after supplementary teaching or a behavioural programme and of children with serious emotional disturbance and/or behavioural problems. Such specialist advice may be sought from psychologists, paediatricians, speech and language therapists, audiologists, etc.

In consultation with the relevant specialist(s), the learning support teacher, resource teacher (if available) and class teacher should then draw up a learning plan that includes the identification of any additional available resources that are considered necessary in order to implement the plan. The parents should be fully consulted throughout this process. This plan should be the subject of regular reviews, leading to revisions of the learning plan and referral for specialist review as necessary.

Supports available for stage three

At stage three, the school will generally request a comprehensive assessment to be carried out by the National Educational Psychological Service or, where this is not yet available, a private psychologist approved by the Scheme for Commissioning Psychological Assessments. On foot of this assessment, further supports may be applied for, e.g. a special needs assistant.

Circular SPED07/02

This circular deals with the recruitment and role of special needs assistants. It will be dealt with comprehensively in Chapter 15 and Appendix 7 on www. gillmacmillan.ie/assistingchildrenwithspecialneeds.

Circular M14/05

This circular deals with the scheme of grants towards the purchase of equipment for pupils with a disability. For details of this circular, see Chapter 11, p. 256.

Circular 0015/09

This circular is the most up to date (as of 2013) in relation to meeting the needs of pupils learning English as an additional language (EAL). This circular replaces 53/07. The circular outlines the department's overall policy in relation to the creation of an inclusive environment. It then outlines the role of the EAL support teacher and outlines how schools should calculate their requirements for EAL support teachers.

Circulars 0007/09 and 0005/09

Circulars similar to these are issued every year to schools. They deal with teacher-in-service courses for qualified teaches wishing to upskill in the area of special needs. This demonstrates the department's ongoing commitment to keeping staff up to date in this area.

Circular 0075/2008

This circular deals with home tuition for children with special needs. It outlines the purpose of the scheme, the criteria for eligibility under the terms of the scheme, how hours are allocated under the scheme and who is eligible to tutor on this scheme.

INTERNATIONAL POLICY IN RELATION TO CHILDREN WITH SPECIAL NEEDS

The practice of including students with special educational needs in mainstream schools is now well-established international policy. Four recent examples of how there has been a movement towards inclusion are illustrated and detailed below.

UN Convention on the Rights of the Child

The United Nations Convention on the Rights of the Child (UNCRC) is an inter-nationally binding agreement on the rights of children adopted by the UN General Assembly in 1989. A child is defined in the UNCRC as a person under the age of 18 years. Ireland signed the convention on 30 September 1990 and ratified it on

28 September 1992. By ratifying the convention, the Irish state committed itself to the promotion, protection and fulfilment of children's rights as outlined by the convention.

The convention incorporates children's:

- **Civil and political rights** (e.g. their treatment under the law)
- **Social, economic and cultural rights** (e.g. an adequate standard of living)
- **Protection rights** (e.g. from abuse and exploitation)

The UNCRC sets out children's rights in **54 articles**. Firstly, the convention has a number of **guiding principles** and it is also divided into four further core principles: **survival, development, protection and participation**.

One of the most important guiding principles for children with special needs is that of **non-discrimination (Article 2)**. The convention applies to all children, whatever their race, religion or abilities, whatever their beliefs are and whatever type of family they come from. It doesn't matter where they live, what language they speak, whether they are male or female, what their culture is, whether they have a disability or whether they are rich or poor. No child should be treated unfairly on any ground.

Other articles also have particular importance, especially **Article 23 (children with disabilities)**. Children with a disability of any kind have the right to enjoy a full life and special care and support as well as the other rights set forth in the convention. The child has a right to access to education, training, health care services, rehabilitation services, preparation for employment and recreation opportunities in a manner conducive to the child achieving the fullest possible social integration and individual development, including his or her cultural and spiritual development.

Salamanca Statement and Framework for Action on Special Needs Education (1994)

The Salamanca Statement and Framework for Action on Special Needs Education was agreed by 91 countries (including Ireland) at the UNESCO world conference held in Salamanca, Spain, in June 1994.

The Salamanca Statement begins with a commitment to education for all and with a declaration of the necessity and urgency of providing access to mainstream schools to students with special needs, whether children, young people or adults:

Regular schools with this inclusive orientation are the most effective means of combating discriminatory attitudes, creating welcoming communities, building an inclusive society and achieving education for all. (UNESCO 1994, section 2)

The fundamental principle of the Salamanca Statement and Framework for Action on Special Needs Education is that children should learn together where possible and that ordinary schools should accommodate all students regardless of their physical, intellectual, social, emotional, linguistic or other conditions.

Council of Europe Political Declaration (2003) and Action Plan (2006)

At the second European conference of ministers with responsibility for policy-making for people with disabilities, held in Malaga, Spain, in 2003, ministers agreed on the principles that should inform future policy development and service provision. The ministers agreed that education is a basic instrument of social integration for people with disabilities and that every effort should be made to give opportunities to children with disabilities to attend mainstream school if this is in the best interests of the individual child. The principle of inclusion and full participation in mainstream schooling was seen as paramount in facilitating the transition for children and young adults with disabilities from education into higher education and employment (Council of Europe 2003).

Ministers met again in 2006 to form an action plan to be implemented by Member States before the end of 2015. The action plan sets out aims, objectives and specific actions for the authorities in Member States to carry out in order to allow inclusion to happen. The report is extensive, so only a small number of relevant actions are mentioned here:

- Unified education system
- Early and appropriate interventions for children with SENs
- IEPs to be closely monitored and evaluated
- Relevant supports available
- Training of teachers and other professionals in special needs education
- All necessary materials, aids and equipment should be made available
- Syllabus should relate to people with special needs
- Disability awareness education is important for non-disabled people
- Parents should be seen and treated as partners
- Guidance towards employment should be given
- Supported employment should be available

- Disincentives to work should be removed
- Barrier-free built environment
- Transport needs to be made accessible, whether public or private
- Health services should be equitable and available to all (Council of Europe 2006)

United Nations International Convention on the Rights of Persons with Disabilities (2006)

The report on the United Nations International Convention on the Rights of Persons with Disabilities (United Nations 2006) in New York contains a total of 50 articles related to the rights of people with disabilities. The articles deal with all aspects of life, including physical accessibility, justice, personal mobility, education, health, rehabilitation, work and employment, social protection and cultural life and recreation. Article 24, on education, states that persons with disabilities have the right to:

- Inclusive education at all levels
- Reach their full potential
- Develop their personality, talents and creativity, as well as their mental and physical abilities, to their fullest potential
- Reasonable accommodations within the system
- Required supports and services
- Use other forms of communication, e.g. sign and Braille
- Access general tertiary education, vocational training, adult education and lifelong learning

For a complete copy of Article 24, see Appendix 4 on www.gillmacmillan.ie/ assistingchildrenwithspecialneeds.

chapter three

Structures within Irish Special Education

THE NATIONAL COUNCIL FOR SPECIAL EDUCATION (NCSE)

The National Council for Special Education was set up to improve the delivery of education services to persons with special educational needs arising from disabilities. It was first established as an independent statutory body by order of the Minister for Education and Science in December 2003. However, it was not until 1 October 2005 that the council was formally established under the Education for Persons with Special Educational Needs (EPSEN) Act 2004 and its general and specific functions were made clear.

Under section 20 of the EPSEN Act, the functions of the council are as follows.

> Plan and co-ordinate the provision of education and support services to children with special educational needs.

> Disseminate information on best practice concerning the education of children with special educational needs.

> Provide information to parents in relation to the entitlements of children with special educational needs.

- Assess and review the resources required by children with special educational needs.
- Ensure that the progress of students with special educational needs is monitored and reviewed.
- Review education provision for adults with disabilities.
- Advise educational institutions on best practice.
- Consult with voluntary bodies.
- Advise the Minister for Education and Science on matters relating to special education.
- Conduct research and publish findings.
- Carry out assessments and compile individual education plans (IEPs) in relation to children with low incidence special needs.
- Publish operational guidelines annually for both primary and post-primary schools in relation to processing Applications for Resources for Pupils with Special Educational Needs (these can be downloaded from their website at www. ncse.ie).

In general, as far as schools are concerned, the NCSE processes and allocates supports for children with low incidence special needs. Details of this are set out in DES circular SPED01/05, which can be downloaded from www.education.ie.

SPECIAL EDUCATIONAL NEEDS ORGANISER (SENO)

Special educational needs organisers (SENOs), of which there are approximately 80 nationwide, are appointed by the NCSE to provide a link between children with special needs, their parents and teachers and the services they require. Each geographical area is allocated a SENO and a list of them is available from the NCSE website. SENOs work with teachers and parents to identify the needs of children with special needs and decide on the level of resources required to provide them with an appropriate education service.

SENOs also link in with services provided by the Health Service Executive (HSE), thus facilitating the inclusion of the child within the school system. Most importantly, they keep parents informed of what decisions are being made on their child's behalf.

THE NATIONAL EDUCATIONAL PSYCHOLOGICAL SERVICE (NEPS)

The National Educational Psychological Service (NEPS) was established in 1999 under the Department of Education and Science to provide an educational psychological service to primary and post-primary schools in Ireland. Clinical psychological services are provided by the HSE.

Psychologists employed by NEPS are located in 10 regions throughout the country. They work directly with a number of schools, and their work includes the following:

▷ Engaging in individual casework with children and young people

▷ Providing a consultation service for teachers and parents

▷ Participating in school-based projects relevant to educational psychology

▷ Promoting mental health in schools

Scheme for Commissioning Psychological Assessments (SCPA)

Not all schools have access to a NEPS psychologist, so a panel of private psychologists was drawn up by NEPS to temporarily fill this gap in provision. People on this panel are not directly employed by NEPS but have been deemed qualified by them. Under this scheme, schools can privately employ the services of a psychologist on the SCPA panel. Usually schools do this if they require an educational psychologist's report quickly in order to secure services and resources for a child with special needs in their care and cannot obtain the services of a NEPS psychologist.

STATE EXAMINATIONS COMMISSION (SEC)

The State Examinations Commission (SEC) is responsible for the development, assessment, accreditation and certification of the second-level examinations of the Irish state: the Junior Certificate and the Leaving Certificate. The SEC also facilitates applications for **'reasonable accommodations'** for children with special needs sitting these examinations. The purpose of these accommodations is to remove the impact of the child's special need on their performance in the examinations but without giving him or her an unfair advantage over those not receiving such accommodations. The fact that reasonable accommodation has been granted will be recorded on the child's certificate, but not the reasons for the accommodation.

Exemptions for examination components

If a candidate's special need is such that it is not possible for him or her to participate in a particular mode of assessment – for example, the aural element of certain examinations may not be appropriate for a candidate with a severe hearing impairment – then the candidate will not have to take this part of the assessment and their mark will be calculated on the parts that they were able to complete.

Written examinations

If a candidate has difficulty with the written component of an examination as a result of a specific learning disability, a range of reasonable accommodations are available, including the following.

- Arrangements to have question papers read to the candidate. The questions may be read as often as the candidate requires. No elaboration or explanation may be given.
- Modified question papers may be supplied substituting alternative questions for those that refer to visual material such as diagrams, photographs and maps.
- Braille translations of question papers may be provided, following any necessary modification.
- Question papers may be provided in enlarged print.
- Candidates may be permitted to record their answers on a tape recorder, typewriter or word processor.
- In the case of Design and Communication or Technical Graphics examinations, candidates may be allowed to use aids such as drafting machines, drawing boards and smaller drawing sheets.
- Answers may be dictated to a person acting as a scribe rather than to a tape recorder. This arrangement may be approved where the candidate's speech would be extremely difficult to interpret on tape or where a tape recording would not meet the particular requirements of the examination, e.g. making calculations in such subjects as Maths and Accounting.
- Ten minutes extra time per scheduled hour of each question paper may be allowed where the candidate needs the help of a scribe or would otherwise be unable to make adequate use of the mechanical aids provided for recording the answers or is visually impaired.
- If a candidate is using a reader, scribe or their answers are being recorded, then he or she will usually sit their examination in an individual exam centre, e.g. an office, and not in the main examination hall.

Oral and aural examinations

In the case of oral examinations, school authorities are requested to liaise with examiners with regard to candidates who have special needs. The arrangements for aural (listening) examinations vary according to degree of deafness and are as follows.

▶ The candidate may remain in the main centre but sit close to the tape recorder.

▶ The candidate may remain in the main centre and be allowed to use a personal stereo player with a personal induction loop. An additional tape of the questions will be provided in such circumstances.

▶ The candidate may be allowed to sit in a separate room and listen to a tape recorder either with or without headphones.

Schools themselves

Schools have the authority to make a number of specified arrangements to facilitate examination candidates with special needs without requesting advance permission from the Commission. The specified arrangements are:

▶ Grant breaks or rest periods in each examination session that are warranted by the physical or medical condition of the candidate. Under this type of arrangement, the time taken for rest or as a break may be compensated for at the close of each examination period, up to a maximum of 20 minutes.

▶ Allow candidates to take medicine, food or drinks into the examination centre where this is required for medical reasons.

▶ Allow the candidate to move within the centre.

▶ Allow the use of a special desk or chair in the classroom.

▶ Allow the use of low vision aids as normally used in the classroom.

▶ Ensure that a candidate with a hearing impairment is positioned close to the superintendent.

Applications for reasonable accommodations are made through the school to the State Examinations Commission, Cornamaddy, Athlone, Co. Westmeath. If a candidate is not being educated in a school or centre of education, e.g. they are being home schooled, then they apply directly to the SEC.

THE SPECIAL EDUCATION SUPPORT SERVICE (SESS)

The role of the Special Education Support Service (SESS) is to enhance and improve the quality of learning and teaching in relation to special educational provision. Under the remit of the Teacher Education Section (TES) of the Department of Education and Skills, SESS provides information and training for school personnel working with students with special educational needs in mainstream primary and post-primary schools, special schools and special classes. SESS provides courses both online and face to face to school personnel together with an online library and other access to other publications and resources, e.g. PowerPoint presentations on important topics.

THE NATIONAL COUNCIL FOR CURRICULUM AND ASSESSMENT (NCCA)

The NCCA was established on a statutory basis in 2001. Its primary function is to advise the Minister for Education and Skills on issues related to curriculum and assessment from early childhood to the end of second level. For example, the NCCA is the body responsible for the development of the new Junior Certificate set to be rolled out in September 2014.

SCHOOL STAFF

The school principal

The school principal has huge responsibility under the EPSEN Act 2004 in the area of special needs. He or she must liaise with parents, class teachers, SENOs and psychologists involved in the child's case. The principal (or their representative) is involved in a child's assessment and the subsequent formation and review of their IEP.

The class teacher

The policy of the Department of Education and Science is that the class teacher has overall responsibility for the education of all children, including those with special needs. In the past, if a child with a special need relating to maths and English was receiving help (what was then called remedial teaching), the class teacher often left teaching maths and English to the remedial teacher, giving the child something else to do if they were in the room when the rest of the class was doing English or maths. Nowadays, children with special needs should be integrated into all aspects of school life and learning support and resource hours should only be considered a source of additional help. In the department's three-stage approach to special needs education (see Chapter 2), the class teacher is the first port of call for concerned parents. During stage one, the class teacher carries out screening tests with the child and forms a plan for him or her. If this plan does not work, it is only then that the class teacher looks outside of his or her classroom for additional help.

SPECIAL EDUCATION TEACHERS

There are a number of other qualified teachers within the system that may be available in a school to support the class teacher in providing services to children with special needs. Nationally, between both primary and post-primary there are approximately 9,000 of these teachers. Teachers classified under the heading of special education teachers include:

- Learning support teacher
- Special education resource teacher
- Visiting teacher service (for visually or hearing impaired children or for Travellers)
- Language support teacher
- Support teacher

Learning support teacher

In the past, these teachers were called remedial teachers. They work in a school on a full- or part-time basis depending on the needs of the school. Learning support teachers mainly work with children who have academic weaknesses (formerly called slow learners) but no special education need. They also provide educational support for some children with special needs, particularly those with dyslexia or borderline mild general disability, if their needs are not great enough to warrant resource teaching. Generally, students whose maths or reading and spelling falls below the 12th percentile but above the 2nd percentile are entitled to help from the learning support teacher (although this varies between schools).

The learning support teacher, together with the classroom teacher and parents, identifies children who are experiencing difficulties, particularly with literacy and maths, and develops an individual intervention plan (or IEP) for each child. Learning support teachers either provide support on a one-to-one basis or in small groups outside of the classroom setting, though in recent times they also offer children learning support within the classroom itself so as to minimise the disadvantages of withdrawal from the classroom. In fact, it is now government policy that learning support is offered as a mixture of individual or small group work outside the classroom and support interventions inside the classroom as well.

Levels of learning support vary from school to school and from child to child, but in general, approximately three half-hour sessions per week is usual. In Ireland, while many learning support teachers do have extra training, they do not have to have any additional qualifications beyond their basic teacher training qualification. This means that the quality of learning support offered in schools can vary from one school to another.

Learning support teachers should formulate weekly plans for the children attending them. These plans should be closely monitored and evaluated for effectiveness. The Department of Education and Skills recommends that the child's progress should be subject to an in-depth review every term (approximately every 12 weeks) and changes made if necessary, as the child may need no further support.

Special education resource teacher

The job of a resource teacher is to provide educational support to those children who have special educational needs as defined by the Department of Education and Skills (see Chapter 1). A big difference between learning support and resource teaching is the amount of time allocated to the child. Children typically get one and a half hours of learning support per week, whereas a child entitled to resource hours could get considerably more, as outlined in Appendix 2 and 3 (how resource hours are allocated; see www.gillmacmillan.ie/assistingchildrenwithspecialneeds).

Like learning support teachers, resource teachers do not need any special qualifications other than their basic teacher training. This is seen as a flaw in the system and has occurred to some extent as a result of the sudden increase in the numbers of resource teachers resulting from the EPSEN Act 2004. Because numbers are small, many resource teaching posts are not full-time posts and therefore are not attractive to the most highly qualified teachers. However, there is a growing number of special education courses being offered by the universities and colleges of education to address this issue.

Most resource teachers work in the primary sector, but there are significant numbers working in post-primary schools as well. As with learning support, resource teaching should not take place exclusively outside the classroom (withdrawal). Instead, the resource teacher should provide support for the child with special needs while they are carrying out their normal daily activities in the classroom setting.

As of 2013, there were 9,950 learning support and resource teaching posts in Irish schools.

Visiting teacher service

There are three main categories of visiting teacher currently working in the Irish system: visiting teachers for the visually impaired, visiting teachers for the hearing impaired and visiting teachers for Travellers. There are not many visiting teachers and they are generally spread between a large number of schools.

Visiting teachers for the visually and hearing impaired (currently there are 14 nationally), while they may provide some direct instruction to visually or hearing impaired children, act more as an advisor to the class teacher on how best to accommodate the visually or hearing-impaired child.

Visiting teachers for Travellers generally act as a link between the school and the child's home. Traditionally, school attendance and attainment rates among Traveller children have been extremely poor. The visiting teacher tries to encourage school attendance and participation by working towards removing barriers to attendance and participation in school life.

Language support teacher

These are relatively new posts created in response to the increasing number of children in schools immigrating to Ireland from countries where the first language is not English. The language support teacher works with these children to help them with English language skills and generally to adapt to school life and the Irish education system (see also Chapter 11).

Support teacher

There is a small number of support teachers working within the Irish education system (fewer than 50). Most are working in the greater Dublin area in schools serving economically and socially disadvantaged communities. Support teachers, formerly called teaching counsellors, work with children who have behavioural problems that are impacting on their ability to learn effectively or the ability of the other children in their class to learn effectively because of their behaviour. Children who are having difficulty controlling their behaviour in class are referred to the support teacher. He or she works with them individually or in small groups, often with their families and their class teacher, to develop anger management and behavioural control strategies.

SPECIAL NEEDS ASSISTANTS

The role of the special needs assistant is dealt with more comprehensively in Chapter 15.

Special needs assistants (SNAs) are employed specifically to assist in the *care* of pupils with disabilities in an educational context. They may be appointed to a special or mainstream school to assist the school in making suitable provision for a pupil or pupils with special care needs arising from a disability. As of 2013, there are approximately 10,000 SNAs working in the country's 3,900 schools.

The allocation of SNA support may be made on a full- or part-time basis, e.g. an hour or more per day, and may be shared by named pupils for whom such support has been allocated. Applications for an SNA must be made to the National Council for Special Education through the local SENO. The SNA will generally not be allocated for general learning disabilities, but more so for physical disabilities and for disabilities resulting in severe emotional or behavioural problems.

While many SNAs do hold additional qualifications, e.g. QQI Level 5 or more, the Department of Education requirements are that SNAs have a minimum of three grade Ds in Junior Certificate or equivalent – QQI Level 3.

chapter four

Special Needs Affecting Physical Health and Development

EPILEPSY

Prevalence

Epilepsy is one of the most common neurological conditions (i.e. affecting the brain), whereby there is a tendency to have recurring seizures as a result of abnormal electrical activity in the brain. According to the Irish Epilepsy Association, epilepsy affects approximately one in every 200 children in Ireland.

Causes

While no cause can be determined for about half to three-quarters of the cases of epilepsy, the following factors are thought to cause epilepsy in some cases.

Brain chemistry

Chemicals called neurotransmitters transmit, or carry, electrical messages along the nerve cells (neurons) of the brain. Someone with epilepsy may have a neurotransmitter imbalance. Researchers believe that some people with epilepsy have too many neurotransmitters that increase impulse transmission (excitatory neurotransmitters) and that others have too few neurotransmitters that reduce transmission (inhibitory neurotransmitters).

Gamma-aminobutyric acid (GABA) is a neurotransmitter that slows electrical transmission between the nerve cells or neurons in the brain. Low levels of GABA in the body have been linked to epilepsy and an increased risk of **seizure**. A number of the drugs used to treat epilepsy stimulate the production of GABA.

Epilepsy may also be caused by changes in brain cells called glial cells. Glial cells help regulate neurotransmission in the brain (brain activity). If glial cells are damaged or defective, then abnormal brain transmissions can result in seizures.

Abnormal brain chemistry can be inherited and can be caused by an injury or disease.

Hereditary causes

Many types of epilepsy tend to run in families, and some have been traced to an abnormality in a specific gene. These genetic abnormalities can cause subtle changes in the way the body processes calcium, potassium, sodium and other body chemicals.

People who have progressive myoclonus epilepsy are missing a gene that helps break down protein. Those with a severe form of epilepsy called Lafora's disease are missing a gene that helps break down carbohydrates.

Hereditary factors are not always a direct cause of epilepsy, but they may influence the disease indirectly. Genes can affect the way people process drugs or can cause areas of malformed neurons in the brain.

Other disorders

Epilepsy can be triggered by brain damage caused by other disorders. Epilepsy can sometimes be stopped by treating these underlying disorders. In other cases, epileptic seizures will continue even after the underlying cause is treated.

Whether or not the seizures can be stopped depends on the type of disorder, the part of the brain that is affected and how much damage has been done. Disorders that may trigger epilepsy include the following:

- Brain tumours, alcoholism and Alzheimer's disease can cause epilepsy because they alter the normal workings of the brain.
- Stroke, heart attacks and other conditions that affect the blood supply to the brain (cerebrovascular diseases) can cause epilepsy by depriving the brain of oxygen. About a third of all new cases of epilepsy that develop in older people are caused by cerebrovascular diseases.
- Infectious diseases such as meningitis, viral encephalitis and AIDS can cause epilepsy.
- Cerebral palsy, autism and a number of other developmental and metabolic disorders can cause epilepsy.

Head injury

Head injuries, e.g. resulting from falls, can cause seizures. The seizures may not begin until years later.

Prenatal injuries

A foetus's developing brain is susceptible to prenatal injuries that may occur if the pregnant mother has an infection, e.g. herpes simplex, doesn't eat properly, smokes or abuses drugs or alcohol. These conditions may cause epilepsy.

About 20 per cent of seizures in children are caused by cerebral palsy or other disorders of the nervous system. Sometimes epilepsy is linked to areas in the brain where neurons may not have formed properly during prenatal development.

Environmental causes

Epilepsy can be caused by:

- Environmental and occupational exposure to lead, carbon monoxide and certain chemicals
- Use of street drugs and alcohol
- Withdrawal from certain antidepressant and anti-anxiety drugs

While the following cannot cause epilepsy to occur in the first place, they may trigger a seizure in children who have epilepsy:

▷ Tiredness
▷ Lack of sleep
▷ Illness
▷ Stress/anxiety
▷ Constipation
▷ Missed doses of medication

Photosensitive epilepsy is the name given to epilepsy in which all, or almost all, seizures are provoked by flashing or flickering lights or some shapes or patterns. Both natural and artificial light may trigger seizures.

Many people think that everybody with epilepsy is photosensitive, but in fact only five in every 100 people with epilepsy are. Photosensitive epilepsy usually begins before the age of 20 years, although it is most common between the ages of seven and 19. Photosensitivity tends to affect girls more than boys. There is also evidence to indicate that photosensitive epilepsy is often genetically transmitted.

Symptoms

There are many different types of epilepsy. They are usually described either in terms of the part of the brain affected by the epilepsy or by the type of seizure the person tends to get. For this reason, symptoms of epilepsy can vary considerably from person to person.

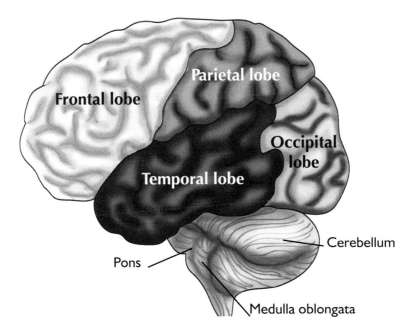

Structure of the brain

As can be seen from the illustration, each of the two hemispheres (halves) of the brain consists of five areas:

- **Occipital lobe:** Responsible for processing visual information.
- **Parietal lobe:** Responsible for processing sensations such as touch and taste and the judgement of the texture, weight, size and shape of objects.
- **Frontal lobe:** Responsible for planning, organising, problem-solving, personality, behaviour and emotions and for movement of muscles.
- **Temporal lobe:** Responsible for memory, speech and comprehension.
- **Cerebellum:** Responsible for balance and muscle co-ordination.

Temporal lobe epilepsy

Temporal lobe epilepsy (TLE) is the most frequent cause of partial seizures and aura (see below). The temporal lobe is located close to the ear. It is the part of the brain where smell is processed and where the choice is made to express a thought or remain silent.

TLE often begins in childhood. Repeated TLE seizures can damage the hippocampus (part of the temporal lobe), a part of the brain that is important for memory and learning. Although the damage progresses very slowly, it is important to treat TLE as early as possible.

Frontal lobe epilepsy

The frontal lobes of the brain lie behind the forehead. They are the largest of the five lobes and are thought to be the centres that control personality and higher thought processes, including language and speech.

Frontal lobe epilepsy usually causes a cluster of short seizures that start and stop suddenly. The symptoms depend on the part of the frontal lobe affected.

Occipital lobe epilepsy

The occipital lobe lies at the back of the skull. Occipital lobe epilepsy is like frontal and temporal lobe epilepsy, except that the seizures usually begin with visual hallucinations, rapid blinking and other symptoms related to the eyes.

Parietal lobe epilepsy

The parietal lobe lies between the frontal and temporal lobes. Parietal lobe epilepsy is similar to other types in part because parietal lobe seizures tend to spread to other areas of the brain.

Cerebellum

The cerebellum lies at the back of the brain below the occipital and temporal lobes. Because the cerebellum is responsible for balance and muscular co-ordination, these will be affected by the seizure.

Seizure types

In general, seizures either affect specific parts of the brain, causing partial seizures, or the whole brain, causing generalised seizures.

Partial seizures

Partial seizures are often named in terms of the part of the brain in which they happen. For example, a person might be said to have partial frontal lobe seizures. About 60 per cent of all people who have epilepsy have this type of seizure.

Recurrent partial seizures are sometimes called **psychomotor seizures**. The term *psychomotor* refers to the interaction between the brain and muscles, and in this case refers to the twitches and hallucinations that characterise the seizures.

There are several types of partial seizures:

1. Simple partial seizures
2. Complex partial seizures
3. Aura
4. Secondarily generalised seizures

Simple partial seizures

People who have simple partial seizures stay awake and aware but may hear, see, smell or taste things that aren't real. They may also suddenly feel afraid, angry, happy or sad for no reason. They may become confused or experience jerking or tingling in an arm or leg.

This type of seizure is sometimes called a focal seizure and may also be called Jacksonian epilepsy, after Hughlings Jackson, a British doctor who was the first to describe it.

Complex partial seizures

Complex partial seizures usually begin with a blank stare that indicates a brief loss of consciousness. People who have these seizures may blink, twitch, chew or smack their lips repeatedly. They may seem drunk, express exaggerated anger or fear and throw things around. They may struggle against restraint. These seizures usually last no more than two minutes.

About 80 per cent of these complex partial seizures take place in the temporal lobe of the brain, which is close to the ear, and they are sometimes called temporal lobe seizures. These seizures may also originate in the frontal lobes.

Aura

Some people who have partial seizures experience unusual sensations that warn them that they are about to have a seizure. This premonitory state is called aura. Auras take several different forms.

- Sometimes it is perceived as a sinking feeling in the pit of the stomach or a sense of déjà vu (already seen).
- Sometimes it takes the form of an auditory hallucination, like an advertising jingle.

A person experiencing an aura is having a simple partial seizure without losing consciousness.

Secondary generalised seizures

Sometimes people have partial seizures that spread to the whole brain and become generalised seizures. This transition can be so rapid that the partial seizure is not noticed.

Generalised seizures

With this type of seizure, a large part of the brain is involved and consciousness is lost. What happens during a generalised seizure varies from individual to individual. Types of generalised seizure include the following.

- **Tonic-clonic convulsive seizure** (still sometimes called a major or grand mal seizure): The person becomes rigid, then falls to the ground and jerks all four limbs. The person's breathing will be laboured and there may be incontinence of urine.
- **Tonic:** There is a general stiffening of muscles without rhythmical jerking. The person may fall to the ground, if standing, with consequent risk of injury.
- **Atonic:** There is a sudden loss of muscle tone and a collapse to the ground (also known as drop attacks).
- **Myoclonic:** Abrupt jerking of the limbs occurs. These often happen within a short time of waking up. These seizures can occur either on their own or with other forms of generalised seizure.
- **Absences:** There is a brief interruption of consciousness without any signs, except perhaps for a fluttering of the eyelids or blank stare. These occur characteristically in children. They were commonly called petit mal seizures.

Diagnosis

The first step in making a diagnosis of epilepsy is for a doctor to take a complete medical history. The doctor will ask questions about:

- Whether the person or someone in the family has a history of seizures.
- What the seizures look and feel like.
- What happened just before the seizures began.
- Possible causes other than epilepsy. In a child, this could be infections or head injury, but in adults it could be alcohol or drug misuse.

A number of tests will be ordered to confirm the diagnosis of epilepsy. These include the following.

Electroencephalography (EEG)

The most frequently used diagnostic tool for epilepsy is the electroencephalograph (EEG). This test uses electrodes attached to the scalp to read the brain's electrical activity. People with epilepsy sometimes have unusual brain wave patterns even when they are not having a seizure, while others do not. EEG is most accurate when it is performed within 24 hours of a seizure. In some cases, a seizure is induced in order to monitor brain activity during this time.

The EEG test usually lasts about an hour and can be done as an outpatient at the hospital. Sometimes longer-term EEG (ambulatory EEG) may be necessary. The person wears a small pack containing a recording device around their waist, with wires underneath their clothing going up to their head. EEG monitoring can then take place over a number of days and the person can carry on with their normal activities.

Portable EEG units can be used to monitor brain waves throughout the day and during many different types of activities.

About half the people who have had an epileptic seizure have normal EEG readings. Therefore, other diagnostic tests may be needed.

Brain imaging

Brain imaging is often used when an adult has had a first seizure or when a child is having convulsive seizures that are not caused by fever.

Computerised tomography (CT or CAT scan) and magnetic resonance imaging (MRI) can be used to reveal the structure of the brain and can detect small structural defects that may be causing the seizures, such as cysts or tumours. Both use computers to produce precise images of the brain.

Positron emission tomography (PET) and functional MRI (fMRI) can be used to monitor the brain's activity and to detect abnormalities in its working. These tests can find damaged areas in the brain that are the focal points for seizures. They can help determine whether a patient is a good candidate for surgery and can be used to guide surgery.

Blood tests

Doctors use blood tests to screen for metabolic or genetic disorders that may be linked to seizures and to look for other conditions that may cause seizures, such as infections, lead poisoning, anaemia or diabetes. Metabolic and genetic screening are most often done when examining a child.

Developmental, neurological and behavioural tests

Tests to measure co-ordination and muscle control, behaviour and intellectual capacity can help find out what is causing the epilepsy and how the seizures may be affecting the patient.

Treatment

Medication

Antiepileptic drugs (AEDs) are the most common treatment for epilepsy. These medications do not cure epilepsy, but rather they treat the epilepsy and help stop the seizures from occurring. There are many different forms of AEDs on the market today. The type of AED prescribed for someone with epilepsy will depend on the type of epilepsy they have. When a child (or indeed an adult) is first given an AED, they will be given a very low dose. As time goes on, the dose of the drug will be gradually increased. This is to minimise the risk of side effects. While it is most desirable if patients are on only one drug to treat their epilepsy (monotherapy), some seizures prove difficult to control, so patients may have to take more than one AED (polytherapy).

AEDs come in tablet, liquid or granule form. The granule form is useful for very young children, as it can be sprinkled over food. Some AEDs are slow release, which means that the drug does not have to be taken as often, e.g. once every day. For these drugs to work effectively, they must be taken at the same time every day so that the patient does not go for a long stretch with only small amounts of the drug in their system.

When someone begins taking AEDs, the drug starts to control the seizures fairly quickly in the majority of cases. In some cases, however, it takes longer and a number of different drugs may have to be tried out singly or used in combination. Most children need to take AEDs until they have gone at least two years without a seizure. After this time, their doctor may consider reducing their treatment gradually.

Surgery

Surgery may be considered for some forms of epilepsy where the focal point of the epilepsy is localised.

Ketogenic diet

The ketogenic diet is a special high-fat, adequate-protein, low-carbohydrate diet that can have an antiepileptic effect. This diet first came to prominence during the 1920s and 1930s, when there were little or no antiepileptic drugs available. It was largely forgotten about until recently, when it came to prominence again in the US for the treatment of children with epilepsy that is difficult to control. Children on a ketogenic diet will be under the direct supervision of a specialist doctor and dietician.

The diet is designed to simulate many of the metabolic effects of starvation. During starvation, the body first uses its store of glucose and glycogen, then begins to burn stored body fat. When there is not sufficient glucose (from carbohydrates in the diet) available, the fats cannot be completely burned and ketones are left as the residue of incompletely burned fat. The ketogenic diet provides dietary fat for the body to burn, but limits the available carbohydrate so that ketones build up in the blood. It appears that it is the high level of these ketones which suppress seizures.

First aid for seizures in a school setting

- Keep calm. Let the seizure run its course and do not do anything to try to stop the seizure, e.g. do not restrain the child.

- If a seizure occurs at school, it is important for the child with epilepsy that you deal with the seizure in a calm way. Say to the other children, 'Child X will be OK in a few minutes, now off you go.' It is important that the child's epilepsy is not highlighted in a negative way.

- If possible, put something soft under the child's head and move away any objects that may cause injury.

- Be aware of how long the seizure lasts.

- After the seizure, lay the child on their side in the recovery position (see photo on the next page) and stay with them until they have recovered completely.

Child in recovery position

- Sometimes when children have seizures they may wet or soil themselves. It is important to check if this has happened in a sensitive way and arrange for a change of clothing when they have had time to recover. How much help will be given will depend on the age of the child.
- It is usually unnecessary to call an ambulance (although school policy may require it) unless the person is injured, if the seizure does not stop after a few minutes, another seizure follows closely afterwards or the child is having trouble breathing.
- Sometimes rescue treatment drugs are administered. In the past, this involved using rectal suppositories, e.g. diazepam. Nowadays, drugs such as buccal midazolam (Epistatus) are usually used instead. These drugs are administered through a syringe (no needle) into the mouth, under the tongue along the gum line. Blood capillaries are close to the surface here and so the drug will be absorbed and act quickly.

Prognosis

In general, the prognosis for epilepsy is reasonably good. Fifty to 60 per cent of children's seizures will be controlled using antiepileptic drugs with minimal side effects. Thirty to 35 per cent will have seizures that are resistant to antiepileptic drugs, so managing their epilepsy will be more difficult. Also, many children simply 'grow out of' epilepsy.

Families also become aware of what triggers a child's epilepsy and will avoid these triggers where possible. Triggers include forgetting or not taking medication, hunger, lack of sleep, stress or worry, flashing or flickering lights, alcohol or street drugs.

Role of the SNA

Usually a child with epilepsy alone (unless it is a very severe case) would not have an SNA of their own. However, if the epilepsy is part of another condition, e.g. cerebral palsy, they may sometimes have an SNA. In addition, some children with epilepsy, because they miss time from school or perhaps are experiencing frequent seizures, may fall behind in their schoolwork. If this happens, the child may be entitled to extra learning support and perhaps time with a resource teacher and SNA. SNAs should help the child by keeping missed schoolwork for them and helping the child organise their books, etc.

In addition, if a child has a seizure, an SNA may be required to administer first aid or remain with the child while he or she is recovering. Seizures should be timed and a written record kept. Depending on the age of the child, an SNA may be required to help children change soiled clothing. Efforts should always be made to ensure the dignity and privacy of the child is maintained. SNAs should be knowledgeable about the condition and know how it is treated. Also, like all children with special needs, children with epilepsy may be a target for bullying, so SNAs, like all school staff, must be especially vigilant for this.

If a child has epilepsy, then for safety an SNA may be asked to accompany and closely supervise the child during certain activities, e.g. swimming lessons. It is also important to inform the lifeguard on duty that the child has epilepsy.

CASE STUDY

Emma started primary school at age four and a half, having attended a local Montessori school in a nearby village for the previous year. She met many other children there, three of whom would be starting at the same primary school as her. Emma was very excited about starting 'big school' and she had little apprehension about going, having collected her brother Seán there since infancy. When Emma started her school she settled in quickly, getting on well with her teacher and new classmates.

Emma did well in all aspects of her schoolwork during junior and senior infants classes. Being chatty and bubbly, she also had little trouble making friends. At the beginning of first class, however, Emma began to turn into a 'dreamer'. Her new teacher sometimes noticed that she would stare ahead blankly and that sometimes she may have the wrong page or the last book that the class had been working on open in front of her. Emma now took part much less often in class discussions. At times she would be her old chatty, bubbly self, but she seemed increasingly withdrawn.

Emma's schoolwork began to become badly affected by her 'daydreaming'. She was now beginning to struggle with her maths, reading and spellings, things she had had no trouble with before. She had become a 'scatterbrain', her work becoming untidy and with gaps left undone at times.

Emma's parents began noticing changes as well. Doing homework became a big chore. Emma's mum, Mairead, usually had to go over the work with her several times to make sure she knew it, which, of course, caused rows. At first her mother thought that Emma's problems at school were because she had a different teacher or that she had extra work to do because she was no longer in the infant classes. But Seán had had the same teacher and really liked her and didn't seem to have had a problem with first class work. Emma's parents also began to notice other slight changes in Emma, such as daydreaming while watching television. Her father would often jokingly say, 'Calling Earth to Emma.' There now seemed to be two Emmas – the chatty, bubbly one and the quiet, daydreaming, often tired one. Mairead did go to see Emma's teacher, who although understanding, thought (perhaps because she had not known Emma beforehand) that she just lacked interest in some subjects.

Emma's daydreaming continued for just over a year, when a couple of weeks after a severe lung infection Emma had her first tonic-clonic seizure. That morning, Mairead was planning on bringing both Seán and Emma shopping for winter clothes and wanted to leave early. By 8.30, Emma still wasn't up, so Mairead had to call her. Emma gave a muffled reply from her bed. Mairead returned to the kitchen. As Emma got up she felt a sudden urge to go to the toilet and ran to the bathroom. Soon after, Mairead heard some sort of scream. Knowing something was wrong, she ran up the stairs and found Emma lying on the bathroom floor at a strange angle. Her limbs were shaking uncontrollably, her eyes were rolling back in her head and she had wet herself. Mairead screamed for her husband John to come help. While waiting for John, Mairead tried to wake Emma up. She also tried to control the jerking, but neither worked. By the time John had come into the bathroom the jerking had slowed down and Emma began to come round, but was still half-asleep and confused.

The family quickly drove to the hospital, where Emma was seen by a doctor. He took a history, where Mairead mentioned her daydreaming. Emma was kept in overnight for observation and was given an appointment to see a neurologist.

Just two weeks later, Emma had her second clonic-tonic seizure, this time at school. Emma had just stood up from her chair in the classroom when she collapsed and had the seizure. Emma's teacher quickly contacted Mairead. The children in the classroom were full of questions, which the teacher didn't really know how to answer. She just said that Emma had had a turn and that she would be OK. Mairead brought Emma to their GP, who referred her directly to the hospital. This time Emma was kept in for three days. She met the neurologist and underwent a number of tests – blood tests, an EEG and a CAT scan. Emma was diagnosed with epilepsy and put on medication.

The next year was nerve wracking for Emma and her parents. She was having one seizure per week on average and was missing a lot of time from school. Emma found the seizures very tiring, as they gave her headaches and sometimes left her arms and legs sore. She would also feel very confused after a seizure.

The children at school used to ask her difficult questions about her 'fits' and a couple made mean comments that upset her. Her friends' mothers were afraid to have Emma over to their homes in case she had a seizure. Mairead tried to get round this by asking children over to their house and also stayed over at birthday parties with Emma in case of a seizure. Mairead was also asked by the school to take Emma out of swimming class.

Over the course of the next two years, Emma had another couple of hospital stays after having a series of seizures close together. The hospital altered and increased her medication a number of times and the frequency of her seizures began to lessen somewhat. Emma's parents attended a few Irish Epilepsy Association (IEA) meetings and found them very helpful. It was nice to meet others who had the same problems and worries as them.

At nine years old, Emma's seizures are averaging three or four months apart. In conjunction with the school, Mairead asked a nurse from the IEA to come talk to Emma's classmates about epilepsy. This seemed to help a lot. Besides, her classmates and teachers were getting used to dealing with the seizures and Emma was getting learning support hours to make up for the class work she was missing due to her absences and seizures.

Over the next number of years, Emma's seizures became less and less regular. By age 14, Emma had gone two years without a seizure and her neurologist was considering weaning her off her medication. Mairead was wary of this at first, fearing that if Emma stopped taking her tablets then the seizures would start again. This proved to be the case. Emma had two seizures while the medication was reduced, so the neurologist increased it again. Emma is currently 17 years old and has been seizure free on medication ever since.

For further information on epilepsy, contact Brainwave (www.epilepsy.ie).

SICKLE CELL ANAEMIA

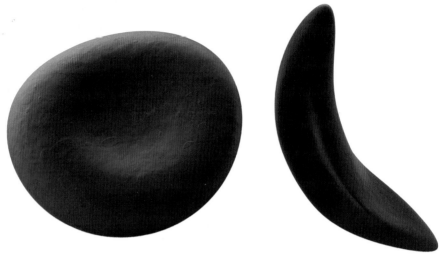

Sickle cells under a microscope

Prevalence

Sickle cell anaemia is a genetically inherited condition whereby a percentage of the red blood cells are sickle shaped as opposed to the normal disc shape. The disease is most commonly found in people of Afro-Caribbean (i.e. African or West Indian) descent. The disease also occurs in people from the eastern Mediterranean and the Middle East, although less commonly so. Sickle cell anaemia rarely occurs in white, Western populations. This distribution is thought to reflect the fact that the sickle cell trait (being a carrier) protects against malaria. The process of natural selection has resulted in high frequencies of the mutant gene in countries where malaria is common.

Sickle cell anaemia is a lifelong condition affecting children from birth. It is thought to occur in one in 500 births worldwide, with some nationalities having a much higher incidence of the disease. In some areas of Sub-Saharan Africa, e.g. parts of Nigeria, Ghana and Uganda, up to 2 per cent of all children are born with the condition. There are currently 400 children in Ireland with sickle cell anaemia (Culliton 2009).

Causes

Sickle cell anaemia, sometimes called sickle cell disease, is a genetically inherited condition whereby the genes controlling the formation of red blood cells are abnormal. Genes come in pairs – one from the father and one from the mother. The gene for sickle cell is recessive, in that the trait (in this case sickle cell anaemia) will not show itself if a healthy gene is also present. The individual will only be a carrier of the disease. Some children of carriers will not inherit the gene at all. The diagram below illustrates how inheritance is passed. Like many genetically inherited conditions, how or why the sickle cell gene mutated in the first place is not known.

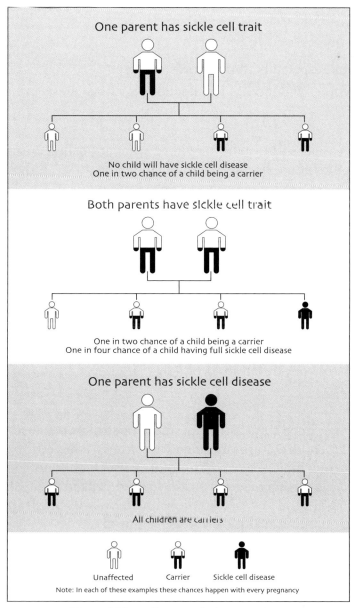

How sickle cell anaemia is passed on

Symptoms

When a baby is born with sickle cell anaemia, they will be initially fit and well with no signs of the disease for four to six months. The disease becomes symptomatic when the baby begins manufacturing new supplies of haemoglobin and new red blood cells. Symptoms include:

- Lack of energy
- Listlessness
- Poor circulation, especially in the hands and feet
- The child becomes vulnerable to infections such as chest, urinary tract and ear infection

As the condition worsens, the child may have what are called crises. During a crisis, the sickle cells in the blood, because of their shape, begin to clump in the tiny blood vessels of the body, causing severe pain (this clumping is also called sickling). The clumped cells stop blood from flowing through the affected blood vessels, thereby blocking blood supply to the tissues. Because of sickling, the area affected may become damaged and the child will have a very high fever. A crisis can be brought on by a number of different triggers, including:

- Infections such as coughs, colds, flu, chicken pox, etc.
- Dehydration
- Extremes of cold, e.g. at a football match, after swimming, in unheated schools or bedrooms
- Stress, e.g. schoolwork or family problems
- Physical exercise

Some children experience transient or permanent strokes because of sickling. Signs of stroke in such children are muscular weakness, slurred speech and severe headaches. They are a major cause of disability in such children.

If a child has a high percentage of sickle-shaped cells in their blood, oxygen will not be transported around the body efficiently. This will result in severe anaemia and an emergency blood transfusion will be required.

Diagnosis

Sickle cell anaemia, like most other genetically inherited conditions, will be diagnosed with a blood test. Early diagnosis is advised, so sometimes a sample of blood from the umbilical cord is taken at birth, especially if it is known that both parents are carriers of the condition.

Treatment

While sickle cell anaemia cannot be cured, there are treatments available that can help relieve its symptoms and treat complications. The goals of treating sickle cell anaemia are to relieve pain; prevent infections, eye damage and strokes; and control complications (if they occur).

Bone marrow transplants may be offered to some patients and haematologists and geneticists continue to look for new treatments for the disease, including gene therapy.

Treating pain

Medicines and fluids

Mild pain is often treated with over-the-counter medicine and heated pads. Severe pain will normally need to be treated in a hospital. Usually the person is given fluids, either by mouth or on a drip, together with anti-inflammatory drugs and a strong painkiller such as morphine.

Hydroxyurea

Children with severe sickle cell anaemia will sometimes be on daily dose of a drug called hydroxyurea (brand names include Hydrea and Droxia). These drugs try to prevent crises from occurring. They also help preserve organ function and will improve growth in children with sickle cell anaemia. The drug can have serious side effects, however, e.g. increased risk of dangerous infections.

Blood transfusions

Blood transfusions are commonly used to treat worsening anaemia and sickle cell complications such as stroke. A sudden worsening of anaemia due to an infection or enlargement of the spleen is a common reason for a blood transfusion.

Having routine blood transfusions can cause side effects, so patients must be carefully monitored. Side effects can include a dangerous build-up of iron in the blood (which must be treated) and an increased risk of infection from the transfused blood.

Complications

Infections

Infections are a major complication of sickle cell anaemia. In fact, pneumonia is the leading cause of death in children who have the condition. Other common infections linked to sickle cell anaemia include meningitis, influenza and hepatitis. If a child who has sickle cell anaemia shows early signs of an infection, such as fever, treatment must be sought right away.

To prevent infections in babies and young children, treatments include:

- Daily doses of penicillin. Treatment may begin as early as two months of age and continue until the child is at least five years old.

- All routine vaccinations and others, such as the swine flu vaccine, should be given to children with sickle cell anaemia.

Eye damage

Sickle cell anaemia can damage the blood vessels in the eyes. Parents should ask their child's doctor about regular check-ups with an eye doctor who specialises in diseases of the eyes.

Strokes

Stroke prevention and treatment are now possible for children and adults who have sickle cell anaemia. Starting at age two, children who have sickle cell anaemia usually have regular brain scans, called transcranial Doppler ultrasound scans. These scans can check the rate of blood flow in the brain, thus identifying children who are at high risk for a stroke. These children are then treated with routine blood transfusions. This treatment has been found to greatly reduce the number of strokes in children.

Treating other complications

Acute chest syndrome is a severe and life-threatening complication of sickle cell anaemia. Treatment usually requires hospitalisation and may include oxygen, blood transfusions, antibiotics, pain medication and intravenous fluids.

New medicines

Researchers are studying several new medicines for sickle cell anaemia, including:

- **Butyric acid:** A food additive that may increase normal haemoglobin in the blood.

- **Nitric oxide:** This medicine may make sickle cells less sticky and keep blood vessels open. People who have sickle cell anaemia have low levels of nitric oxide in their blood.

- **Decitabine:** This drug increases haemoglobin F levels (this type of haemoglobin carries more oxygen) in the blood. It may be used instead of hydroxyurea.

Ongoing management of the condition

▷ The child needs to be kept free of as many infections as possible. The school should inform parents if there has been an outbreak of anything in the school, e.g. chicken pox, as a child with sickle cell anaemia may have to remain at home.

▷ Children with sickle cell anaemia need to get the same immunisations as other children as well as some others, e.g. the yearly flu vaccine (usually given only to the elderly).

▷ Children need to eat a balanced diet.

▷ The environment, e.g. classroom toilets, need to be kept spotlessly clean.

▷ Children with sickle cell anaemia need to drink more fluids, so will need to visit the toilet more often. If in a playschool or crèche and in nappies, they will need changing more often.

▷ Children with sickle cell anaemia should avoid strenuous sports in wet or cold playgrounds and fields.

Prognosis

In the past, people with sickle cell anaemia often died from organ failure between the ages of 20 and 40. As a result of a better understanding and management of the disease, today patients can live into their fifties or beyond.

Role of the SNA

▷ Make sure your knowledge of sickle cell anaemia is accurate and up to date.

▷ Be aware of infection and the importance of keeping the child's environment clean.

▷ Make sure the child washes his or her hands before eating and after using the toilet.

▷ Encourage the child to eat well at lunchtime.

▷ If the day is particularly cold, you may be asked to supervise the child indoors during playtime, as it may be too risky for him or her to play outside.

▷ Remind the child to take frequent drinks of water.

▷ Because children with sickle cell anaemia often miss a lot of time from school, SNAs may be asked to keep a note of what the child has missed and to keep any handouts or activities for them. Sometimes work is sent home for the child to do.

CASE STUDY

Mercy was born seven years ago in Ireland to Nigerian parents and has sickle cell anaemia. She has just started her third year at her local primary school. She has a younger sister, Delight, who is four, and a brother, Sam, who is almost two. Neither of her siblings have the condition.

Mercy feels quite well most of the time, though she does get tired easily and suffers frequent lung and kidney infections. Every so often, Mercy has a crisis and has to go into hospital. Because of this and the infections, she misses a lot of school and is finding it difficult to keep up with the work. When Mercy is at school, she attends learning support three times a week and also sees the resource teacher. Joan, the SNA, also helps her out in class.

When Mercy has a crisis, the pain is unbearable. She can barely walk and has to be carried around the house by her dad. When she returns to school after having a crisis, she is sometimes on a crutch and has to stay in at lunchtime so that she won't get cold and have another one. She is constantly on an antibiotic and had to get a blood transfusion recently.

Mercy is a very quiet little girl and is finding it difficult to make friends at school. This could be due to the fact that she is absent so often and that she isn't always able to go out to play at break time. Her parents are worried about this and are beginning to ask some of her school friends over at weekends to play. This seems to be helping somewhat.

DIABETES MELLITUS

Prevalence

The term 'diabetes' means excessive urination and the word 'mellitus' means honey. There are two main categories of diabetes: type 1 and type 2. Type 1 diabetes tends to occur in childhood or early adult life and always requires treatment with insulin injections. It is caused by the body's own immune system destroying the insulin-making cells (beta cells) of the pancreas. Type 2 diabetes usually develops slowly in adulthood. It is progressive and can sometimes be treated with diet and exercise, but more often, type 2 diabetes may require anti-diabetic medicine and/or insulin injections. In terms of prevalence, it is estimated that approximately 2,000 Irish children have diabetes. The vast majority of these children have type 1, but an increasing number of obese older children and young adults are developing type 2.

Causes

Diabetes mellitus is a lifelong condition caused by a lack or, or insufficiency of, insulin. Insulin is a vitally important hormone made by the pancreas. Insulin acts like a key to open the doors into body cells, letting sugar (glucose) in. With diabetes, the pancreas makes too little insulin to enable all the sugar in the blood to get into the muscle and other cells of the body to produce energy. If sugar can't get into the cells to be used, it builds up in the bloodstream. Diabetes is therefore characterised by high blood sugar levels. Excess sugar is also excreted in the urine, hence the practice, in days gone by, of tasting urine to diagnose the condition.

Type 1 diabetes can be caused by both genetic factors and environmental triggers. Type 1 diabetes is classified as a polygenic disease, meaning it is caused by a number of different genes. The risk of a child having type 1 diabetes is 10% if their father has it, 10% if a sibling has it, 4% if their mother has it and has the baby before age 25 and 1% if their mother has it and if she has the baby after age 25. These statistics show that the disease has a strong genetic component (Joslin Diabetes Center 2013).

Environmental factors are also important in type 1 diabetes. In one study of identical twins, when one twin had type 1 diabetes, the other twin only had it 30 to 50 per cent of the time. Despite having exactly the same genetic make-up, one twin had the disease but the other did not. This suggests that environmental factors, in addition to genetic factors, can cause the disease (Todd 1990). Other studies that indicate an environmental influence include the presence of a tenfold difference in occurrence among people living in certain parts of Scandinavia, and a tendency to acquire the incidence of the disease of the destination country for people who migrate (Knip et al. 2005). The reason for the high levels of type 1 diabetes in northern Scandinavia is thought to be linked to low levels of vitamin D due to severely reduced daylight hours in the winter months.

Some research has also found that certain viruses (rubella is one that has been studied) can trigger an autoimmune response in some people, causing the person's immune system to attack both the virus-infected cells in the body and the beta cells in the pancreas. Not everyone who contracts the virus has this reaction, so it is thought that genetic factors are significant here too.

Some researchers have found a link between cow's milk and type 1 diabetes and also between low levels of vitamin D and diabetes (these findings came from a study conducted in northern Finland, where children were given large doses of dietary vitamin D to compensate for the lack of sunlight during winter months).

Some drugs used to treat pancreatic cancer have also been shown to cause type 1 diabetes. Children who have experienced trauma to the pancreas may also develop diabetes.

Symptoms

The five most common symptoms of diabetes in children are:

- An increase in thirst and frequency of urination
- Lethargy
- Increased appetite with sudden or unexplained weight loss
- Vision changes
- A fruity odour to the breath

A doctor should be consulted if a child is displaying these symptoms. These symptoms may have other causes besides diabetes.

Diagnosis

Diagnosis will be made via blood and urine tests. Patients will be asked to fast (blood sugar levels would normally drop as a result) and if blood sugar levels remain high even with fasting, this will normally indicate diabetes. In addition, because blood sugar has not been used for energy production, protein and fat stores in the body will have been used. A by-product of protein metabolism for energy production is ketones in the urine. This will be picked up by a urine test.

Treatment

Currently, diabetes cannot be cured but it can be treated. Diet and insulin therapy are the two main ways diabetes can be controlled. Generally, the person with diabetes monitors their blood sugar levels at intervals throughout the day and administers insulin to themselves by way of a subcutaneous injection. Children are usually taught to do this from a relatively early age. In terms of diet, people with type 1 diabetes generally avoid foods high in refined sugars, e.g. cakes, sweets, in favour of foods that release energy more slowly. Individuals with type 1 diabetes must eat regular meals and snacks. The Diabetes Federation of Ireland has produced a very good booklet on diabetes for children. This booklet can be downloaded at www.diabetes.ie.

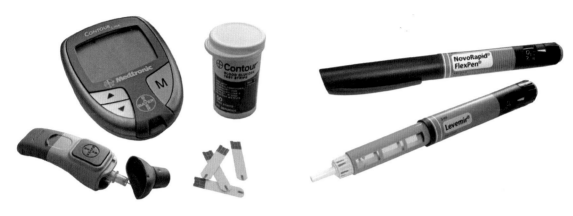

Blood sugar monitor   **Insulin pen**

Prognosis

Many people with diabetes live long and healthy lives. However, even when diabetes is well controlled, it does put the individual *at risk* of long-term complications. The major long-term complication is damage to the blood vessels. Diabetes doubles the risk of cardiovascular disease, including the risk of stroke and heart attacks. Diabetic retinopathy is a condition whereby the blood vessels of the retina in the eyes are affected, sometimes causing visual impairment. Diabetic nephropathy occurs when the blood vessels of the kidneys become damaged, sometimes causing kidney failure and requiring dialysis. Diabetic neuropathy occurs when the nervous system is affected by diabetes, causing numbness and tingling in the extremities, especially the hands and feet. People with diabetes need to take good care of their feet in particular, as they are at increased risk of skin ulcers, which can be very difficult to heal and sometimes result in amputation. Therefore, it is vital that people with diabetes monitor their blood sugar levels, eat slow-release energy foods regularly and are absolutely meticulous with their insulin injections. Doing this lessens the risk of the long-term complications outlined above.

In the short term, if an individual's blood sugar becomes too low they may have what is called a hypoglycaemic attack. This may occur because (a) too much insulin has been injected or (b) blood sugar has been used up too quickly, e.g. the person has expended a lot of energy, or (c) not enough food has been consumed, e.g. the person has skipped meals. Symptoms of hypoglycaemia include blurred vision, a fast or pounding heartbeat, feeling cranky, nervous or aggressive, headaches, shaking, trembling or sweating, weakness and confused thinking. The person may faint or in severe cases go into a diabetic coma. If this occurs, medical attention should be sought immediately.

On the other hand, if blood sugar levels are too high this is called hyperglycaemia. This is not as immediately dangerous as hypoglycaemia, but if it occurs frequently over periods of time it can cause organ damage and failure.

Role of the SNA

The main role of the SNA is to remind the child with diabetes to monitor their blood sugar, eat their regular meals and snacks and take their insulin injection at the prescribed time. In addition, SNAs, like all school personnel, need to be able to recognise the signs of a hypoglycaemic attack at its earliest stages and know what to do. If a child is showing signs of hypoglycaemia, they need to consume an easily absorbed form of sugar, e.g. sugar lumps, granulated sugar or milk (usually 200ml). If necessary, the child should be given more within 10 minutes in addition to food with a slower energy release, e.g. bread.

If a child has difficulty controlling diabetes, those caring for him/her may be given a special injection for use in emergencies containing glucagon. This injection would be given if the child was beginning to lose consciousness or perhaps having a seizure due to low blood sugar levels. If this were to occur in a school, it is a medical emergency and an ambulance would need to be called immediately.

ASTHMA

Prevalence

Asthma is a common condition that affects the airways carrying air in and out of the lungs. When an individual has asthma, their airways become overly sensitive and react to things that would not normally cause a problem, e.g. cold or dust. When someone has an asthma attack the walls of the airways tighten up, making them narrow and making it difficult for air to flow in and out of the lungs. This tightening of the muscles around the airways can happen quickly and is the most common cause of mild asthma. This can normally be successfully treated with the correct inhaler. However, sometimes the lining of the airways can become swollen and sticky mucus is produced, clogging up the airways further. This can take longer to clear up and can cause more persistent, serious asthma problems.

Ireland currently has the fourth highest incidence of asthma in the world (behind the UK, Australia and New Zealand), with approximately 14.6 per cent of the population having the condition. Rates are higher among children than adults; for example, 19 per cent of 13–15-year-old Irish children have asthma (Global Burden Report 2003).

Causes

The causes of asthma are not fully understood. An individual can develop asthma at any time in life, although it most commonly begins in childhood. Genetics are thought to play a role with asthma in that it often runs in families, but it can occur out of the blue. Individuals with other conditions such as hay fever, eczema or other allergy-type conditions are more prone to asthma. Environmental factors are also thought to be important. Most Irish children, for example, now live in centrally heated, very well-insulated homes, which may be contributing to our increasing asthma levels. Another factor thought to be contributing to increasing levels of asthma in children is the increase in processed foods in their diets. Adult onset asthma usually develops after a serious respiratory tract infection.

Symptoms

The most common symptoms of asthma are listed below. They may be brought on by exercise, changes in air temperature or irritants in the air, e.g. pollen, dust or animal hair. Colds or chest infections can bring on attacks or worsen symptoms. Some people experience these symptoms on a regular basis.

- Difficulty breathing/shortness of breath
- A feeling of tightness in the chest
- Wheezing
- Coughing, particularly at night
- Hoarseness

Diagnosis

Before diagnosing asthma, the individual's doctor will take a patient history. He/she will establish how long the symptoms have existed, how frequently they occur, how the symptoms are affecting the individual's quality of life, whether the symptoms get worse at night or affect sleep and whether the individual coughs or wheezes after exercise or is sensitive to airborne pollutants such as dust, pollen or animals. The doctor will often ask whether there is a family history of asthma and about any chest infections, e.g. do they normally take longer than 10 days to clear?

   If the doctor suspects that the individual may have asthma, he/she may carry out a simple breathing test called a spirometry, which measures lung function both before and after a dose of asthma reliever is given. The individual may be asked to take an exercise test to check if exercise worsens symptoms.

Treatment

The main treatment for asthma is medication. Preventers, controllers and relievers are all terms that people with asthma are familiar with.

- **Preventers/controllers:** These are inhalers that help prevent the swelling and inflammation of the airways. This helps the airways to become less sensitive to irritants and reduces the risk of attacks. The effect of preventers/controllers builds up over time, so they need to be taken every day, usually once in the morning and once in the evening. It is important that the person with asthma takes their preventer/controller even when they are well, as this is what is keeping them well. Preventer inhalers usually contain a low dose of steroid, which reduces inflammation. For some people, preventers/controllers alone are not sufficient and a combination inhaler may be prescribed. This inhaler will contain a steroid plus a long-acting reliever (see below).

- **Relievers:** Everyone with asthma will have a reliever. Relievers are taken immediately when the symptoms of asthma occur. Relievers work by quickly relaxing the muscles around the airways, allowing them to widen and helping the person to breathe more easily. They do not reduce swelling and inflammation, like preventers/controllers do. If relievers are taken before exercise, they reduce the chances of an attack. Relievers normally come in a blue inhaler. Examples include Salbutamol (e.g. Ventolin) and Terbutaline (e.g. Bricanyl). Individuals should not have to use relievers too often (more than once or twice a week), as this would indicate that their asthma is not well controlled. If this is happening, then the individual's preventer/controller medication may have to be reviewed or other 'add-on' therapies used.

- **Add-on therapies:** One of the first add-on therapies that is usually tried is called a leukotriene receptor antagonist (LRA). This therapy works by blocking the action of a group of naturally occurring chemicals in the lungs that cause inflammation, called leukotrienes. A long-acting reliever is usually prescribed with an LRA. Doctors will not normally change a patient's medication without finding out if he/she is taking their existing medication properly. Sometimes a patient's asthma is out of control because he/she is not taking their preventer or they are aggravating their asthma by smoking.

- **Steroids:** If an individual's asthma gets particularly bad at a particular time, a short course of steroid tablets may be prescribed, usually over the course of three to 14 days. A small number of people with asthma may have to take longer courses. The type of steroid given to people with asthma is called corticosteroids. They mimic those naturally produced in the body and are very unlike the anabolic steroids used by body builders, etc. Doctors generally prescribe the lowest effective dose.

Prognosis

Asthma is usually chronic, meaning that it does not go away. It may go into long periods of remission (where the individual does not get symptoms). Severity varies among people with asthma. Many children with mild to moderate asthma seem to grow out of it, becoming symptom-free adults. Prognosis is generally improved when asthma is treated early and effectively, before damage has been done to the airways. Unfortunately, in a minority of cases lungs become permanently damaged and the individual may experience problems throughout their lives. People with asthma who also smoke have a much more negative prognosis, as they are prone to other conditions affecting the lungs, especially emphysema. Death from asthma is relatively uncommon and most are preventable. It is rare for a person receiving proper treatment to die of asthma. Asthma that is not properly controlled can interfere with aspects of the individual's life, e.g. attendance at work or school and participation in sports or other activities.

Role of SNA

Preventer/controller medication is normally taken in the mornings and evenings, so it will not usually have to be taken by the child while at school. The main function of school personnel, including SNAs, is to help the child with asthma avoid known triggers and to help them cope with an attack should it occur.

If a child is having an asthma attack:

1. Stay calm yourself.
2. Immediately give them their reliever inhaler (usually blue) and have them take two puffs.
3. Sit the child upright and help them remain calm. They are likely to have had attacks before, so they will often know what to do themselves.
4. Tell them to take slow, steady breaths (again, they will probably know this).
5. If there is no immediate improvement, it is usual for the child to take another puff once every minute (up to 10 puffs in 10 minutes) until symptoms improve. For children under six years of age, it is usually up to six puffs in six minutes.
6. If symptoms do not improve, call an ambulance. Repeat steps 1 to 4 until it arrives.

It is important not to let the child lie down and do not put your arm around him/her, as this further restricts breathing. Do not restrict the use of their reliever: during an attack, extra puffs of reliever are safe. Listen to what the child is saying – they are likely to have had attacks before and know what they are talking about. With young children, a spacer is often used to administer reliever.

Asthma reliever inhaler with spacer attached

DEVELOPMENTAL DYSPRAXIA

Developmental dyspraxia, which is sometimes called developmental co-ordination disorder (DCD), clumsy child syndrome, motor learning problems or sensory processing disorder, can be defined as:

> an impairment or immaturity of the organisation of movement. It is an immaturity in the way that the brain processes information, which results in messages not being properly or fully transmitted. The term dyspraxia comes from the word praxis, which means 'doing, acting'. Dyspraxia affects the planning of what to do and how to do it. It is associated with problems of perception, language and thought. (www.dyspraxiafoundation.org.uk)

Prevalence

Dyspraxia is thought to affect up to 10 per cent of the population and up to 2 per cent severely. Males are four times more likely to be affected than females. Dyspraxia sometimes runs in families, and there can often be an overlap between dyspraxia and other related conditions, such as dyslexia, ADHD, dyscalculia (difficulties with maths) and Asperger's syndrome. This means that in a class of 30 children, there is likely to be at least one child with dyspraxia.

Causes

Dyspraxia is a specific learning disability resulting from an immaturity of the neurological development of the brain. Problems occur as a result of the brain transmitting incomplete or scrambled messages to the muscles. It is not fully understood why the neurological pathways in the brain fail to develop or mature properly in children with dyspraxia.

Symptoms

The symptoms of dyspraxia are numerous and varied. Not everyone with dyspraxia shows all symptoms, and symptoms may be complicated further by the fact that a child with dyspraxia may also have other related conditions, as mentioned above.

In a preschool child, the following indicators may be present:

- Babies are usually irritable from birth and may exhibit significant feeding problems.
- They are slow to achieve expected developmental milestones – sitting up, crawling and walking.
- Many children with dyspraxia fail to go through the crawling stages, preferring to 'bottom shuffle' and then walk.
- They usually avoid tasks that require good manual dexterity, e.g. making jigsaws, colouring.
- They will have difficulty dressing, e.g. pulling up pants after using the toilet.
- Artwork will be immature when compared to peers.
- Immature pencil grip at three to four years of age.

Children in the early years of school may show the following indicators:

- Very high levels of motor activity, including feet swinging and tapping when seated, hand-clapping or twisting.
- Unable to stay still.
- High levels of excitability, with a loud, shrill voice.
- May be easily distressed and prone to temper tantrums.
- May constantly bump into objects, trip and fall over.
- Hands flap when running.
- Difficulty with pedalling a tricycle or similar toy.
- Lack of any sense of danger (jumping from heights, etc.).
- Continued messy eating – inability to eat skilfully with a knife, fork or spoon.

May prefer to eat with their fingers and may frequently spill drinks or knock over other tableware.

- Avoidance and disinterest in constructional toys, such as jigsaws or building blocks.
- Poor fine motor skills. Difficulty in holding a pencil or using scissors. Drawings may appear immature.
- Lack of imaginative play. May show little interest in dressing up or role play.
- May be isolated within the peer group. Rejected by peers, the child may prefer adult company.
- Laterality (left- or right-handedness) still not obvious by four or five years.
- Persistent language difficulties.
- Sensitive to sensory stimulation – dislikes loud noises, being touched or hugged, dislikes new clothes close to skin.
- Inability to process verbal instructions. May have to be told to do something several times.
- Short concentration span. Tasks frequently left unfinished.

Children in the middle and late years at primary school may show the following indicators:

- Difficulties in adapting to a structured school routine, e.g. forgetting PE day or to bring in equipment on a certain day, e.g. tin whistle on a Wednesday
- Dislike of and difficulties with physical education classes
- Slow at dressing. Unable to tie shoelaces
- Barely legible handwriting
- Immature drawing and copying skills
- Limited concentration and poor listening skills
- Literal use of language and inability to 'read' situations
- Inability to remember more than two or three instructions at once
- Slow to complete class work
- Continued high levels of motor activity, e.g. foot tapping, rocking
- Hand flapping or clapping when excited
- Tendency to become easily distressed and emotional
- Problems with co-ordinating a knife and fork – may still use hands to eat
- Inability to form relationships with other children – poor social and communication skills

- Sleeping difficulties, including wakefulness at night and nightmares
- Reporting of physical symptoms, such as migraine, headaches and feeling sick

By the time many children reach secondary school, they may have become disillusioned with the education system. Many will have fallen significantly behind and often have poor attendance rates.

Diagnosis

Dyspraxia will usually be diagnosed by a psychologist, occupational therapist or speech and language therapist (depending on who the child has been sent to) by observing the child and taking a complete developmental history, e.g. asking what age the child walked at, etc. A dyspraxia checklist (see Appendix 5 at www.gill macmillan.ie/assistingchildrenwithspecialneeds) may be used initially before more detailed testing is done with the child using a specialist professional test. Diagnosis is frequently not clear cut, however, because other conditions may be present along with the dyspraxia, as mentioned earlier.

Treatment

While there is no cure for dyspraxia, there are a number of different options available that can help the child improve their skills and deal with the emotional and social effects of having dyspraxia. Depending on the particular characteristics of their dyspraxia, children will often work with a combination of occupational therapist, physiotherapist and speech and language therapist. In school, children may also have access to learning support, resource hours and perhaps an SNA.

Children with dyspraxia are often not able to correctly position what are called the speech articulators (face, tongue, lips and jaw) and may have difficulty pronouncing sounds, syllables and words. With two or more years of intensive speech therapy, most children will eventually be capable of communicating orally.

If the child has poorly developed gross motor skills, e.g. running, jumping, throwing, catching or kicking a ball or riding a bicycle, they may begin working on balance and co-ordination skills with a physiotherapist, who can build up the child's muscle strength and tone and increase awareness of his or her limbs. For children experiencing problems with their fine motor skills, e.g. handwriting, tying laces or putting on clothing, an occupational therapist can concentrate on the child's co-ordination using skills such as threading, cutting, colouring and copying shapes and patterns.

In school, teachers and support staff such as SNAs can help the child with dyspraxia in many ways.

For the development of gross motor skills:

- Ten minutes of exercises should be carried out daily.
- Games and exercises such as star jumps, crab walk, wheelbarrow, hokey pokey, hopscotch, tag, Simon says, skipping, hopping, marching to rhymes and clapping.
- Give very specific instructions.
- Start with 'big' activities for the hips and shoulders, e.g. bat a balloon from one child to another using cardboard tubes. Do it lying down to exercise the hips.
- Throw a silk scarf or other light material to one another.
- Fishing game using a cardboard tube (two handed) with string and magnet to pick up letters or fish – this can also be played in a kneeling position.
- Draw letters on your back – guess which letter.
- Paint letters on the wall with water using a big brush (outdoors).
- Tray with shaving foam – teacher makes a letter and the child traces it and then copies the teacher.
- Make letters with chalk on carpet squares or in the playground.
- Unscrew lids from bottles.
- Pegs – good for strengthening and improving hand function.
- Game – use box with pegs attached. Start with big pegs and then use all sizes. Throw a dice and the child must remove the number of pegs thrown. Reverse and child must clip the pegs to the box.
- Ball skills – start with big, light beach balls or foam balls.
- Position the child sitting on the floor with his or her back to the wall and practise throwing/rolling from this position. Repeat the same exercise kneeling and then standing.
- Use an apron as a 'catcher'. Other catchers can be a bin or basket or a hoola hoop with a net attached. These catchers ensure success.
- Older children can play volleyball using a light ball, short-tennis and badminton.
- Kicker-flickers – attach ball to waist with elastic string and practise kicking.

For the development of better spatial awareness and perception:

- Spatial awareness – children with dyspraxia sometimes have problems with social distance and constantly 'invade your space'. Teach them to stay literally at arm's length from the person they are talking to.
- Sit in front of a mirror, side by side. Identify by pointing and outlining with the index finger all the parts of the body, from large/general to detailed.

- Stand with the child in the middle of the room and indicate by pointing at certain features of the room, e.g. the corner by the door, the wall with the window. Turn the child and ask him or her to indicate the same things from a new position.
- Begin with imitated hand and feet movements – clapping hands, right hand to left shoulder, etc. Repeat with ears, knees, elbows, etc.
- Sequence daily life, e.g. ask the child to name people around the table, scanning from left to right.
- Have name cards of each item of clothing, describe the movements required to dress.
- What do you do when you wash your hands, brush your teeth, lay the table, etc?
- Practise days of the week, months, seasons, etc.
- Count from one to 20.
- Repeat name, address, telephone number, etc.
- Music – march in time to rhythm – arms and legs co-ordinated.
- Ask the child to close their eyes and listen to a clock ticking, keys jangling, fingers tapping, etc. Ask them to describe in a sentence what they heard.
- You say what I say – Hello, it's a nice day; I'm tired; I'm hungry; I want to play; I would like some sweets; I would like to go shopping. Practise in different tenses.
- A programme called the Frostig Programme of Visual Perception can be useful to establish left/right hand, etc.
- Children with dyspraxia can have trouble taking things down from the black or white board in the correct sequence. Colour coding what is written on the board can be helpful. Use a green–red system. Write the first sentence in green chalk or marker, the second in orange and the last in red.

For the development of better organisation and time management skills:
- Plan the week with the child.
- Have a notice board on the wall with a timetable of activities – use pictures for smaller children.
- Give plenty of notice for changes in routine.
- Remind the child 10 minutes before the next activity.
- Use a timer – give it to the child for different tasks, e.g. set it for 10 minutes for reading.
- Mark shoes with an X on the side of the sole to make them easy to match up.

- Make sure the child has a schoolbag with plenty of room in it.
- Have two see-through pencil cases, one for school and one for home.
- Recommend an elastic loop to hang coat.
- Different-coloured covers for different subjects.
- Recommend velcro and elastic shoelaces.
- Use a ruler with a handle.
- Use a dycem mat to prevent books and copies from slipping.
- Do not expect the child to wait in line for too long – maybe put him or her in front.
- Help children to develop a concept of time – this helps them to feel more in control.
- Use a calendar to mark off the days and months of the year.
- Have a buddy system; write down or photocopy homework for the child.
- Check the child has the relevant books to take home with them.

For the development of handwriting skills:
- Use a sloping surface – this is essential.
- The child should be allowed to experiment with a variety of pencils and pens.
- Try wrapping a pencil with silly putty to give grip.
- Use a dycem mat to prevent copybooks from slipping.
- Colour code, e.g. a green dot to start and a red dot to finish.
- Endless repetition of prewriting skills.
- Some experts encourage a cursive style.
- Dictaphones, laptops and computers, PalmPilots, AlphaSmart (these are small, relatively inexpensive computers that connect to a main teacher computer).
- To test writing – child copies writing, teacher dictates, child writes, child writes independently.
- Never place a left-handed child beside a right-handed child.
- Useful computer programs – Type to Learn or speech-to-text software, e.g. Dragon Naturally Speaking, Clicker 5.

(Adapted from www.dyspraxiaireland.com)

Prognosis

Dyspraxia is a lifelong developmental condition. Many individuals are able to compensate for their disabilities through effective teaching and support, physiotherapy and occupational and speech therapy. With this help, these individuals can go on to train for and hold jobs. Others who do not receive proper interventions can become very frustrated, suffer from low self-esteem, develop behavioural and emotional problems and generally fail to reach their true potential. In general, therefore, prognosis depends on the level of intervention and support the child receives to learn to live with their condition.

Role of the SNA

Although SNAs do not have a direct teaching role, they are invaluable in supporting the work the teacher is doing with a child, e.g. by supervising and offering one-to-one encouragement and support while the child is carrying out various tasks. Help the child with physical exercises and also with tasks such as putting on their coat at break time, putting on and tying shoes and packing their bag. Help the child organise themselves and check and support the child while they are taking down material from the board. Make sure the child is not being left out at lunchtime, as sometimes children with dyspraxia can be excluded by their peer groups. Be patient and listen carefully to what the child is saying, as their speech may not be very clear.

CASE STUDY

Alex was an irritable baby. He didn't sleep well and had problems feeding. His mother, Jenny, thought it was colic and changed his feeds several times in an effort to improve things. He was slightly late in sitting and didn't really crawl, preferring to bottom shuffle before walking at 20 months. As a young child, Alex was always covered in bruises. He was forever tripping and falling over things. Once he hit his head on the corner of a radiator and had to be taken to hospital, where he got five stitches in his forehead. Jenny bought him a tricycle for his third birthday, but he was not able to pedal it.

Jenny kept Alex at home until he was five and a half before sending him to school, as she didn't think he was ready. He still had difficulty with things that his cousins the same age seemed to be able to do easily, such as dress themselves, put on their shoes and eat with a knife and fork. Jenny also felt that Alex was a bit immature and that he found it difficult to get along with others, often irritating them with his constant chatter and clumsy behaviour.

When Jenny bought Alex his first school uniform, he went mad, saying he wasn't going to wear it because it was itchy. Jenny had to wash it over and over before he would wear it. Alex is often fussy about his clothes. Jenny always has to remove care labels before he will wear them.

As Alex progressed through the early years in primary school, Jenny began to worry about him and his lack of progress. He seemed to be struggling in most areas despite making an effort. His handwriting was almost totally illegible, he was not reading well for his age and he was very far behind his peers in maths. Homework was a struggle. Oftentimes he would not have a notion about what homework he was meant to do, and he would have nothing recorded in his homework journal and Jenny would end up having to ring one of the other mothers to ask. Because of Alex's inability to sit and concentrate even for short periods, the most basic homework was taking over two hours to do. Often these marathon homework sessions ended up with Alex crying in frustration and Jenny tearing her hair out with him. Thursday nights were the worst, when he would have English and Irish spellings to learn together with tables for a test the next day. He just didn't seem able to keep what he was learning in his head and invariably got only one or two right the next day. He found this very demoralising, because he, like Jenny, realised that he was spending longer than everyone else trying to learn his work, yet was getting nowhere.

He began to feel he was stupid and started to hate school. He would often complain about pains in his stomach and head, hoping not to have to go to school. Jenny feels now that a lot of the time he actually did feel unwell, but not because of a bug or infection but because of the sheer stress of sitting in a classroom while feeling stupid and unable to do what everyone else could.

By the start of second class, Jenny decided that because Alex was making such slow progress, she would go into the school and ask for an assessment to be done with Alex. His teacher and the headmaster agreed that an assessment should be done, but explained that waiting lists were long at the minute. They explained that if she could pay for the assessment to be done privately, that would speed things up. Jenny was annoyed that her son did not have access to a free psychologist but felt that the sooner he got help, the better, so she decided to employ someone privately.

The psychologist carried out extensive assessments and tests with Alex. He took a detailed family history with Jenny and her husband, Paul, including information about Alex as a baby and also Jenny and Paul's own experiences of school. Paul explained that he had also had difficulties at school and had left as soon as he could with no qualifications. The assessment took all day and cost €500. A couple of weeks later, the results of the assessment came back. The psychologist believed that Alex had dyspraxia. Paul and Jenny had heard of dyslexia, but not dyspraxia – they knew nothing about it. That evening they read everything they could find on the internet, and much of what they found matched what they already knew about Alex. The diagnosis was both a relief and also a huge worry for them. It was a relief because now perhaps Alex would get the help he needed, but a huge worry because now they knew that his problems would never go away – he would never just grow out of this.

The school principal sent Alex's reports to the National Council for Special Education. Due to the report's findings, he was allocated three resource teaching hours per week, three half-hour learning support hours and also access to an SNA for parts of the school day. As a result of this support, Alex is coming on slowly but surely.

For further information on dyspraxia, see www.dyspraxiaireland.com.

DYSGRAPHIA

Dysgraphia sometimes appears as a special need on its own or with other disorders, especially autistic spectrum disorders such as Tourette syndrome, Asperger's syndrome and ADHD. Depending on the type of dysgraphia, people can usually write, but at a very basic and untidy level. Other fine motor skills may also be lacking, e.g. tying shoes, buttons or doing other tasks that require good hand–eye co-ordination. They can also lack basic spelling skills, e.g. they have difficulties with the letters p, q, b and d, and will often write the wrong word when trying to record their thoughts on paper.

In childhood, the disorder generally emerges when the child is first introduced to writing. The child may make inappropriately sized and spaced letters, or write wrong or misspelled words despite thorough instruction. Children with dysgraphia alone may have no other learning or social problems. Approximately 6 per cent of children are thought to have dysgraphia.

Causes

Like dyslexia and dyspraxia, dysgraphia tends to run in families, so there is thought to be a genetic link. In some cases, dysgraphia can also be caused by brain injury during birth, childhood or even adulthood or as part of another condition, particularly ADHD and autistic spectrum disorders.

Types of dysgraphia

Dyslexic dysgraphia

With dyslexic dysgraphia, spontaneously written work is illegible, copied work is fairly good and spelling is bad. Finger tapping speed (a method used to identify fine motor problems) is normal, indicating the deficit does not likely stem from cerebral damage. A dyslexic dysgraphic does not necessarily have dyslexia (difficulty reading), but both conditions do often appear together.

Motor dysgraphia

Motor dysgraphia is characterised by poor fine motor skills, poor dexterity and poor muscle tone. Generally, written work is poor to illegible, even if copied straight from another document. The child may be able to write short sentences relatively neatly, but this will require huge concentration and will take an unusually long time to accomplish. If the child has to write long passages of text, letter shape and size become increasingly inconsistent and illegible. Writing is often slanted due to holding a pen or pencil incorrectly. Spelling skills are not impaired. Finger tapping speed results are below normal.

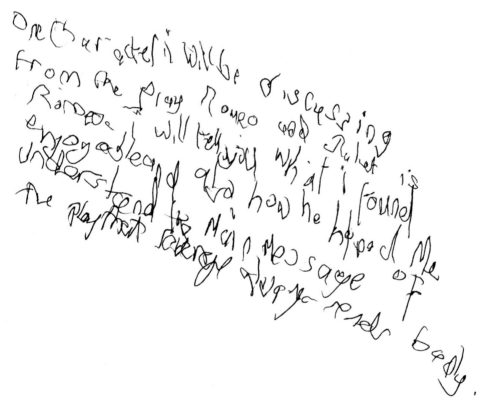

A sample of motor dysgraphic handwriting. This is the translation: One character I will be discussing from the play Romeo and Juliet is Romeo. I will tell you what I found enjoyable and how he helped me understand the main message of the play – that revenge always ends badly.

Spatial dysgraphia

Due to poor spatial awareness, a person with spatial dysgraphia has both illegible spontaneously written work and illegible copied work. They will, however, have normal spelling and normal finger tapping speed.

Symptoms

As there are a number of different forms of dysgraphia, symptoms will vary from child to child. Children with dysgraphia generally take much longer than their peers to complete a written assignment despite having normal or even above average intelligence. The child will show a reluctance or even refuse to complete writing tasks. The child strongly prefers to print instead of using cursive (joined) writing.

The child may use a mixture of upper and lower case letters within the same words, use all upper case letters, use irregular letter sizes and shapes or write unfinished letters. He or she may find it difficult to stay within the lines of the page and have an unusual writing grip. Most will have many written spelling mistakes (even though verbally some can spell very well), frequent reversal of letters within words, the speed of writing will be uneven and they may experience muscle cramping in the arm and shoulder.

Many people who are dysgraphic actually experience pain while writing. The pain usually starts in the centre of the forearm, sometimes spreading to the entire body. Other people with dysgraphia feel as if they are lifting a heavy weight while writing – this is despite normal arm and finger strength. Children with dysgraphia often have difficulty using a spoon, knife and fork.

Diagnosis

Diagnosis will usually be made by observing the child while writing and studying samples of their writing. A comparison may be made between written work and work produced using a word processor. While dysgraphia does sometimes appear on its own, it often appears with another condition, most commonly dyslexia, ADHD, Asperger's and autism, and as such it may be seen as a feature of that condition.

Treatment

Dysgraphia is a lifelong condition that can be helped in one of three ways:
- Carrying out exercises to improve fine motor movements of the hands
- Using techniques to aid handwriting
- Allowing the person to use other means of communication other than writing

Children with dysgraphia should be given small pencils, e.g. golf pencils, or cut down triangular-shaped pencils to promote their grip. They will need to have been given good, clear handwriting instruction with practice. Before a child begins handwriting, it is useful to have them do some warm-up exercises, e.g. free drawing or colouring (depending on age). Children should be allowed extra time to complete written work in class. If possible, the child could dictate what it is they want to say to an adult who writes it down for the child to copy in their own writing. It is important that the child's creativity is not stunted just because they cannot physically write well. For this reason, the use of computers is invaluable for a child with dysgraphia. Children should be introduced to the keyboard early on and taught to type well. They should be allowed to use a laptop in class. Speech recognition software, such as Dragon Naturally Speaking, can be very useful. Children with dysgraphia may be able to avail of reasonable accommodations in state examinations, e.g. a scribe or dictating exam answers onto tape.

Prognosis

While someone will have dysgraphia for life, if it exists on its own without being part of another, more debilitating condition, then the child should experience no major difficulties as a result of the condition. Children will only experience problems if those around them refuse to accommodate them. Teachers or parents who insist on good handwriting and who criticise the child for their efforts can unnecessarily contribute to problems such as low self-esteem in children with dysgraphia. If children are permitted to use the technology that is available and are given reasonable accommodation in their examinations, the condition should not pose any major problems. Most jobs now require little handwritten work.

Role of the SNA

As an SNA, you should ensure that the child has the correct writing materials with him or her, i.e. a short golfer's or triangular pencil. Sit beside the child and offer support and encouragement. You may be asked to act as scribe for the child – writing down what they wish to say so that they can copy out what you have written afterwards – so make sure your writing is clear and totally legible. If the class is expected to use cursive writing (although the child with dysgraphia may be exempt from this), make sure you write in the style being taught by the teacher, as there are a number of different styles of handwriting currently being taught in Irish schools (the two most popular are script style and cursive style). Help the child use their laptop and any software they are using, e.g. speech recognition software.

Aaron started school at age four and a half after attending preschool for a year. In the preschool they didn't really notice that Aaron had any difficulties, perhaps just that he didn't enjoy colouring and drawing as much as the other children and his work seemed much more untidy. As Aaron progressed through school, however, his mother began to suspect that something was wrong. By age eight, his younger brother, who was only five at the time, was able to write much more legibly than him. A lot of the time you would not know what Aaron was trying to write. He didn't seem to be able to write on the lines, his letters alternated between big and clumsy and tiny. The spacing between his words was very irregular. Above all, he hated writing and complained that it hurt when he wrote. Homework became a nightmare. It would take him an hour to write out two or three sentences. This led to rows, which inevitably resulted in Aaron crying in rage and frustration and his mother becoming frustrated and worried. On Thursday nights, Aaron's mother would ask him his spellings for his test the next day. He was actually quite good at spelling as long as he didn't have to write them down. Usually he would come home with three or four spellings marked wrong in his spelling test notebook, which his mother couldn't understand, as he seemed to know them very well the night before.

As Aaron progressed into third class, he got a new teacher. She noticed the difference between Aaron's verbal and written ability almost straight away. One day she called Aaron's mum into the school, explaining that she thought Aaron might have dysgraphia, something she had come across in a previous school she had worked in. This was the first time Aaron's mum had ever heard this word. The teacher explained what she knew about the condition, and later that evening, Aaron's mum looked it up on the internet. Most of what she found seemed to match Aaron to a tee.

The school supported Aaron very well. They had a psychologist assess Aaron and a report completed detailing his needs. Through the local SENO, they applied for and got a laptop computer and voice recognition software for him. Now Aaron does most of his written work on computer and he is coming on very well in all his subjects.

VISUAL IMPAIRMENT

In the context of special education needs, the Department of Education (circular SPED02/05) defines visual impairment and outlines what additional resources are available:

Such pupils have a visual disability which is so serious as to impair significantly to see, thus interfering with their capacity to perceive visually presented materials, such as pictures, diagrams, and the written word. Some will have been diagnosed as suffering from such conditions, such as congenital blindness, cataracts, albinism and retinitis pigmentosa. Most require the use of low-vision aids and availing of the services of a visiting teacher.

(This category is not intended to include those pupils whose visual difficulties are satisfactorily corrected by the wearing of spectacles and/or contact lenses.)

Schools that have a pupil who has been assessed as having a visual impairment, and no other assessed disability, may be allocated a maximum of 3.5 hours teaching support per week from a resource teacher, or from a visiting teacher and resource teacher combined.

Where a pupil with a visual impairment also meets the criterion for another low incidence disability category, provision is allocated as for multiple disabilities. In addition, under circular M14/05, the child may be eligible for grants towards **assistive technologies**. Circular SPED07/02 also indicates that an SNA may be provided for a child with a sensory impairment who has what is called a **care** need resulting from their disability.

Prevalence

The World Health Organization (WHO) defines blindness as being unable to count fingers held up at a distance of 6 metres (20 feet) or less while the person is using the best correction possible. Only about 10 per cent of people who are termed legally blind have no vision at all. There are approximately 240 children under age 18 in Ireland today that are legally blind. In addition, there are approximately 450 to 500 children who, although not termed legally blind, have a visual impairment severe enough to be considered a special educational need. Worldwide there are thought to be approximately 1.4 million blind children, three-quarters of whom live in developing countries.

Causes

Visual impairment can be caused by failure of the eye to develop properly, damage to the eye itself or damage to the optic nerve or other parts of the nervous system connected to it, e.g. the visual cortex of the brain. These problems can arise at different times during a child's development.

Before birth:
▶ There may be a family history of blindness, whereby blindness is genetically inherited.

- Maternal rubella or other infections such as syphilis during pregnancy.
- Toxoplasmosis, an infection that comes from parasites found in animal faeces or undercooked meat. This is why pregnant women should avoid farm animals (or if they are in contact with them, should make sure to be extra cautious with personal hygiene) and lightly cooked meats. Some professionals also advise pregnant women to stay away from unpasteurised dairy products and shellfish that may swim in polluted waters.

Around birth:
- Prematurity – babies who are born earlier than 35 weeks gestation are at risk of eye defects
- Infections, e.g. herpes simplex, during the birth process
- Oxygen poisoning or toxicity (too much oxygen given at birth)
- Asphyxia during the birth process (deprived of oxygen at birth)

After birth:
- Head and eye injuries
- Infections, e.g. measles
- Cataracts – a clouding over the eye lens
- Inflammatory diseases, e.g. conjunctivitis
- Vitamin A deficiency (in the developing world)

Structure of the eye

- **Conjunctiva:** The delicate thin outer skin that covers the eye and inner eyelids.
- **Cornea:** The window of the eye, which allows light through to the retina.
- **Aqueous humour:** A clear, jelly-like substance.
- **Iris:** The area of the eye that gives the eye its colour. It is in front of the lens, but behind the cornea.
- **Pupil:** The central hole in the eye. It widens and narrows to allow more or less light in.
- **Lens:** A capsule of clear fluid that helps focus images on the retina.
- **Vitreous humour:** A clear, jelly-like substance.
- **Retina:** The inner lining of the eye. It receives and transmits messages about images to the brain via the optic nerve.
- **Macula:** A small area of the retina that is needed for seeing detailed images.

> **Choroid:** The layer between the retina and the sclera. It contains the blood vessels in the eye.
> **Sclera:** The tough white protective covering on the eye.
> **Optic nerve:** Messages are sent along this nerve from the retina to the brain.

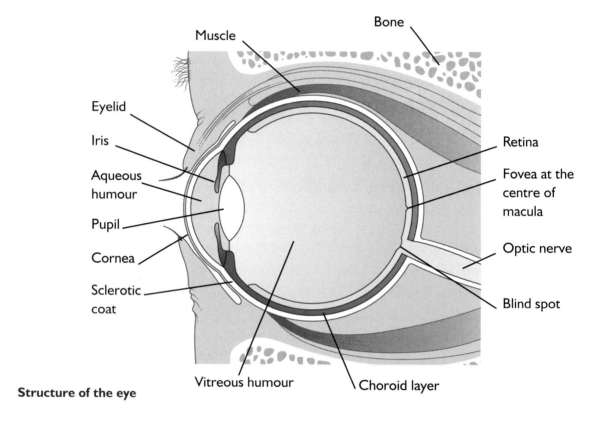

Structure of the eye

Types of visual impairment

Degrees of visual impairment will depend on what form the individual has. Listed below are the main types of visual impairment in the Western world. Patterns of visual impairment are different in developing nations, where more children are visually impaired as a result of environmental reasons or lack of medical care.

Albinism

Albinism is a genetically inherited condition where the eyes, hair and skin lack normal levels of the pigment melanin. As the gene for albinism is usually recessive, both parents have to be carriers of the gene, though some rare forms are inherited from only one parent. Also, there is a rare form of albinism called ocular albinism that affects only the eyes. It is carried on the X chromosome, so while females can be carriers, only males have the condition.

Eye conditions common with albinism may include:

▶ **Nystagmus:** Irregular rapid movement of the eyes back and forth or in a circular motion.

▶ **Strabismus:** Eye misalignment – crossed eyes or lazy eye. If left untreated (usually with special glasses or a patch), then this can cause visual impairment and blindness.

▶ **Myopia** (short sightedness – difficulty seeing items far away) or **hyperopia** (long sightedness – difficulty seeing close up).

▶ **Astigmatism:** The cornea of the eye is misshapen, resulting in blurred vision.

▶ **Photophobia:** Hypersensitivity to bright light and glare.

▶ **Macular hypoplasia:** Underdevelopment of the fovea, which is an area in the centre of the retina.

▶ **Optic nerve hypoplasia:** Underdevelopment of the optic nerve.

▶ **Abnormal decussation** (crossing) of the optic nerve fibres going to the brain.

▶ **Amblyopia:** This condition is sometimes incorrectly mixed up with strabismus and called lazy eye. This is not accurate, because with amblyopia, the eye is quite normal – it is the area of the brain meant to interpret visual images that is not working correctly. Thus, lazy brain would actually be more accurate.

Of course, all of the above conditions can occur alone without albinism and cause visual impairment.

Congenital blindness

Congenital blindness means blindness from birth. It can be inherited or caused by something that occurs during the prenatal period, e.g. the mother contracting German measles (rubella).

Congenital cataracts

A congenital cataract is present at birth and causes a clouding of the lens of the eye. Because the lens is cloudy, light cannot focus properly on the retina and sight is impaired. Cataracts at birth are rare and may be caused by maternal rubella or appear with other syndromes, e.g. Down's syndrome. Cataracts will usually be removed shortly after birth unless they have been caused by maternal rubella, in which case they cannot be removed for a number of months. There is usually a lasting effect on vision, especially if caused by rubella.

Cortical visual impairment

Someone with cortical visual impairment may be totally or partially blind. Someone with cortical visual impairment alone will have nothing wrong with their actual eyes rather, the brain does not process visual messages either properly or at all.

Glaucoma

Glaucoma is a serious eye condition that results from the excessive build-up of pressure in the fluid of the eye. It is quite rare, occurring in approximately one in 10,000 children. As eye pressure builds up, the various parts of the eye, particularly the optic nerve, become damaged, thus causing blindness or partial blindness. Early symptoms of glaucoma include cloudy corneas, a prominent eye or eyes, sensitivity to bright light (tilting of the head away or eye closure), excessive tearing or one eye larger than the other. Glaucoma is usually treated with surgery and medication that reduces eye pressure. Unfortunately, damage caused before treatment is irreversible, so early detection is vital.

Retinitis pigmentosa

Retinitis pigmentosa is a genetically inherited progressive eye condition whereby the photoreceptors (rods and cones) located in the retina develop abnormally. The condition usually takes years to develop, although it can develop more quickly and therefore can be a cause of visual impairment in children. Someone with retinitis pigmentosa will normally experience night blindness first (an inability to see in dim light), followed by a gradual reduction in their perceptual vision (tunnel vision). Retinitis pigmentosa can cause total blindness if central vision becomes affected as well, although this is rarely, if ever, seen in children. There is no real effective treatment for the condition.

Retinopathy of prematurity

Retinopathy of prematurity (ROP) is an eye disorder that predominately affects prematurely born babies. The blood vessels of the eye develop between the sixteenth and thirty-sixth week of pregnancy. Babies born prematurely can have a disorganised growth pattern of the blood vessels in the retina, which may result in scarring and retinal detachment (pulling the retina out of shape). ROP can be mild and may resolve spontaneously, but it may lead to blindness in serious cases. As such, all preterm babies are at risk for ROP. Very low birth weight babies (1 kg or 2.4 lb and under) are at an additional risk. Both oxygen toxicity and oxygen deprivation can contribute to the development of ROP. All premature babies are examined for the condition, as early laser surgery can help prevent the condition worsening. If untreated, then blindness or partial blindness can result. Even if treated, babies born with ROP are at a much greater risk of developing other eye conditions, e.g. glaucoma, cataracts, myopia and strabismus.

Diabetic retinopathy

Diabetic retinopathy is retinopathy (damage to the retina) caused by complications of diabetes mellitus, which can eventually lead to blindness. People who have poorly controlled diabetes, whereby their blood sugars fluctuate (perhaps because of lifestyle or irregular insulin intake), can damage the blood vessels of the retina, causing visual impairment. Diabetic retinopathy would not normally be seen in diabetic children, but if their diabetes is badly controlled, they are likely to develop it later in life.

For further information on eye conditions that cause visual impairment, see the Royal National Institute of Blind People website, www.rnib.org.uk. Click on Eye Health, then Eye Conditions, and you will find an A to Z list of conditions.

Diagnosis

Diagnosis will depend on the type and cause of the visual impairment. All babies' eyes are examined in hospital after birth and during early developmental check-ups. At-risk babies, especially those who are very premature and low birth weight, will be given more extensive and more invasive examinations. Parents and childcare staff should also be vigilant.

Signs to look for in babies:
- No eye contact
- Does not react to light
- Abnormal eye movement (nystagmus)
- Eyes do not follow objects at eight weeks
- Failure to locate objects at six to 12 months

Signs to look for in older children:
- Cloudy, bloodshot, sore eyes, excessive rubbing or blinking
- Unusual eye movements
- Clumsiness and poor hand–eye co-ordination
- Child moves their head rather than eyes when following a story
- Holds objects close to their face or sits 'on top' of the television
- Loses interest in activities that require good vision

) Child may not get work copied down off the white/black board or have it copied down in a patchy, disorganised way despite normal reading and writing ability

Treatment

Treatment will depend on the cause and symptoms of the visual impairment. It may involve surgery (cataracts, retinopathy, glaucoma, prematurity), medication (glaucoma) or there may be no treatment available and efforts will be concentrated on helping the child work around their disability in order to develop to their full potential. In childcare settings and schools, this is where special needs workers have a vital part to play.

) It is thought that sight is involved in 80 per cent of a child's learning. It is therefore vital that visually impaired children are encouraged and facilitated to develop their other senses, e.g. sand and water play.

) For partially sighted children, ensure that the childcare setting or school classroom is well lit.

) Always describe what is going on to the child.

) Encourage self-help skills, e.g. putting on coats and shoes, washing hands, feeding. Be patient and allow the child as much time as they need.

) Tell the child before you touch him or her, e.g. 'I am going to change your nappy now, Samantha.' The child cannot see you, so they could get a fright if they are suddenly whooshed up and laid down on a changing mat.

) Ensure the environment is safe and secure. Parents will be invaluable here, as they will have had experience with their child and should be involved in the safety audit carried out before the child starts the crèche, preschool or school.

) Use storytelling, rhymes and action songs.

) Speak clearly, but not patronisingly. When someone speaks to us, we use many visual clues to figure out what they are saying. Visually impaired children rely only on auditory information and it is therefore more difficult for them to hear what has been said, especially in a noisy classroom.

) Assist the child so that he or she can take part in all activities, e.g. swimming lessons.

) Encourage the other children to name themselves while speaking to the visually impaired child. This will only have to be done initially, as the child will quickly be able to differentiate voices.

) Some children will have insufficient sight to read print (even enlarged print) and will need to learn Braille. Develop the child's abilities to discriminate by touch in preparation for learning Braille by playing games that require him or her to differentiate subtle differences in objects. Braille can be learned by those working with the visually impaired through various courses nationwide. Details of Braille courses can be obtained from the National Braille Production Centre (www.braille.ie).

▶ For children who wear glasses, ensure that they wear them in class. Perhaps they could have a spare pair kept in school at all times. Show positive images of children wearing glasses, e.g. Harry Potter.

Children will be entitled to the services of the visiting teacher for the visually impaired. The job of this teacher is to provide extra support for the visually impaired child and to advise the preschool or school on how best to provide for the needs of that child. They conduct assessments and give advice in relation to equipment commonly used by the visually impaired, i.e. technology, large print, tapes, and on additional personnel resources, when needed. Teachers can also advise schools on any necessary adaptations to the school environment required by the child with a visual impairment.

The National Council for the Blind in Ireland (NCBI) offers a wide range of services to children and adults with visual impairments. Those working with visually impaired children should be aware of these services and help the children avail of them.

Library

▶ **Talking book service:** The NCBI library stocks thousands of talking books for both adults and children.

▶ **Large print book service**: The NCBI holds the largest collection of large print novels for children in Ireland. The collection of adult large print books also contains titles on all topics and interests.

▶ **Braille book service:** As with audio books, the NCBI specialises in the production of Irish interest titles in Braille.

▶ **Magazines and newspapers on tape**: NCBI's professional readers read extracts from a wide range of newspapers and magazines onto tape.

▶ **Talking educational books:** Every year, the NCBI library produces an audio recording of textbooks from the Irish primary and second-level curriculum.

The NCBI also has a shop. Orders can be placed online for products such as:

▶ Copies with large squares (sums) and wider, more defined lines

▶ Writing frames to help the child keep writing straight

- Braille calendar and diary
- Embossed (raised) graph paper
- Scented coloured markers
- Talking calculators
- Braille rulers
- For classes such as home economics there are talking measuring jugs, talking weighing scales, talking tape measures or a talking microwave.
- Some board and card games have been made suitable for the visually impaired – dominos, Connect 4, solitaire, large print Scrabble and playing cards and audible mitre football. Some companies have manufactured versions of their games suitable for the visually impaired, but they need to be specially ordered, as the games generally available in shops are not this version, e.g. Ludo, Monopoly, snakes and ladders and Staunton chess sets.

Prognosis

The prognosis for a child with a visual impairment will largely depend on the nature of the impairment, the amount of support the child receives and whether there are other conditions present. With good levels of both practical and emotional support, visually impaired children can reach their full potential, going on to lead successful, independent lives.

Role of the SNA

Children with significant visual impairments will normally be allocated an SNA, either on a full- or part-time basis. The visiting teacher for the visually impaired will give detailed guidance for each individual child, but generally, SNAs can help children use computers (computer shortcuts are very important because the child generally cannot see the cursor) and other assistive technology (text-to-speech scanners and software) and also help them in terms of physically moving around the classroom, school and playground safely. The SNA can read information displayed on the blackboard for the child and generally keep them in touch with what is going on. Of course, the role of the SNA also includes giving the child plenty of positive feedback and encouragement for their efforts. Children who have partial sight may benefit from having class work enlarged on the photocopier.

Sasha was born prematurely at 28 weeks, weighing just over 1 kg (2 lb 4 oz). She remained in hospital for almost four months, the first two months of which she spent in an incubator on oxygen. During her time in hospital, she picked up a number of serious infections and had a small heart defect, which surgeons repaired. Sasha also has retinopathy of prematurity (stage 3), affecting both eyes. While surgeons were able to halt the condition and prevent it getting worse with laser surgery, Sasha is visually impaired and registered as legally blind.

During her early years, Sasha's parents were very protective of her. Sasha's mum, Lynette, gave up work to care for her full time. However, this meant that Sasha had little contact with other children and therefore didn't really know what to do if she did encounter other children at relations' and neighbours' birthday parties, etc. When Sasha was three and a half, Lynette decided that Sasha should join a preschool. When she went to look, however, she had great difficulty finding one to take her daughter. Many she approached said that they did not have the facilities or the personnel to accommodate someone with Sasha's needs. In the end, Lynette enrolled her daughter in a preschool three mornings per week. Before Sasha began attending, Lynette had a number of meetings with the staff in the preschool to discuss Sasha's needs. Once she started she began to progress well, though she continued to have difficulty relating to other children, and most of the time engaged in solitary play. The preschool staff were concerned that Sasha had few self-help skills – she couldn't put on her coat and shoes or toilet or feed herself unaided. Lynette knew that she was guilty of doing too much for Sasha and began to teach her self-help skills such as brushing her teeth, allowing her more independence.

Sasha began primary school at age five. The school again tried to accommodate Sasha's needs. She sat at the top of the room to be able to hear what the teacher was saying clearly, and an SNA enlarges all work onto dull paper (avoiding glare) so that she can use it. Sasha also has a magnifying glass that she uses and has a desk lamp plugged in at her desk so that she can see her work more clearly. Sasha has specially lined copies (the lines are dark in colour and more widely spaced), a talking calculator and access to text-to-speech software. With all of these facilities, Sasha is doing quite well at school. Her literacy is coming along, although she does need learning support in this area, which she gets three times a week.

At lunchtime, the other children take care not to bump into Sasha. She is restricted in the games that she can play. One or two of the girls in her class help her manoeuvre round the playground at lunchtime.

For further information on visual impairment, the National Council for the Blind of Ireland (www.ncbi.ie) is a useful website.

CYSTIC FIBROSIS

Cystic fibrosis (CF) is a genetically inherited condition that causes one or more of the glands of the body to produce a thick, sticky mucus that affects organ functioning. The most common organs affected by CF are the lungs and the organs of the digestive tract, although the reproductive system may also be affected.

Prevalence

Cystic fibrosis (also called mucoviscidosis) is Ireland's most common life-threatening inherited disease. Ireland has the highest incidence of CF in the world – approximately one in 19 Irish people are carriers of the CF gene and there are more than 1,100 children in Ireland living with CF.

Causes

CF is caused by mutations in a gene called gene CFTR on chromosome 7. CFTR is a gene that provides instructions for making a protein called the cystic fibrosis transmembrane conductance regulator. Through the process of osmosis, this protein regulates the movement of water in and out of the mucus membranes of many of the organs, particularly the lungs, digestive system, liver, pancreas and reproductive organs. When the CFTR gene is faulty, the mucus becomes overly thick, causing the organs to clog and malfunction. CFTR also regulates salt loss from the body via the sweat glands. Patients with CF usually secrete large amounts of salt in their sweat (before the availability of genetic testing, this was how CF was diagnosed).

As the gene CFTR is recessive, for someone to have CF, both their parents must either be carriers of the defective gene or actually have the condition itself. Most babies born with CF have parents who are just carriers of the condition. This is because many people (particularly males) who actually have CF experience fertility problems and therefore often cannot have children.

Symptoms

CF affects the glands and damages many organs, including the lungs, the pancreas, the digestive tract and the reproductive system. CF primarily affects the lungs and the digestive system. It causes thick, sticky mucus to be produced, blocking the bronchial tubes of the lungs. The mucus also makes it difficult to clear bacteria from the lungs, leading to cycles of serious lung infections and inflammation. This can eventually cause permanent damage to the lungs.

The thick mucus also prevents the body's natural enzymes (especially the enzymes from the pancreas) from digesting food properly. This makes it difficult for someone with CF to digest and absorb adequate nutrients from their food, causing malnutrition.

The reproductive system is also affected in some people with CF. It is estimated that 95 per cent of males and 80 per cent of females with CF have serious reproductive problems and would have difficulty having children.

Diagnosis

CF can be diagnosed either before or after birth. An early diagnosis after birth is very important so that therapy can begin right away before there is significant organ damage.

Before birth, if a woman and her partner know they are carriers of the CF gene, then they may be offered prenatal tests that can determine whether the foetus has CF or not (remember, the chance of the foetus having CF is one in four). Two of the most common testing methods are chorionic villus sampling and amniocentesis.

Chorionic villus sampling

This test is usually conducted between the tenth and twelfth week of pregnancy, when a sample of cells is taken from the placenta and sent away for testing. This is an invasive testing technique and carries a small risk of miscarriage (1 per cent). It can detect with a very large degree of accuracy the presence of a faulty CFTR gene.

Amniocentesis

This test is usually conducted between the fifteenth and eighteenth week of pregnancy, when a sample of amniotic fluid is withdrawn using a fine needle and sent away for testing. Like chorionic villus sampling, this is an invasive testing technique and carries with it a small risk of miscarriage (0.5 per cent). It can detect with a very large degree of accuracy the presence of a range of genetic conditions, including CF.

After the baby is born, it can be tested for CF by taking a blood sample and by conducting a sweat test. For the sweat test, doctors trigger sweating on a small patch of skin on an arm or leg. They rub the skin with a sweat-producing chemical, then use an electrode to provide a mild electrical current, which may cause a tingling or warm feeling. Sweat is collected on a pad or paper and then analysed. The sweat test is usually done twice. High salt levels confirm a diagnosis of CF.

Some babies (about 10 per cent) with CF are unable to pass their first stool (called meconium) because of blockage. This is one reason why babies are generally not permitted to leave hospital until they pass their first stool.

Other signs to look out for include:

▷ Baby tastes salty when kissed
▷ Baby coughs and wheezes
▷ Baby fails to gain weight
▷ Baby's stools are bulky and foul smelling (because they are essentially undigested, rotten food)
▷ The baby may vomit when coughing

Once diagnosed, children will be given chest X-rays, sinus X-rays and lung function tests and their sputum (spit) will also be tested for bacteria present. These tests will determine how severe the CF is and therefore how aggressively it should be treated with antibiotics and steroids, etc.

Also, people who have a family history of CF can be tested to find out if they are a carrier of the faulty CFTR gene.

Treatment

Treatment for CF generally centres around five different areas:
▷ Maintenance of good nutrition
▷ Prevention of infection, particularly lung infections
▷ Physiotherapy to keep the airways clear
▷ Organ transplants
▷ New medications

Maintenance of good nutrition

The pancreas is usually affected by CF and the child will need to take a synthetic pancreatic enzyme replacement called pancrelipase to help digest their food. Popular brands of pancrelipase include Pancrease, Pancreacarb, Ultrase and Creon. The replacement is usually taken 15 minutes before a meal. Pancrelipase will need to be continued for life or the child would fail to thrive and would be prone to illness and infection.

The following are some general dietary guidelines for children with CF. Each child with CF will be different and will be under the care of their own dietician.
▷ Most children with CF require a high-calorie diet. This is because even though they are taking enzyme supplements, a proportion of what they eat is not digested and utilised by the body. A child aged seven to 10 normally needs to consume approximately 2,000 kilocalories per day, but a child with CF may need to consume up to 4,000 kilocalories per day, depending on the extent of their condition.

- Children will need to eat three good meals per day with at least two nutritious snacks.
- It is important that the foods that the child consumes are of a high nutritional content and that they do not fill up on junk foods with little nutritional value.
- Because children with CF are unable to absorb fat, they are given fat-soluble vitamin supplements (vitamins A, D, E and K).
- Fat content in a child's diet will be reduced if they are suffering side effects from consuming fat, e.g. abdominal pain.
- If babies are not breastfed, then modified formula milk will usually be given that contains higher levels of protein and energy than ordinary formula milks.
- As a baby is weaned, they will be given increasing amounts of pancreatic enzyme as the amount of food they are eating increases.

Prevention of infection, particularly lung infections

One of the biggest challenges facing children with CF is keeping their lungs free of infection. Some children will be on a continuous dose of antibiotic medicine, while others may be on inhalers and steroids when the need arises. It is important that children with CF are kept away from potential causes of infection and that they are given appropriate vaccinations, e.g. swine flu (H1N1). Other suggestions include the following.

- Bedrooms and classrooms should be well ventilated to prevent the spread of airborne infections.
- Crèches, preschools and schools should have a strict policy of not allowing children to attend if they are unwell.
- Children should be encouraged to use a tissue if they cough or sneeze and put it immediately into the bin.
- Encourage hand washing after using a tissue and after toileting.
- Try to stop contact with children or other adults who have colds or coughs (although it is also important not to become overly protective).
- It is often not advisable to bring a child with CF into very crowded situations.
- Ensure that everyone working with a child with CF has current immunisations.
- Maintain good levels of general hygiene in the home, crèche, preschool or school.
- Inform parents of children with CF if there has been an outbreak of general infection in the crèche, preschool or school.

Physiotherapy to keep the airways clear

Even when children with CF are symptom free, it is important to take measures to make sure their lungs remain clear. Children with CF will have a physiotherapist working with them who should provide training for the child's parents and other people caring for the child, e.g. an SNA. The following physiotherapy methods are commonly used.

- **Drainage:** The child is positioned downwards at different angles in order to drain mucus from the lungs.
- **Chest clapping:** A cupped hand is used to clap the chest firmly in order to free mucus from the lungs. The child is encouraged to cough up secretions.
- **Chest shaking:** As the child breathes out, the adult places his or her hand flat on the child's chest, shaking it firmly and pressing inwards.
- **Breathing exercises**.

If the child has a lot of mucus, sessions lasting up to one hour may need to be carried out three or four times per day. If a child is well and does not have a lot of mucus, then only shorter, less frequent sessions may be necessary. Sessions will normally be carried out with babies over the adult's knee. With older children, a foam wedge is usually used. Physical exercises such as jumping on a trampoline should be encouraged.

Organ transplants

Both life expectancy and the quality of life for people with CF can be significantly improved through a lung transplant. As of May 2009, there were 13 young people with CF awaiting lung transplants in Ireland. Ten CF transplants were undertaken in Ireland in 2012. The Cystic Fibrosis Association of Ireland urges people to carry an organ donor card.

Gene therapy is another avenue being explored by medical science today. The hope is that one day, doctors will be able to replace defective CF genes with healthy genes, thus curing the condition. While progress has been made in this area, a breakthrough is some way off.

New medications for cystic fibrosis

From March 2013, a new drug called Kalydeco was made available to individuals with CF caused by the G551DE mutation. As just over 10 per cent of patients in Ireland have this form of CF, it means approximately 120 patients will be suitable for treatment with the new drug. The drug has many benefits, including significant improvements in lung function, increased body weight, improvement in patients' quality of life and a 55 per cent reduction in pulmonary infections. It is the first drug that has come on the market that treats the causes of CF instead of just treating its symptoms. While the drug is very costly, costing approximately €234,000 per patient per year (this figure has since been negotiated downwards to approximately €160,000 per patient per year), it makes a huge improvement in the quality of life of people with CF, reducing time spent in hospital and out of school and work. It is hoped that further research building on the work already done with this drug will find similar treatments for other forms of the disease.

Prognosis

Up until the 1960s, the prognosis for children with CF was very poor indeed. Most children did not live beyond their fifth birthday. Today, with advances in medicine, better knowledge of nutrition and physiotherapy, children are not only living longer, but also healthier lives with CF. Organ transplant also significantly improves life expectancy. Today, the average life expectancy of someone with CF is 30 years, with some people living well beyond this.

Role of the SNA

An SNA working with a child with CF may have the following roles.

- Carry out physiotherapy sessions with the child, several times a day if necessary.
- Make sure the child is eating their lunch and has taken their enzyme supplement.
- Remind children and perhaps administer other medication, e.g. antibiotics or inhalers.
- Ensure that children cough into tissues and dispose of them safely.
- Help young children with good personal hygiene.
- Help to keep the child's environment clean and well ventilated.
- If a child misses a lot of school due to their CF, keep handouts, etc. for the child, as the teacher may ask you to put together an activity pack for the child to do at home.

Simon was born on a sunny April day. Everything seemed fine at first and Simon and his mother, Tanya, left the hospital the next day to go home to Simon's dad, Paul, and older brother, Josh.

Tanya began to worry early on, after recovering from the initial overtiredness and mayhem a newborn brings. She noticed that Simon wasn't putting on weight and often brought feeds back up. She mentioned it to the public health nurse when she came around. The nurse advised changing Simon's feeds to a different formula, so she put him on a feed for 'hungrier babies'. After a month there was still no routine yet with his feeds and Tanya also noticed that his nappies smelled very bad.

At his six-week check-up, Tanya told the doctor that she was worried that Simon wasn't putting on weight. The doctor said to give it a little time to see how things went. At eight weeks, Tanya took Simon to the GP with a chest infection. This time, Tanya told the doctor that Simon's nappies smelled very badly compared with her memory of Josh's nappies. The doctor gave Tanya an appointment for Simon to attend the local hospital and a course of antibiotics. At the hospital, Simon had a number of tests done, including a sweat test and chest X-ray. A number of days later, Tanya and Paul got the devastating news that their son had cystic fibrosis. They hadn't even known that they were carriers. Both of them knew how serious the condition was because each had cousins with the condition.

Over the next few months, Tanya and Paul met with dieticians, physiotherapists and paediatricians and learned how to manage Simon's condition. They were told to wean Simon at 12 weeks and introduce high-protein foods such as puréed chicken, fish and meat as soon as possible in order to boost Simon's food intake. They also started him on an enzyme replacement powder that they mixed with his yoghurts. They also learned how to do his physiotherapy, and did this daily.

Simon continued to do fairy well, though he did get more infections than his brother and it always took him a lot longer to get over them. Tanya didn't send him to preschool, as she thought it would just be asking for trouble. As a consequence, Simon was a quiet, shy and timid child.

Starting school was a big day for Simon. His mother had arranged to meet the school staff in advance to explain Simon's condition and his special requirements. The school put a policy in place for the storage and dispensing of Simon's enzymes and medicines and also applied for and got a part-time SNA who trained to carry out his physiotherapy chest clapping sessions.

During Simon's first year at school, he contracted swine flu and was admitted to hospital. His condition became very serious at one stage and he was in intensive care. Thankfully, the doctors were able to get the virus under control and Simon came through the ordeal. During his second year he got a number of serious lung infections, again requiring hospitalisation and long spells at home from school to recuperate. During these periods, his school arranged for home tuition with the Department of Education and Skills. This meant that Simon, who is a very capable student, was able to keep up with his schoolwork.

His primary school years progressed much like this and now Simon is in his Junior Certificate year. His health is sometimes good and sometimes not so good, when he has to go on oxygen. He finds it difficult to put on any weight and is very thin, something he doesn't really like about himself. Simon does fear what the future will bring for him and hopes to have a lung transplant one day, as he knows his lungs are getting more and more damaged because of the years of infections and drugs.

For further information, contact the Cystic Fibrosis Association of Ireland (www.cfireland.ie).

SPINA BIFIDA

Prevalence

Spina bifida is the most common neural tube defect (NTD), which causes incomplete development of the spinal cord. Translated, it literally means 'split spine'. Spina bifida is a relatively common condition that affects about one in every 1,000 children born in Ireland each year. Ireland has one of the highest incidences of spina bifida births in the world.

Causes

The spine is made up of separate bones, called vertebrae, that normally cover and protect the spinal cord. With spina bifida, some of these vertebrae are not completely formed. Instead, they are split and the spinal cord and its coverings usually protrude through a sac-like bulge on the back, covered with a thin membrane. What causes the spine to fail to close completely is not fully understood, but it is thought to be a combination of both genetic and environmental factors. One environmental factor that is thought to contribute to spina bifida is a lack of folate in the diet or the inability to naturally absorb folate. This is why women who are pregnant or are considering pregnancy should take folic acid supplements, as it is found to reduce occurrences of spina bifida by up to 75 per cent.

Symptoms

The symptoms or effects of spina bifida on the individual will largely depend on the form or type of spina bifida and the extent to which the spinal cord has been exposed. Effects can include hydrocephalus, varying degrees of paralysis, pressure sores, loss of sensation in the lower limbs, malformations, social and sexual issues and bowel and bladder incontinence. A small number of people with spina bifida are allergic to latex. Many health care products, e.g. surgical gloves, tubing and catheters, have latex in them, so those with a severe allergy to latex should wear a MedicAlert bracelet or carry a card.

Common forms of spina bifida

Spina bifida occulta

Spina bifida occulta is very common and is sometimes called hidden spina bifida. The split in the bone of the spine is so small that the spinal cord and main nerves cannot bulge out, and so little or no damage is done to the nervous system. The only thing that is visible on the back may be a dimple, tuft of hair or a red mark. Someone with spina bifida occulta may not have any problems at all and may not even know they have this condition unless an X-ray of the back is taken.

Meningocele

With meningocele (pronounced men-in-jo-seal), the split in the bones is not big enough for the spinal cord to come through, but a 'balloon' of skin filled with fluid and blood vessels bulges out. This fluid, which comes from around the spinal column, is called cerebrospinal fluid (CSF). The nerve supply is not usually affected. The degree of disability is usually not very severe, but this can only be determined as the child develops.

Myelomeningocele

Myelomeningocele (pronounced my-lo-men-in-jo-seal) is the most common form of spina bifida, and depending on the location of the split, it can cause the most problems. The split is so large that the spinal cord and nerves bulge out into the balloon filled with fluid. The spinal cord and nerves become exposed and the degree of damage will determine the extent of disability. Myelomeningocele is most frequently found in the lumbar area, but can occur anywhere along the spine.

Myelomeningocele spina bifida

Encephalocele

In a small number of cases of neural tube defects, the split is high up and involves the back of the head (skull). There will be a balloon-like swelling, but this does not contain important nerves of the spinal column. Some encephaloceles (pronounced en-cef-a-lo-seals) are small and covered with skin and the children usually grow up without major implications. Sometimes, however, if it is large it may contain some of the brain, which can severely affect the baby's eyesight and can cause learning disabilities. Sometimes, the balloon-like swelling will contain significant amounts of brain tissue, so that the remaining brain is small, poorly developed and severely hydrocephalic. This will cause profound learning disabilities.

Anencephaly

Anencephaly (pronounced an-en-cef-a-lee) is the most severe neural tube defect. The skull does not form and the entire brain above the brainstem fails to develop.

Unlike spina bifida, the condition is inoperable and the prognosis is extremely poor. Due to the extent of brain damage, the affected babies are unlikely to survive outside the uterus. They may be stillborn or die shortly after birth.

Diagnosis

In most cases, spina bifida is diagnosed before birth (prenatal). However, some mild cases may go unnoticed until after birth (postnatal). Very mild cases, in which there are no symptoms, may never be detected.

Prenatal diagnosis

The most common screening methods used to look for spina bifida during pregnancy are second trimester maternal serum alpha-fetoprotein (MSAFP) screening and foetal ultrasound. The MSAFP screen measures the level of a protein called alpha-fetoprotein (AFP), which is made naturally by the foetus and placenta. During pregnancy, a small amount of AFP normally crosses the placenta and enters the mother's bloodstream. If abnormally high levels of this protein appear in the mother's bloodstream, however, this may indicate that the foetus has a neural tube defect. The MSAFP is just a screening test and not specific for spina bifida; therefore, the test cannot definitively determine that a foetus does or does not have spina bifida. If a high level of AFP is detected, the doctor may request additional testing, such as an ultrasound or amniocentesis, to help determine the cause.

Amniocentesis, as mentioned earlier, is usually done between the fifteenth and eighteenth week of pregnancy. The doctor removes samples of amniotic fluid from the amniotic sac surrounding the foetus. If high levels of AFP are found, this strongly indicates that the disorder is present. However, amniocentesis cannot reveal the severity of the spina bifida.

Postnatal diagnosis

Mild cases of spina bifida not diagnosed during prenatal testing may be detected postnatally during a routine examination (where spinal lesions will be visible) and X-rays. Doctors may use magnetic resonance imaging (MRI) or a computed tomography (CT) scan to get a clearer view of the spine and vertebrae. Individuals with the more severe forms of spina bifida often have muscle weakness in their feet, hips and legs. If hydrocephalus is suspected, the doctor may request a CT scan and/or X-ray of the skull to look for extra fluid inside the brain.

Treatment

There is no cure for spina bifida. The nerve tissue that is damaged or lost cannot be repaired or replaced, nor can function be restored to the damaged nerves. Treatment depends on the type and severity of the disorder. Generally, children with the mild forms of spina bifida need no treatment, although some may require surgery as they grow.

The key priorities for treating myelomeningocele are to prevent infection from developing through the exposed nerves and tissue of the defect on the spine and to protect the exposed nerves and structures from additional trauma. Typically, a child born with spina bifida will have surgery to close the defect and prevent infection or further trauma within the first few days after delivery.

Doctors have recently begun performing foetal surgery for treatment of myelomeningocele. Foetal surgery is performed *in utero* (within the uterus) and involves opening the mother's abdomen and uterus and sewing shut the opening over the developing baby's spinal cord. Some doctors believe the earlier the defect is corrected, the better the outcome is for the baby. Although the procedure cannot restore lost neurological function, it may prevent additional loss from occurring. However, this surgery is considered experimental and there are risks for both foetus and mother. The major risk for the foetus is that if surgery stimulates premature delivery, the foetus may suffer the effects of organ immaturity, brain haemorrhage and even death. Risks to the mother include infection, blood loss leading to the need for transfusion, gestational diabetes and weight gain due to bed rest. Having said this, the benefits of foetal surgery are promising, and when fully developed will hopefully reduce the exposure of the vulnerable spinal nerve tissue and bones to the intrauterine environment, particularly the amniotic fluid, which is considered toxic.

Some children with myelomeningocele develop a condition called progressive tethering, or tethered cord syndrome. With this syndrome, their spinal cord (which is usually movable within the spinal column) becomes fastened to the vertebrae of the spinal column, causing the spinal cord to become abnormally stretched and the vertebrae elongated as the child grows and moves. This condition can cause loss of muscle function to the legs, bowel and bladder. Early surgery on the spinal cord to free it from the vertebrae may allow the child to regain a normal level of functioning and prevent further neurological deterioration.

Some children will need subsequent surgeries to manage problems with the feet, hips or spine. Individuals with hydrocephalus generally will require additional surgery to replace the shunt, which can be outgrown or become clogged.

Some individuals with spina bifida require assistive devices such as braces, crutches or wheelchairs. The location of the malformation on the spine often indicates the type of assistive devices needed. Children with a defect high on the spine and more extensive paralysis will often require a wheelchair, while those with a defect lower on the spine may be able to use crutches, leg braces or walkers.

Treatment for paralysis and bladder and bowel problems typically begins soon after birth, and may include special exercises for the legs and feet to help prepare the child for walking with braces or crutches when he or she is older.

Because of nerve damage, many children with spina bifida do not have normal bowel and bladder control. Effective bowel and bladder management are extremely important because:

- Failure to empty the bladder or bowel can lead to infection and constipation.
- A smell of urine or faeces can be hugely detrimental to the child's relationships with peers and his or her self-esteem.
- Effective management ensures the skin is kept clean and free from sores.

Some children with spina bifida will have a catheter or penile sheath (males) fitted which drains into a bag. The bag is then emptied several times each day. Pads and special pants may also be used. The bowel can be trained by the child using the lavatory at the same time each day. The bowel then becomes accustomed to being emptied at this time. Sometimes children with spina bifida also need to use enemas or suppositories to stimulate the bowel, have bowel washouts, take medication and in some cases have surgery.

Prognosis

The prognosis for spina bifida largely depends on the form the individual has. Some children have such a minor form of the condition that they have few, if any, adverse effects. Others with more severe forms will have varying degrees of paralysis. For such people, prognosis will depend on how well or otherwise their environment is adapted to their needs. People with even severe forms of spina bifida can succeed in school, college and university, hold down jobs, get married, have children and generally lead fulfilling lives, provided they have adequate and appropriate supports.

Role of the SNA

Many children in mainstream schools and preschools with spina bifida have the support of an SNA. The principal role of the SNA in this case shall be catering for the child's physical care and mobility needs.

- With babies and young children, make sure to change the baby's position to prevent pressure sores.

- Keep the nappy area clean, dry and moisturised. Pay special attention to creases in the flesh.
- Assist older children with toileting, emptying their urine bag and helping the child sit on the toilet safely, clean themselves properly and dress. Be aware of the child's need for privacy.
- Assist the child in getting from one class to the next; this may involve using a lift.
- The child may need assistance during practical classes.

CASE STUDY

Philip was born with myelomeningocele spina bifida in the mid to lower lumbar region. This resulted in him being paraplegic, whereby he has little control from the waist down. Philip is in a wheelchair and wears pads; as such, he needs assistance with toileting. He attends a mainstream primary school where he has a male SNA whom he gets on very well with. Academically, Philip is progressing very well and is also popular with his classmates. He does not allow his disability to get in his way, and he plays in goals in the yard at lunchtime, stopping the ball very effectively with his wheelchair.

Philip is currently in sixth class, and his parents are finding it somewhat difficult to find a secondary school that can accommodate his needs because the boys' school in the town is quite old and on a number of different levels. They are considering sending Philip to a community school in a town a number of miles away because it is relatively new and all on one level. They are hoping that Peter, his SNA, will be able to transfer with him, as he has worked with Philip since he started school and Philip's parents feel that he has contributed a huge amount to Philip's happiness and success in primary school.

For further information on spina bifida, see the Irish Association for Spina Bifida and Hydrocephalus website (www.sbhi.ie).

HYDROCEPHALUS

Hydrocephalus literally means 'water in the head' and is caused by an accumulation of cerebrospinal fluid (CSF) within the ventricles of the brain, resulting in raised pressure inside the head. At least 80 per cent of those born with spina bifida have some degree of hydrocephalus and many premature babies also develop the condition. In babies and young children, the skull bones are not yet fused together and the raised pressure causes the head to increase in size.

In some cases, hydrocephalus arrests itself and does not require treatment, but in the majority of patients, it is progressive and is treated by the insertion of a shunt (tube) to drain excess fluid from the brain. Problems associated with hydrocephalus include seizures, eye problems, sensitivity to noise, learning disability and language and speech difficulties. However, not all children with hydrocephalus develop these problems.

Prevalence

The overall prevalence of hydrocephalus is approximately 0.5 per cent of all children, i.e. one in every 500 live births. There are two main types of hydrocephalus: congenital, i.e. present at birth, and acquired, i.e. occurs after birth.

Causes

There are believed to be over 180 causes of hydrocephalus, the most common of which is **premature birth**. With a premature baby, the baby's brain is still developing when it is born, so the blood vessels of the brain are very fragile. Hydrocephalus is caused if the blood vessels become damaged, as this causes a build-up of fluid that cannot be drained effectively.

Eighty per cent of children with **spina bifida**, especially myelomeningocele and sometimes meningocele, have hydrocephalus.

Meningitis is an infection of the linings or meninges of the brain and spinal cord. The debris and inflammation or swelling caused by the infection can cause blockages of the drainage pathways of the brain and thus cause cerebrospinal fluid to build up.

Brain and spinal tumours may compress the brain and spinal cord, narrowing the drainage pathways and causing a cerebrospinal fluid build-up.

Symptoms

) Excessive head growth – all babies should have their heads regularly measured and charted on a percentile chart. A baby head with hydrocephalus will normally be above the 97th percentile, meaning that his or her head will be bigger than 97 per cent of babies his or her age

) A bulging, tense fontanelle (soft spot)

) A restless baby with a high-pitched, shrill cry

) Vomiting

) Sleepiness

- Bulging eyes and uneven pupil size
- Downward deviation of the eyes (also called sunsetting), where the baby appears to be looking at their bottom eyelids
- Seizures
- Delayed closing of the anterior fontanelle (soft spot) in the skull. This normally closes by 10 to 14 months

If hydrocephalus is left untreated, as it can be in many developing nations, then coma and death will occur. If treated (usually with the insertion of a shunt), then it can be brought under control.

Even if treated, hydrocephalus can cause brain damage or delayed brain development, which may lead to strabismus (lazy eye), nystagmus (rapid involuntary eye movement), hypersensitivity to noise, learning difficulties such as short attention span, poor short-term memory, and spatial awareness and perception problems causing clumsiness and delayed fine motor control, e.g. writing with a pencil. Emotional and behavioural problems are also five times more likely in a child with hydrocephalus. One in four children with hydrocephalus also develop epilepsy.

Diagnosis

Hydrocephalus is diagnosed through clinical neurological evaluation and by using cranial imaging techniques such as ultrasonography, computed tomography (CT), magnetic resonance imaging (MRI) or pressure-monitoring techniques. The child's doctor will select the appropriate diagnostic tool based on the child's age, clinical presentation and the presence of known or suspected abnormalities of the brain or spinal cord.

Treatment

The main treatment for hydrocephalus is the surgical insertion of a shunt (a small plastic tube) into the brain. The shunt works by draining fluid off the brain, either into the stomach or into the heart (see the illustration overleaf). The shunt will not be visible from the outside – there will only be a slightly raised area on the head behind the ear. As the child grows, their shunt will be regularly replaced. Early insertion of a shunt is vital so that brain damage does not occur. Shunts cannot repair damage that has already been done to the brain; they can only prevent further damage.

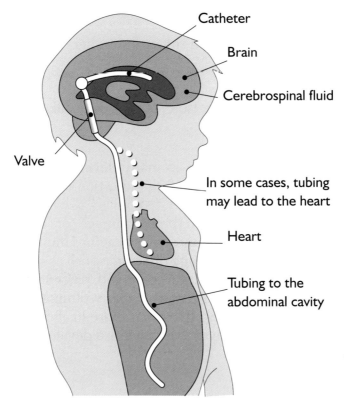

Catheter

Brain

Cerebrospinal fluid

Valve

In some cases, tubing may lead to the heart

Heart

Tubing to the abdominal cavity

Child with shunt due to hydrocephalus

Important signs that there may be something wrong with a shunt

Sometimes a child's shunt becomes blocked or infected. It is very important that this is detected and treated. The following are the most common signs that there is something wrong with a child's shunt. (Please note, however, that every child is different and that these are just the most common symptoms.) Some symptoms will vary with the age of the child.

- Enlargement of the head (babies and toddlers)
- Full, tense fontanelle (babies)
- Dividing of skull sutures (babies)
- Swelling or redness along the track of the shunt (all)
- Fever (all)
- Irritability (all)
- Seizures (all)
- Vomiting (toddlers and children)
- Headache (toddlers and children)

- Sleepiness (toddlers and children)
- Personality change (children)
- Loss of bowel and bladder control (children)
- Staggering (children)
- Lethargy and listlessness (children)

Prognosis

Prognosis will largely depend on the degree of damage that was done to the brain before the child was treated and whether there are any other conditions present, e.g. spina bifida.

Many children will experience few, if any, effects of having hydrocephalus as long as their shunt functions effectively and remains infection free. Others, many of whom have other complications, can have generalised learning difficulties, speech and language problems, problems with eyesight, or co-ordination and emotional problems. For these children, prognosis will be better if sufficient resources and supports are put in place for them.

Role of the SNA

Many children with hydrocephalus do not have any special needs and therefore will not require any special assistance. Having said this, though, school personnel need to be educated about the condition and be aware of the signs that the child's shunt is not functioning properly. Also, the school should ensure that the child does not get any knocks to the head and that their head is adequately protected while playing sports, especially contact sports such as camogie and hurling. Some sports, e.g. rugby, may not be suitable for a child with hydrocephalus.

For other children whose development is more affected by their hydrocephalus (particularly if there are other conditions present), there may be a wide range of needs that an SNA will be required to assist with. These may include:

- Help with toileting
- Mobility needs – the child may be in a wheelchair or have a frame
- Use of assistive technology, e.g. computers
- If the child has behavioural difficulties, the SNA may be required to sit with the child to help him or her stay on task. (See also the role of the SNA for visual impairment (p. 90), learning disability (p. 135) and emotional and behavioural difficulties (p. 197).)

CASE STUDY

Thomas was born prematurely at 28 weeks, weighing just 1,200 grams (2 lb 10 oz). Shortly after he was born, the medical team in the special care baby unit noticed that his head was swelling. Over the next few days he had a series of tests and brain scans and on day four a shunt was fitted. His parents were able to bring him home after six weeks, when he reached the 2.2 kg (5 lb) mark. When Thomas first came home, his parents were very nervous with him, especially with his shunt. Thomas's father, Peter, was afraid to lift him in case he dislodged or damaged the shunt.

Like all premature babies, Thomas's development was slower than average. He was not able to sit up alone until 11 months and didn't walk until he was almost two. He also picked up a lot of chest infections and had very bad eczema all over his body. Often his skin would get so dry that it would split and bleed. His mum, Hannah, had to smother him in Silcock's base and wrap him in bandages from head to toe. This meant that Hannah could not really go out much with Thomas, which she found very isolating, and she became somewhat depressed as a result.

Thomas went to school at five years of age. Peter and Hannah met with the principal and class teacher beforehand to explain that Thomas had hydrocephalus. They explained that Thomas could not play contact sports and also gave the school a copy of the symptoms to look for if the shunt was not working. Thomas is now in first class and is getting on well in school. His main problem is that he still tends to get infections frequently, so he misses a lot of school. He goes to learning support three times a week to help him catch up. His eczema also flares up at times, making things uncomfortable for him.

MUSCULAR DYSTROPHY

Muscular dystrophy (MD) refers to a group of genetically inherited muscular diseases that weaken the muscles of the body. Muscular dystrophies are characterised by progressive weakening and wasting of the muscles of the body. There are at least nine different forms of muscular dystrophy: Duchenne, Becker, limb girdle, congenital, facioscapulohumeral, myotonic, oculopharyngeal, distal and Emery-Dreifuss. In addition, there are more than 100 diseases with some similarities to muscular dystrophy. Most types of MD are multi-system disorders affecting the musculature, heart, gastrointestinal and nervous systems, endocrine system, skin and eyes, as well as other organs. Duchenne muscular dystrophy, which was first diagnosed by the French neurologist Guillaume Duchenne, is the most common and unfortunately the most severe form of the condition and is the focus of this section.

Prevalence

It is estimated that Duchenne muscular dystrophy affects approximately one in 3,500 male births.

Causes

Duchenne MD is caused by a mutation of a gene located on the X chromosome (Xp21). This gene is needed for the production of the protein dystrophin, an important structural component of muscle tissue. Because the mutated gene is located on the X chromosome, Duchenne MD affects only males except in exceptional cases. Because females have two X chromosomes (only one is usually affected), they are generally carriers. Since Duchenne MD is genetically transmitted, it tends to run in families, although it can occur spontaneously.

Symptoms

Symptoms will usually begin to appear in male children before the age of six, although some may be visible in early infancy. They include the following.

▶ Babies do not show any symptoms initially, though the child may be late walking

▶ Progressive muscular wasting, causing muscular weakness

▶ Poor balance and frequent falls

▶ Enlargement and pains in the calves of the legs

▶ Low endurance and difficulties in standing unaided or climbing stairs

▶ Difficulty walking, with a waddling gait (usually by age 10, the child will need braces and/or a frame to walk)

▶ Limited range of movement

▶ Respiratory difficulties

▶ Drooping eyelids (ptosis)

▶ Gonadal atrophy (decrease in size of penis and testes)

▶ Scoliosis (curvature of the spine)

▶ Eventually the child will be unable to walk (most children will need to use a wheelchair by age 12)

▶ Paralysis

▶ About a third of boys with Duchenne MD have intellectual disabilities, although the severity of disability does not increase with age

▶ Some types of muscular dystrophy can affect the heart, causing cardiomyopathy or arrhythmias (irregular heartbeats)

Diagnosis

As Duchenne muscular dystrophy is inherited, families will often be aware of other relatives with the condition. However, for a significant percentage of boys there will be no family history and the genetic abnormality occurs spontaneously. Diagnosis normally takes the form of a blood test – a child with the condition will have raised levels of serum creatinine kinase (CK). In addition, a sample of muscle tissue (muscle biopsy) will be taken to confirm diagnosis.

Treatment

There is no known cure for muscular dystrophy, but good management can ensure a good quality of life for the child and limit the disease's associated problems. Inactivity (such as bed rest or prolonged sitting) can worsen the condition. It is also important that the child does not become overweight, as this puts extra strain on the muscles. Thus, a well-balanced, varied diet is essential. A smoke-free, healthy environment is very important as his chest muscles weaken.

Physiotherapy can help the condition considerably. The child may have to carry out as much as four hours of physical therapy a day. Sometimes physiotherapy involves passively moving the child's limbs to prevent **contracture** of the muscles, i.e. the muscles shortening and tightening up. Hydrotherapy can be extremely beneficial, as limb movement is much easier in water. Occupational therapy teaches and practises skills such as self-care and self-feeding, which are important for the child to maintain as much independence as possible. An occupational therapist may advise the home or school regarding changes to the child's environment that would increase the child's level of independent functioning. Speech therapy and mobility aids such as crutches, leg braces or callipers, wheelchairs and frames are also very important. It is necessary to ensure that mobility aids are comfortable and do not rub the skin.

It is important that the adults in the child's world help him maintain social relationships and friendships. The child should be encouraged and facilitated to be out and about as much as possible and to take part in activities with his peers. Hobbies that he will be able to take part in as his condition worsens should be encouraged, e.g. reading, computers and listening to music.

Environmental considerations

▷   Doors should be wide enough to accommodate mobility aids and handles should not be too high. In an ideal world, doors of public buildings such as schools should be automatic or at least push button operated.

- The child's environment should be clutter free to safeguard against falls.
- Handrails should be fitted, especially in bathrooms and along long corridors.
- Ramps are required to allow wheelchair users access to buildings.
- Bathrooms should be wheelchair accessible.
- Teachers should make a point of using class materials that depict children using wheelchairs, callipers or crutches.

At present, research is being conducted into a specific virus that has been found to carry healthy dystropin genes. It is hoped that by introducing this virus to the body, healthy genes will be introduced to combat the effects of the child's unhealthy genes.

Prognosis

The prognosis for muscular dystrophy varies according to the form of MD the child has. Some cases can be very mild and progress very slowly over the normal lifespan. Others, such as Duchenne MD, produce severe muscle weakness resulting in paralysis and death. In the past, children with MD tended to die at a very early age. Nowadays, with proper care, people with Duchenne MD are living into their thirties, forties and even fifties.

Role of the SNA

Children with Duchenne muscular dystrophy will generally have a full-time SNA assisting them while at school. The main role of an SNA is to look after the child's care needs. The level of care required will largely depend on how advanced the child's condition is. Older children may require assistance getting from one class to the next or around the classroom or playground, although if chairs are electric he will be able to remain independent for longer in this regard. The muscles of the child's bowel and bladder may have weakened, resulting in the child being catheterised or wearing pads and thus requiring assistance with toileting. SNAs may be required to move the child, so it is important that he or she has attended a manual handling course to be able to do this safely. For general guidelines on moving and handling children with mobility difficulties, see pp. 276–9.

Alan was diagnosed with Duchenne muscular dystrophy shortly before his first birthday. He was a few months behind in terms of reaching his developmental milestones, only now beginning to sit for prolonged periods and to crawl. Annette, his mother, suspected MD long before the official diagnosis came through, as her brother had died from the condition three years previously at the age of 39. Annette and her husband, David, were absolutely devastated. They cried continuously for their little boy, knowing all too well exactly what lay ahead for him. After extensive counselling, both Annette and David realised that they owed it to their son to put their own devastation aside and do everything in their power to make Alan's life as full and interesting as it could possibly be.

Over the next few years, Annette and David began working with Alan's occupational therapist, helping Alan feed and dress himself. They learned from Alan's physiotherapist what physical exercises Alan had to do and also tried to keep Alan's limbs from tightening up by passively moving his limbs. Alan started primary school aged six, and at that stage he did not yet need any walking aids. In senior infants he was diagnosed as having a borderline mild general learning difficulty. He was able to avail of extra learning support in basic literacy and maths. Socially, Alan was getting on very well at school. He was attending a small country school and the children there got on well with him, helping him out in whatever way they could.

As time progressed, so too, unfortunately, did Alan's condition. By fourth class Alan was using a wheelchair and needed help toileting. The school applied for and received a full-time SNA for Alan, who worked with and cared for him daily at school. Alan was finding it very difficult to write, so the school applied for and received funding for a laptop with voice recognition software. Jenny, Alan's SNA, worked with him to train the software to recognise Alan's voice and also helped him use his laptop. Alan is now transferring to a local secondary school. His parents are worried about him leaving his small, secure primary school, where every child knows and accepts him.

For further information, see the Muscular Dystrophy Ireland website (www. mdi.ie).

CEREBRAL PALSY

Cerebral palsy (CP) is an umbrella term used to describe a group of non-progressive, non-contagious motor conditions that cause physical disability. CP is caused either by damage or failure of the brain to develop in the specific area that controls movement.

Prevalence

It is thought that approximately one in every 400 babies born in Ireland has some degree of cerebral palsy. Given that approximately 75,000 babies are born annually in Ireland, an estimated 190 babies are born with some degree of cerebral palsy each year.

Causes

CP is caused by damage to the motor control centres of the brain and can occur during pregnancy (about 75 per cent), during childbirth (about 5 per cent) or after birth (about 15 per cent).

Before birth:
- Infections, particularly rubella, toxoplasmosis (an infection that comes from parasites found in animal faeces or undercooked meat) or other viral infections
- Failure of the placenta to develop and function effectively
- Some drugs
- 'Vanishing twin' – some cases of cerebral palsy are thought to be caused by the death of an identical twin sharing the same placenta. The death of one twin is thought to cause a disruption in the flow of blood to the surviving twin. In the past it was common practice not to inform mothers if a very small dead foetus was found attached to the placenta so as not to cause feelings of grief and loss

Around birth:
- A prolonged, difficult labour
- Prematurity – between 40 and 50 per cent of babies born with cerebral palsy are premature
- Infections
- Multiple births

After birth:
- Physical brain injuries – falls, physical abuse, shaken baby syndrome
- Infections such as meningitis, encephalitis, severe jaundice
- Hypoxia (oxygen deficiency to the brain) caused by near drowning, choking or poisoning
- Brain tumours

Symptoms

There are three main types of cerebral palsy, each of which will have different symptoms:

- Spastic cerebral palsy
- Athetoid cerebral palsy
- Ataxic cerebral palsy

Spastic cerebral palsy

This is the most widely known and most common form of CP, affecting up to 60 per cent of all children with the condition. Damage occurs to the cortex or outer layer of the brain. This area of the brain is concerned with thought, movement and sensation. This causes an abnormally strong and sometimes painful tension in the muscles of the arms and legs. If the person tries to move a joint, the muscles contract and block or stop the movement. Arms are often held at an angle. The child's fist may be clenched. The child may have what is called scissoring, where the legs come inwards at the knees with toes pointed outwards. The term *spastic*, while it is a medical term, should never be used to describe someone with CP, as it is hurtful and offensive.

Child with spastic cerebral palsy using a stander

Athetoid cerebral palsy

Athetoid cerebral palsy is less common, thought to affect 20 to 25 per cent of children with CP. Athetoid CP results from damage to the basal ganglia, which is located in the middle of the brain, below the cortex. The basal ganglia is involved with co-ordinating and controlling the movement of the muscle groups. All limbs may or may not be involved. Movement will be jerky and irregular and the child will normally make twisting movements with their fingers and wrists. If the legs are affected, then the child will walk in a writhing, lurching, stumbling manner with uncoordinated arm movements. Emotional stress may make the condition worse. A baby with athetoid CP, unlike a baby with spastic CP, will be floppy, slow to gain head control and to sit.

Ataxic cerebral palsy

Ataxic cerebral palsy is the rarest form of CP, affecting between 1 and 10 per cent of children with CP. It results from damage to the cerebellum, which is the area of the brain concerned with balance. A child with ataxic CP will have difficulty balancing and will sometimes walk with a high stepping motion. The child may also have difficulty typing, writing or using scissors. Nystagmus (rapid eye movement) is often present with this type of CP.

Some children may have a combination of all three types and many also have other conditions (Johnson 2002):
- General learning disability (IQ < 50): 31 per cent
- Epilepsy: 21 per cent
- General learning disability (IQ < 50) and not walking: 20 per cent
- Blindness: 11 per cent

Children with CP are also described in terms of how many limbs are affected by the condition.
- **Quadriplegic:** This is most the most severe form of CP – all four limbs are affected
- **Hemiplegia:** One side of the body is affected
- **Paraplegia:** Only the legs are affected

Diagnosis

Early signs:
- Asymmetry of movement between one side of the body and the other
- Feeding difficulties – poor sucking or swallowing

- Listlessness or irritability
- Excessive, feeble crying
- Failure to thrive

Later signs:
- Failure or delay in reaching developmental milestones, e.g. sitting up, crawling, walking
- Persistence of primitive reflexes (most disappear by three or four months)
- Weakness
- Early hand preference (by 12 to 14 months) – hand preference is normally not fully established until four to six years
- Delayed or impaired speech
- Unusual posture

If a child is suspected of having CP, a full developmental history will be taken and a neurological examination will be carried out by a paediatrician. Sometimes a CT or MRI scan will be carried out, especially if the cause of the CP is not known. Scans will also be carried out to detect other treatable conditions, e.g. hydrocephalus, that frequently accompany CP.

Treatment

There is no cure for CP, but various forms of therapy can help a person function and live more effectively with their condition. In general, the earlier the treatment begins, the better chance the child will have of overcoming developmental disabilities and learning new ways to accomplish the tasks that challenge them. The earliest proven intervention occurs during the infant's recovery in the neonatal intensive care unit (NICU). Interventions include the following.

- **Early nutritional support** with premature infants is thought to help prevent the development or worsening of cerebral palsy. Dietary supplements may have to be given because of difficulty eating sufficient quantities of food.
- **Physiotherapy** programmes are designed to encourage the child to build a strength base to improve gait and movement. Stretching programmes are also used to limit contractures. Some experts believe that lifelong physiotherapy is crucial to maintain muscle tone, bone structure and to prevent dislocation of joints.
- **Occupational therapy** maximises the child and later adult's ability to adapt to their limitations and to live as independently as possible. Occupational therapy

takes many forms, from teaching living skills such as dressing, feeding, toileting and self-care to vocational or work skills, e.g. computer skills.

- **Orthotic devices** such as ankle-foot orthoses (braces) minimise gait irregularities and help improve walking.

- **Mobility devices** such as walkers and wheelchairs give the child with CP mobility. Electric wheelchairs give greater mobility to people with CP and some can be chin operated if the person is quadriplegic.

- **Microchip technology** means that computers and other communication aids can be worked with fingers, toes, tongue, voice, eye and breath movements. Communication aids such as Lightwriters, Go-Talk talkers and Advocate can be used and allow synthetic speech or pre-recorded speech.

- **Speech therapy** helps control the muscles of the mouth and jaw, thus improving clarity of communication. Just as CP affects the way a person uses their arms and legs, it can also affect the way they move their mouth, head and face, making it difficult to breathe, talk clearly, bite, chew and swallow food. Speech therapists help the child train their muscles to carry out all these skills more effectively and will usually work with the child on an ongoing basis.

- **Massage therapy and yoga** are recommended to help relax and strengthen tense muscles and to help keep joints flexible. The breathing exercises involved in yoga can also help keep the lungs free from infection.

- **Surgery** is sometimes recommended for people with CP. Surgery may be used for a number of reasons.
  - To loosen tight muscles and release fixed joints. This surgery is usually performed on the hips, knees, hamstrings and ankles. It is performed less often on the elbows, wrists, hands and fingers.
  - To insert a baclofen pump. This device is surgically inserted into the abdomen and is connected to the spinal cord. The pump releases set amounts of a muscle relaxant called baclofen, which helps reduce muscles contractions.
  - Surgery may be carried out on the bones of the legs. Because the muscles of someone with spastic CP contort and spasm, this often causes the bones to contort or twist during childhood, when they are soft and still forming. Once the bones have hardened (when the child is older), this surgery cuts the bones and realigns them.
  - Rhizotomy is a surgical procedure whereby the nerves of the limbs most affected by movements and spasms are cut. This has the effect of reducing spasms and allows more flexibility.
  - Botulinum Toxin A, commonly known as Botox, is injected into muscles that painfully spasm and contract.

A number of alternative therapies have been developed to work with children with CP and other conditions causing motor dysfunction. Some of these are described below.

- **Conductive education** is an intensive holistic learning programme first developed in Hungary by Professor András Pet. Conductive education is designed to help children with motor disorders to improve bodily movement and function. Children engage with the programme five hours a day, five days a week. The underlying philosophy of the programme is that children will only learn new skills if they are actively involved themselves in the learning process. Traditional therapies, where the child with CP is a passive recipient of physical therapy and care, do not promote self-help and independence.

- The **Bobath concept** was developed in the US by Bertha Bobath and her husband, Karel. Patients engage in systematic physical therapy (with children, exercises will be done through play). The idea is that because the brain is adaptable (plasticity), practising certain movements will reinforce sensori-motor pathways, thus aiding movement.

Management of the condition

In addition to treating the condition, someone with CP may have to be cared for and their condition and its symptoms managed. The following points should be taken into account by anyone working with or caring for a child with CP.

Handling the child:

- Make sure that you handle the child's limbs with care. Never hurry a movement and always tell the child when you are going to move a limb. This is to prevent the limb contracting.

- Tension and stress will cause increased muscle spasm. Try to keep the child's environment as calm and stress free as possible.

- Never try to control a limb that is in spasm by force. Gently rock the part in spasm to relax it.

- For your own safety and the safety of the child, ensure that you know how to move the child correctly (see p. 276–9).

- If you are helping a child to stand, position yourself in front of him or her. Ensure his or her feet are spaced out and placed firmly on the floor. Encourage the child to lean forward before putting weight on their feet, then lift.

Feeding:

- When feeding, ensure the child is in a comfortable position. Keep his or her head upright and central to aid swallowing and reduce the risk of choking. He or she may have his or her own extra support chair.
- Always tell the child what you are offering to him or her.
- Always check the temperature of the food and allow plenty of time for feeding.
- Always use plastic spoons and beakers because sometimes people with CP can have a strong reflex bite, which could cause injury if metal or ceramic tableware was used.
- If spoon feeding, place food far back on the tongue and to the side to aid chewing and swallowing.
- Avoid crumbly foods, as there is an increased risk of choking.
- Children should be encouraged and shown how to self-feed if at all possible. Special easy-to-grip spoons are available.
- Use bowls and cups with suction pads to prevent slipping.
- Allow for mess and protect the child's clothing.
- Try to introduce a variety of textures – in the past, children with CP were often fed puréed foods only.
- Offer plenty of praise and encouragement.

Drinking:

- Sometimes the child's lower jaw will move up and down as he or she drinks, making it difficult for the child to keep fluids in his or her mouth. To help this, support the lower jaw from behind. Help the child to hold their mug, ensuring that their thumbs are turned outwards.
- Use mugs with two handles to encourage the use of both sides of the body. Weighted mugs are available that are easier to control.
- Tongue thrust (the tongue continuously coming forward) can make it difficult for a child to drink. Sucking through a straw can help limit this.

Physical care:

- Encourage independence in dressing. Clothes should be easy to put on and remove. Put clothes on the affected limbs first. Never pull arms through, as this will increase elbow flexion and spasm.
- Before putting on socks and shoes, the child's legs should be bent. This reduces ankle and foot stiffness and toe curling.

◗ Encourage the child to choose what they want to wear themselves.

◗ Use non-slip bath mats. As the child grows, shower chairs, etc. may have to be used.

◗ Pay particular attention to dental hygiene, as the child's reduced chewing and swallowing capacity can cause extra plaque build-up in the mouth.

◗ Children may require help with toileting. There may be a delay with bowel and bladder control, resulting in the child wearing nappies for an extended period. The child's physiotherapist should work with him or her on developing the bowel and bladder muscles.

◗ Children's sleep position may have to be changed during the night to prevent pressure sores. Most children sleep on their side or tummy when they are old enough, as it is more comfortable for them.

Games:

◗ Play games that encourage the development of fine motor skills, e.g. jigsaw work.

◗ Develop games that encourage balance and control of movement (these will be recommended by the child's physiotherapist).

◗ Carry out speech and language exercises as recommended by the child's speech therapist.

◗ Use music and action stories and rhymes.

Prognosis

Cerebral palsy is not a progressive disorder (meaning the actual brain damage neither improves nor worsens), but it cannot be cured. A person with the disorder may adapt to their condition well during childhood if he or she receives extensive care and education from specialists such as physiotherapists, occupational therapists and speech therapists. Once bones and muscles become fully established, orthopaedic surgery may be used to correct bone deformities. People who have CP also tend to develop arthritis at a younger age than normal because of the pressure placed on joints by excessively toned and stiff muscles.

While people with CP are more likely to have some form of learning disability, the majority have normal levels of intellectual functioning and should be given opportunities to maximise their learning potential.

The ability to live independently with CP varies widely, depending on the severity of the person's condition. Some individuals with CP will require assistance for all activities of daily living. Others can lead independent lives with little or no support or support only for certain activities. The need for personal assistance often changes with increasing age and associated functional decline. However, in most cases people with CP can expect to have a normal life expectancy. As the condition does not directly affect reproductive function, many people with CP can have children. CP is not a genetically inherited condition, so people with CP are not any more likely to have a child with CP than the general population.

Role of the SNA

Most children with cerebral palsy, except those with mild forms of the condition, will have a full-time SNA assisting them while at school. The principal role of an SNA is to look after and assist with the child's physical care needs. The child may need assistance getting around the classroom or from one classroom to the next, or around the yard. The child may require help toileting or feeding themselves. SNAs may be asked to help the child use assistive technology or help the child ready class materials. It is vital that the SNA provides plenty of praise and encouragement and helps keep the child's morale up when tasks are proving difficult for them.

CASE STUDY

Alanna was born prematurely with athetoid cerebral palsy. She was in hospital for some time after birth, feeding through a gastrointestinal tube. She was slow reaching all of her physical milestones – she still had a good degree of head lag at six months, didn't sit unaided until she was 18 months and then only for short periods, and by four years old she was not yet walking unaided and was not yet completely toilet trained. She also has epilepsy. Her language development was also affected in that while she had a good vocabulary, she was not yet speaking clearly at four years. Apart from her physical development and spoken language, Alanna was a very engaged and capable child. She loved being read to and playing on her computer and could walk for short periods with the aid of a walker.

By six years she could read well and started her local primary school. The school was very supportive. As the building was old with no disabled access, the principal applied for money under the Summer Works Scheme to have a ramp fitted up to the school front door. Alanna is now in first class and gets assistance from the school's SNA, though only for short periods throughout the day. She has a special desk and chair, which gives her support. If she were to sit in a regular school chair and desk it would be too tiring for a full school day. Alanna's fine motor skills are affected by her cerebral palsy in that she finds it difficult to write neatly, but she is learning. Alanna's classmates have become used to the fact that she has cerebral palsy and don't really notice any more. They help her out if she is having trouble doing something.

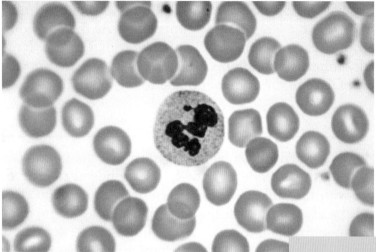

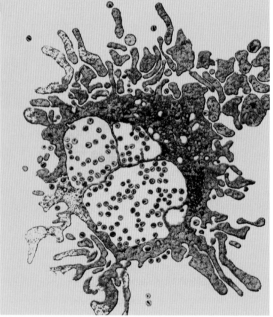

A healthy white blood cell (left) and one infected with HIV (below)

HIV AND AIDS

Acquired immune deficiency syndrome (AIDS) is a disease of the human immune system caused by the human immuno-deficiency virus (HIV). Dr Beatrice Hahn of the University of Alabama in the US and her research team discovered that the first human known to be infected with HIV was a man from the Congo who had his blood stored in 1959, just prior to his death. The blood was tested again once AIDS was known to exist; it was positive. The first live case was not diagnosed until 1981.

By destroying the body's white blood cells, this condition progressively reduces the effectiveness of the immune system and leaves individuals susceptible to infections and tumours. HIV is transmitted through direct contact of a mucous membrane or the bloodstream with a bodily fluid containing HIV, such as blood, semen, vaginal fluid, preseminal fluid and breast milk.

Transmission can be as a result of anal, vaginal or oral sex, blood transfusion, contaminated hypodermic needles, exchange between mother and baby during pregnancy, childbirth, breastfeeding or other exposure to one of the above bodily fluids.

The focus of this section is on HIV and AIDS in children living in Ireland.

Prevalence

According to the Health Protection Surveillance Centre, as of 2011, there have been a total of 6,287 confirmed cases of HIV infection in Ireland, with 320 new cases notified in 2011. Of these new cases, three were children (see www.hpsc.ie for the most up-to-date figures).

Causes

In Ireland, the principal way the HIV virus is transmitted to children is from mother to baby during pregnancy, birth or breastfeeding. This is called **vertical transmission**. In total during 2011, 90 babies were born to HIV-infected mothers in Ireland, but because of antiviral medication, only two babies were born HIV positive (68 did not have the virus and the status of the remaining 20 has not yet been fully determined). If a woman were to have no antiviral drugs, to give birth naturally and to breastfeed, the rate of transmission from mother to baby would be 25 per cent, so of the 90 HIV-positive mothers who gave birth in Ireland during 2011, at least 22 of their children would have been born HIV positive.

Once the HIV virus enters the system, it begins to infect and destroy the body's white blood cells (T-cells, macrophages and dendritic cells). This impacts the body's immune system, making the person prone to infection and disease. Once large numbers of white blood cells have been infected and destroyed and the immune system is severely compromised, the person is said to have developed AIDS.

Symptoms

Infants

At birth, infants born to an HIV-infected mother may test negative for the virus and have no symptoms. This does not mean that the infant does not have the virus. Blood tests will be done at various stages after birth, up to and past six months of age, to determine an infant's HIV status. Symptoms may include the following.

- Failure to thrive – delayed physical and developmental growth as evidenced by poor weight gain and bone growth
- Swollen abdomen (due to swelling of the liver and spleen)
- Swollen lymph nodes
- Intermittent diarrhoea (diarrhoea that may come and go)
- Pneumonia

⟩ Oral thrush – a fungal infection in the mouth that is characterised by white patches on the inside of the cheeks and tongue
⟩ Painful lesions (sores) on the inside of the mouth

Children

Symptoms seen in children older than one year of age can be divided into three different categories, from mild to severe. They may include the above symptoms, but may also include the following.

Mild	Moderate	Severe
Swollen lymph nodes	Pneumonitis (swelling of the lung tissue)	Two serious bacterial infections within a two-year period, often meningitis, septicaemia or pneumonia
Swelling of the parotid gland (salivary glands located in front of the ear)	Oral thrush that lasts for more than two months	A yeast infection that occurs in the lungs or digestive tract
Constant or recurring sinus infections	Constant or recurring diarrhoea	Encephalopathy (an infection of the brain that may cause deterioration of brain function)
Constant or recurring ear infections	A fever that persists for longer than two months	Tumours or malignant lesions
Dermatitis (an itchy skin rash)	Hepatitis and inflammation of the liver, which is often caused by infection	Severe pneumonia
	Chicken pox infection, which may include intestinal tract	
	Kidney disease	

Diagnosis

HIV is not tested for in newborns in the same way as in adults. In adults, a blood sample is tested for HIV antibodies. If they are present, then this indicates that the person is HIV positive. During pregnancy, however, a mother's antibodies, including those for HIV (if the mother is HIV positive), will pass across the placenta and into the baby's bloodstream. This is why the traditional blood test will not be able to determine if a baby is HIV positive. Instead, a **viral load test**, sometimes called a DNA PCR test, will be used that detects the genetic material that makes up the HIV virus itself. This test will be carried out shortly after birth, at six weeks and then again at 12 weeks. The traditional test for HIV will not be used until the baby is 18 months old.

Treatment

HIV cannot be cured, but there are drugs available that try to slow down the rate at which the virus attacks the immune system. Drug treatment regimes for HIV are called antiretroviral therapy (ART) and generally involve taking a number of different drugs every day of the child's life. Without drug treatment, a third of HIV-positive children die before their first birthday and half die before their second.

For therapy to work well, children must be diagnosed early. This is because HIV reproduces much more rapidly in children than in adults. There is debate about when is the best time to start children on ART – should it be started when they are still well, or should it wait until they are showing some symptoms? The disadvantage of starting early is that children will be on ART for many years, perhaps building up a resistance to the drugs, and there are also side effects of the therapy.

To judge whether an HIV-positive person requires treatment, a CD4 test is usually carried out. This measures the number of T-helper cells (a type of white blood cell) in a person's blood that have been attacked by HIV.

A falling CD4 count is a sign that HIV is progressing and that the immune system is becoming weaker. In healthy, uninfected adults, absolute CD4 count is usually between 500 and 1,500 cells per cubic millimetre of blood. When an HIV-positive adult's CD4 count falls below 350, it is usually recommended (in economically developed countries) that they start receiving antiretroviral treatment.

For children below the age of five, though, these adult guidelines are generally irrelevant. Absolute CD4 counts vary with age, and younger children usually have a much higher CD4 count than adults. This makes it difficult to judge the health of a child's immune system based on CD4 count. In recent times, the general guideline is that babies born HIV positive should be treated straight away, whether symptomatic or not (World Health Organization 2008).

As with adults, antiretroviral therapy with at least three drugs is recommended for children, as this prevents HIV from becoming resistant to any single drug. How the drugs function is very complex, but in essence they help prevent the HIV virus from multiplying inside the while blood cells. The amount of drug given to a child depends on their height and body weight. Also, as they are growing rapidly, their drug regime may frequently change. Children generally metabolise drugs more quickly than adults, so they are usually on a higher dose for their height and weight than an adult. Drugs are available in tablets, syrups and powders. In some cases, drugs can be combined into a single tablet.

The drugs taken as part of ART usually cause side effects. These can range from mild to severe and may include abdominal pain, severe ongoing diarrhoea, nausea, vomiting, weight loss, fatigue and anaemia, fever, dry mouth, headaches, insomnia and skin rashes.

Children on HIV treatment may need to take three or more types of ARVs every day for the rest of their lives (unless they can avail of a single tablet dose, though this does not suit everyone). If drugs are not taken routinely at around the same time every day, HIV may become resistant to the therapy, causing it to stop working. For some children with HIV, adherence to their drug regime can be problematic. Syrups and reconstituted powders do not taste good and infants may refuse to take them, perhaps actually bringing them back up. Many children who are HIV positive have very ill parents who may not be functioning well in their role as parent. Some ARV drugs have to be taken with food, several times a day, and as such, parents might not take children outside of the home through fear of their illness being discovered.

Children living with HIV need to eat a well-balanced, healthy diet. On average, a child with HIV also requires 10 to 20 per cent more calories per day than a child without the condition.

In order to prevent the child from picking up opportunistic infections, care must be taken that children with HIV receive recommended vaccinations. It is not recommended that they get live vaccinations, such as the one for polio, as their system may not be strong enough to prevent contracting the disease from the vaccination. Efforts should be made to limit the child's exposure to infection, e.g. the parents of a child with HIV should be informed if there are cases of conditions such as chicken pox in a crèche or school. Common sense should prevail at all times, e.g. do not allow a child with HIV to play football on a cold, wet day.

Prognosis

With current drug therapy, most children born today with HIV infection live well beyond the age of five, and about 50 per cent live beyond age 10. More and more children are surviving well into adolescence and early adulthood. However, physical prognosis is only one factor. Children living with HIV and AIDS have many other issues to contend with – discrimination, prejudice, bullying, exclusion and fear. How negatively a child with HIV is treated by his or her community can have a huge impact on that child's prognosis. In communities where HIV and AIDS are properly understood, children can lead more fulfilling, happy lives. In communities where there is a widespread lack of understanding and information, children's lives can be very difficult indeed.

Role of the SNA

As with other physical conditions, the role of an SNA working with a child with HIV would be predominantly looking after the child's care needs. SNAs may be required (depending on policy) to supervise the child taking his or her medication and also to help ensure all children in the setting follow strict health and safety procedures as laid down by the school under the guidance of the health authorities.

CASE STUDY

Vanessa was born HIV positive. Both her mother and father are HIV positive as a result of drug use. Vanessa's mother did not go to a doctor until she was almost six months pregnant and she was not aware of her HIV-positive status. Doctors did give Vanessa's mother antiviral drugs for the remainder of the pregnancy, but by that stage it was too late. Immediately after birth, Vanessa was taken into the care of the HSE, which had great difficulty finding a foster home for Vanessa because of her HIV status. In the end, they found a couple willing to foster Vanessa, living just outside Dublin. Vanessa was started on ART at six weeks, and her foster parents were excellent. They ensured she took her medication exactly on time, even though sometimes it was very difficult to get Vanessa to take it. Vanessa is now three years old. She does get sick a lot – she has had pneumonia, kidney infections, ear infections and numerous bouts of thrush. Her foster mother, Linda, thinks she needs to begin mixing with other children, but has not been able to find a playschool willing to take her on. Everywhere she has approached so far has said that they do not have anybody trained to deal with a child with Vanessa's needs. Linda does not know what the future will hold for Vanessa. Her parents have not seen her since she was six months old.

chapter five

Special Needs Affecting Intellectual or Cognitive Development

ASSESSMENT AND ACADEMIC TESTING

General learning disability (GLD) is the name given to a group of disabilities with one thing in common. The child will have a general level of intelligence (as measured by an individually administered intelligence test by a psychologist) that falls below the average range. A wide variety of tests are used by psychologists, which shall be discussed here.

Academic testing and assessment is just one tool in the bag of a qualified psychologist trying to understand a particular child's special learning needs. Results or information gathered as a result of testing must be interpreted in terms of the whole child, e.g. their background, family situation, learning history (such as how often they attend school), their behaviour, their motivation for school and their health status. This can be difficult for a psychologist to do when they have only been called in to carry out an assessment in a school and do not know the child personally. What a psychologist will often do is carry out interviews with people who do know the child, such as their teacher and parents, in order to get a clearer understanding of the problems the child is facing at school.

Critics of academic testing and assessment argue that such tests take a very limited view of intelligence, focusing narrowly on linguistic and mathematical skills. The psychologist Howard Gardner (1983) believes there are many other valuable forms of intelligence that are not measured by traditional tests. His original theory of multiple intelligence proposed seven different intelligences, although he has since added others. The original seven are as follows.

1. **Linguistic intelligence:** Ability to use words (read and speak).
2. **Logic and mathematics:** Ability with numbers, logic and sequential thinking.
3. **Interpersonal skills:** Ability to read and be sensitive to the needs of others.
4. **Intrapersonal skills:** Knowing oneself, one's beliefs, attitudes and values.
5. **Musical intelligence:** Ability to respond to or perform music.
6. **Bodily-kinaesthetic intelligence:** Ability in athletics, sport, dance.
7. **Artistic intelligence:** Ability to create art, sculpture, photography, fashion, interior design.

Schools, particularly primary schools, place great emphasis on acquiring the first two forms of intelligence – large parts of the school day are spent reading, writing and doing mathematics. From first class, children begin taking what are called group administered tests of achievement, mainly in reading and mathematics. The most common of these used in Irish schools are the **Drumcondra test** (reading and maths), the **Micra-T test** (reading) and **Sigma-T test** (maths). Results from these tests are usually presented as **percentile scores**. Percentile scores indicate how well the child is doing in comparison to other children his or her age. If a child achieved a score at the 26th percentile for maths, for example, this would mean that on average, he or she would score better than 25 per cent of children his or her age, but worse than 74 per cent of them. Children who are not performing well in class or on group administered tests such as these may be put forward for further assessment by an educational psychologist.

Intelligence tests

Most intelligence tests measure the following cognitive skills. However, results from intelligence tests are only useful if they are taken in the context of the whole child, as discussed earlier.

- Verbal skills
- Non-verbal skills
- Attention and concentration

▶ Memory
▶ Social judgement and comprehension
▶ Hand–eye co-ordination skills
▶ Perceptual organisation skills
▶ Abstract reasoning skills

If there are behavioural or emotional problems, tests will also sometimes gather information on:
▶ Frustration tolerance
▶ Impulse control
▶ Anger management skills
▶ Coping skills
▶ Interpersonal judgement (what other people's intentions are)
▶ Stress tolerance
▶ Anxiety levels
▶ Fears and phobias
▶ Moral development (knowledge of right from wrong)
▶ Social problem-solving skills
▶ Motivation for school
▶ Preoccupations and obsessions
▶ Existence of mood swings

Psychological reports should be easily read and understood by teachers and parents alike. They are only useful if the psychologist also outlines specific recommendations for the child in terms of supports and strategies that should be put in place to help the child progress.

Wechsler Intelligence Scale for Children

The Wechsler Intelligence Scale for Children, which was first developed in 1949 by David Wechsler in New York, is one of the most popular tests used by psychologists in Irish schools. The test can be completed without reading and writing and is suitable for children aged six to 16 years. For younger children, the Wechsler Preschool and Primary Scale of Intelligence test is used, and there is also a version for use with those aged over 16, called the Wechsler Adult Intelligence Scale. The original test for children aged six to 16 years and 11 months old has been updated a number of times. The current version, the WISC-IV, was produced in 2003. It is divided into four broad categories, each of which is divided again into subsets. The four broad categories are:

1. Verbal comprehension
2. Perceptual reasoning
3. Working memory
4. Processing speed

Sometimes a child will be asked to respond verbally to a question asked (verbal scale), while other times the child will be asked to do something in response to a question or a task (performance scale).

The fourth edition of the test has a total of 15 subsets, each one measuring a different aspect of intelligence. The 15 subsets are as follows.

WISC-IV verbal comprehension subtests

1. **Similarities:** This test requires the child to identify the similarity between two apparently dissimilar items.
2. **Vocabulary:** For the picture items, the child is required to name the pictures in the stimulus book. For the verbal items, the child is required to give definitions for words the examiner reads aloud.
3. **Comprehension:** This test requires the child to answer questions based on his or her understanding of general principles and social situations.
4. **Information:** The test requires the child to answer questions that address a broad range of general knowledge topics.
5. **Word reasoning:** This test requires the child to identify the common concept being described in a series of clues.

WISC-IV perceptual reasoning subtests

6. **Block design:** This test requires the child to view a constructed model or a picture in the stimulus book and use red and white blocks to recreate the design within a specified time limit.
7. **Picture concepts:** The child is presented with two or three rows of pictures and chooses one picture from each row to form a group with a common characteristic.
8. **Matrix reasoning:** This test requires the child to view an incomplete matrix and select the missing portion from five response options.
9. **Picture completion:** This test requires the child to view a picture and then point to or name the important part that's missing within a specified time limit.

WISC-IV working memory subtests

10. **Digit span:** The Digit Span Forward task requires the child to repeat numbers in the same order as read aloud by the examiner. Digit Span Backward requires the child to repeat the numbers in the reverse order of that presented by the examiner.

11. **Letter-number sequencing:** Requires the child to read a sequence of letters and numbers and recall the numbers in ascending (smallest to biggest) order and the letters in alphabetical order.

12. **Arithmetic:** Requires the child to mentally solve a series of orally presented arithmetic problems within a specified time limit.

WISC-IV processing speed subtests

13. **Coding:** Requires the child to copy symbols that are paired with simple geometric shapes or numbers.

14. **Symbol search:** Requires the child to scan a search group and indicate whether the target symbol(s) matches any of the symbols in the search group within a specified time limit.

15. **Cancellation:** Requires the child to scan pictures and mark target pictures within a specified time limit.

Depending on the child, the test normally takes between 50 minutes and 1 hour 15 minutes to complete. Once the test has been completed, a number of different results can be obtained:

- Verbal scale IQ (how the child performed on tasks requiring a verbal response)
- Performance scale IQ (how the child performed on tasks requiring the child to do something)
- Full-scale IQ (an overall score)

A full-scale score in the range 90 to 110 is considered average. The tester can also look closely at how the child performed on particular subsets of the test. A child may score significantly higher in one or two subset areas compared with their overall score. This would warrant further investigation. In addition, a very big difference between verbal scale IQ and performance scale IQ could indicate a specific learning difficulty, e.g. dyslexia (performance IQ much higher than verbal IQ).

Standard scores are also frequently used to report the results of assessment.

BORDERLINE GENERAL LEARNING DISABILITY (BGLD)

Children in this category will have a full-scale score in the 70 to 79 range (2nd to 8th percentile) as measured by a test such as the Wechsler Intelligence Scale for Children outlined above. Children with borderline general learning disability will not appear any different from their peers outside of school. They may have good social skills and be popular with their peers. In school, however, children will not learn in the same way or as quickly as their peers. They often have difficulty with abstract concepts and making generalisations. Material may have to be practised and repeated several times before the child masters it. In the past, children with borderline general learning disability were called 'slow learners'. This is now considered a derogatory term and should not be used, even though to some extent the term does accurately describe a child with a BGLD learning style. These children can learn if information is taught in an appropriate way. The teacher needs to present material in a concrete format, work through the material in a step-by-step fashion and allow plenty of time for practice. For example, if a teacher was teaching the concept of area to the class, for some children it would be sufficient to tell them that you multiply the length by the width to get the area – they would understand this and be able to apply this information to real-life situations themselves. For other children, including children with BGLD, it would be better if the teacher showed them and allowed them to practise in a concrete way how to get the area of various things, e.g. their desk, the classroom door or the actual room they are in, using rulers, sticks, metre sticks, etc.

Some other characteristics of children with borderline general learning disability may include:

- Delayed conceptual development
- Slow speech and language development
- Limited ability to abstract and generalise
- Limited attention span
- Poor retention ability
- Poor adaptive behaviour
- Inappropriate or immature personal behaviour
- Low self-esteem
- Emotional disturbance
- General clumsiness and lack of co-ordination and of gross and fine motor skills

If their needs are not recognised and addressed, children with borderline general learning disability often develop behavioural problems and become disruptive in the classroom. School can become a negative experience for these children, somewhere they experience failure on a daily basis. They feel powerless in the school environment, so they begin to try to exert their own kind of power by disrupting the lesson or making people laugh. Other children with BGLD zone out instead and try to become invisible. Busy teachers sometimes let them do this, rarely calling on them for answers or giving them unchallenging, repetitive work to do.

Children with BGLD should be given learning support and have an individual education plan (IEP) developed for them. In the classroom, teachers will need to adapt what and how they teach children with BGLDs. In 2007, the NCCA produced a set of guidelines for teachers teaching children with general learning difficulties. Suggestions include the following:

- Use objectives that are realistic for the students, ensuring that the learning task is linked to prior learning.
- Choose material and activities that interest and motivate the student, e.g. if you discover the student has an interest in football, then source materials that reflect this interest.
- Provide opportunities for interacting and working with other students in small groups – students can learn effectively from more able peers.
- Spend more time on tasks.
- Organise the learning of a task into small, manageable stages. Tasks should have a clear beginning and end point to avoid ambiguity.
- Use models or samples so that the student has a clear, concrete example of what is expected.
- Ensure that language used is pitched at the students' level of understanding and does not hinder their understanding of the activity.
- Introduce tasks or steps one at a time.
- The same task can be presented at different levels to different students.
- Pose key questions to guide students through the stages/processes and to assist in self-direction and correction.
- Use graphic symbols as reminders to assist in understanding the sequence/steps in any given task/problem.
- Model task analysis by talking through the steps of a task as it is being done.
- Have short and varied tasks.
- Create a congenial learning environment by using concrete and, where possible, everyday materials and by displaying word lists and laminated charts with pictures.
- The teacher's attitude should be positive and patient. (NCCA 2007b)

If a child with BGLD is still failing to make progress despite access to learning support and adapted teaching, the school principal may decide to apply for resource teaching hours for the child. Resource teaching can be done on a withdrawal basis or else within the classroom setting (the latter is what is now recommended). The resource teacher works alongside the class teacher, assisting children either individually or in small groups with what is being learned by all children in the class. This practice is called co-operative teaching. In terms of an SNA, generally a child with borderline general learning disability would only be allocated such support if their behaviour, because of persistent failure to make progress, was posing a danger to themselves or other children. An SNA could also be asked to supervise and help children with individual or small group activities as set down by the class teacher.

In mainstream secondary schools, children with borderline general learning disabilities can be accommodated in the following.

- **Mixed-ability classes:** Most schools now have mixed-ability classes. Some schools have mixed-ability classes only for the first year and then stream, others have mixed-ability classes for some subjects and stream for others (usually maths, English and Irish), others stream after Junior Certificate, while still others never stream. Children with mild GLD do well in mixed-ability classes if the classroom environment meets their needs. For this to happen, teachers need to be able to adapt content and teaching methods, classes cannot be too big and good resources and equipment need to be made available.

- **Streamed or banded classes:** A decreasing number of schools stream from first year. This means students are placed in particular classes according to their assessed level of achievement or ability on an entrance examination. Streaming can have advantages for children with BGLDs, but there are also many disadvantages. Lower-stream classes are usually small, which means teachers have more time to spend with individual students and lesson content and teaching methods can be geared more towards the needs of the class. However, streaming encourages children to have preconceived ideas about their ability to achieve – 'If I'm in this class, I must be stupid, so what's the point in trying?' Teachers can also have low expectations of lower-stream classes, which may translate into reality. If streaming is to work, lower-stream classes need to be small, be given the best, most experienced teachers and have access to good resources.

- **A special class:** Some schools have a designated special class or unit for students with particular special needs. Children with a borderline general learning disability would not normally be in a designated class.

Information and communications technology (ICT) can be used to great effect with students with BGLD.

⬗ ICT can provide a non-threatening environment where students can learn at a pace and level suited to them.

⬗ Software programs present material in such a way that students are repeating tasks and skills in different ways without even being aware of it – something that is needed for mastery.

⬗ ICT can offer graphics, sound effects and immediate rewards to help encourage the learner.

⬗ When carrying out a task using ICT, the student does not feel as exposed – they can fail, try again, fail and try again without anybody knowing. ICT is non-judgmental and allows students to work at their own pace.

⬗ ICT can be used to introduce and reinforce simple concepts, such as matching and sorting, as well as basic literacy and numeracy skills in a fun way.

⬗ ICT facilitates the development of motor skills, eye tracking and hand–eye co-ordination.

⬗ ICT aids language development – the student is motivated to read on-screen instructions, etc. in order to play the game.

⬗ If used in groups, ICT facilitates social interaction and gives students an opportunity to experience turn-taking and co-operation.

MILD GENERAL LEARNING DISABILITY

Children in this category will have a full-scale score in the 50 to 69 range (below the 1st percentile) as measured by a test such as the Wechsler Intelligence Scale for Children outlined above. They will have difficulty with basic skills such as reading, writing and mathematics. In addition, children with mild general learning disabilities will also have what are called deficits in adaptive behaviour. Adaptive behaviours are life skills that we use every day, e.g. tying shoelaces, putting shoes on the right feet, personal hygiene routines and, later, cooking meals, going to the shop to buy groceries, washing clothes, travelling on a train or a bus or doing housework. Many of these skills are not taught directly to an individual, but are learned through observation. Children with mild general learning disabilities usually have to be taught these skills directly. Some students may display inappropriate or immature personal behaviour, e.g. handling their genital area, low self-esteem, emotional disturbance, general clumsiness and lack of co-ordination of fine and gross motor skills.

Sometimes children with mild GLDs have syndromes such as Down's syndrome, while other times their disability can be a result of a birth injury, trauma or illness. Frequently, however, the exact cause is not known.

For children with mild GLDs, education is not just about reading, writing and maths. Education should also include the learning of life skills – dressing, cooking, cleaning, personal hygiene, shopping, using public transport, etc. Education is also about the development of social skills and emotional development.

Nowadays, many children with mild GLDs are being educated more frequently in mainstream schools with the help of resource teachers and SNAs (for example, there are a total of 236 primary schools in Ireland presently catering for children with mild GLDs). Having said this, there are still a large number of special schools and a number of post-primary and primary schools that have special classes for children with mild and more severe general learning disabilities or more specific special needs, such as sensory or physical disabilities, language and communication disabilities or autistic spectrum disorders.

Normally in a secondary school, students have different teachers for different subjects all day. In most special classes attached to post-primary schools there will be one resource teacher timetabled to teach that class for most of the day. This is seen as important and is advantageous if:

- The teacher has additional qualifications and/or skills
- The teacher is motivated and wants to teach this particular group
- The teacher is patient, understanding and positive towards the group
- The teacher has access to sufficient equipment and resources

Students will be taught by other teachers for particular subjects, e.g. woodwork or home economics. This can happen either if students from the special class join mainstream classes for specific subjects or if the subject teacher team-teaches the group with their resource teacher. Some schools adopt an approach of reversed integration whereby students from mainstream classes join the special class for certain subjects in the special class setting. This gives students from mainstream classes the opportunity to become peer tutors and offer valuable support to students in special classes.

Special schools

Currently in Ireland there are 107 special schools, 30 of which cater for students with mild GLDs. Generally, special schools cater for children aged five to 18 following the primary, Junior Certificate and Leaving Certificate curricula as appropriate. Emphasis is also put on the teaching of life skills.

MODERATE GENERAL LEARNING DISABILITY

Children with moderate GLDs have been individually assessed by a psychologist and found to have a level of intelligence that is within the range of 35 to 49 in standard scores (well below the 1st percentile). These children will have more severe adaptive behaviour deficits and more severe special learning needs. Children with a moderate GLD have impaired development and learning ability in respect of language and communication, social and personal development, motor co-ordination and basic literacy and numeracy as well as independent living skills. They may also have additional or multiple disabilities, such as physical impairment, hearing impairment, visual impairment, cerebral palsy, autistic tendencies, emotional disturbance, sensory losses or behavioural problems.

At present in Ireland, most children with moderate GLDs are being educated in special schools (of which there are 33 nationwide) and special classes attached to mainstream schools. With the Department of Education policy of integration and inclusion, though, this could be set to change over the coming years.

Children with moderate GLDs will normally be in classes where the pupil to teacher ratio is small. They will have access to a resource teacher and an SNA.

An IEP is essential for a student with a moderate GLD. This allows the student to follow a pace and learning style that suits their needs and particular abilities. Language development, social and personal skills development and functional skills development, i.e. self-help skills, as well as leisure and vocational skills and activities to develop gross and fine motor skills should all be part of the curriculum.

As the student may be receiving services from a multidisciplinary team (physiotherapists, occupational therapists, speech therapists), it is important that all members of the team, as well as the student's parents, work together to plan and co-ordinate the necessary services.

Two-way communication between the home and school is very important to ensure that the best possible programme is always in place for the student. Assistive technology and adaptive aids such as computers and communication devices may provide valuable assistance for students with moderate disabilities. In terms of the development of vocational skills, many schools now use work experience programmes and placements to help students learn how to function outside the sheltered settings of school and home.

SEVERE OR PROFOUND GENERAL LEARNING DISABILITIES

Children with severe or profound GLDs have a measured level of intelligence (IQ) that is in the range below 35 (significantly below the 1st percentile). Children will also display significant adaptive deficits and it is also very common for them to have significant physical disabilities and severe communication problems. Each child will have a carefully worked-out IEP. The main focus of the IEP is to work towards the child being able to communicate their needs, e.g. to be toileted, to be fed or to be read to. In Ireland, there are currently six special schools that cater for the needs of children with severe or profound GLDs.

SPECIFIC LEARNING DISABILITIES – DYSCALCULIA

As mentioned in Chapter 4 (in the sections on dysgraphia and dyspraxia) and again in Chapter 6 (dyslexia), children with specific learning disabilities will have average or above average intelligence (90 to 110 standard score points, which is in the 25th to 75th percentile) as assessed by a psychologist through the use of an individually administered test such as the WISC-IV discussed above. Despite this, they will have significant deficits in one or more specific areas.

- **Dyslexia:** Difficulty with writing, reading and spelling (see Chapter 6).
- **Dyscalculia:** Difficulty with mathematics (see below).
- **Dysgraphia:** Difficulty with handwriting (see Chapter 4).
- **Dyspraxia:** Difficulty with motor co-ordination (see Chapter 4).

Dyscalculia is a specific learning disability whereby the child (and later adult) has an innate difficulty in learning or comprehending mathematics. In some ways, it is to mathematics what dyslexia is to reading, writing and spelling.

Prevalence

Current estimates suggest that dyscalculia may affect about 5 per cent of the population. However, some psychologists suspect that at least some children diagnosed with dyscalculia may not have the disability at all, and instead their difficulties with mathematics are due to environmental factors resulting in an intense dislike and/or fear of mathematics, avoiding the subject if at all possible. As a result, the child gets little practice and falls further behind, continuing the cycle of dislike and avoidance. It is thought that this could be an important factor in some cases, rather than an innate developmental problem with mathematics. There may also be an overestimation of this and some other special learning needs due to the fact that many extra resources are only available to children if they have a diagnosis.

Causes

Like many other special learning needs, what causes dyscalculia is not fully understood. The first cases of dyscalculia were diagnosed in brain-damaged patients where damage was predominantly found at the junction between the temporal and parietal lobes of the cerebral cortex. It can be hereditary, which suggests a genetic link, and it is also associated with low birth weight and prematurity. Other conditions that frequently occur with dyscalculia include dyslexia (see Chapter 6), attention deficit hyperactivity disorder (see Chapter 7), epilepsy (see Chapter 4) and fragile X syndrome (see Chapter 8). Adams and Hitch (1997) suggest a connection between dyscalculia and deficits or problems with the working memory.

Symptoms

- Frequent difficulties with arithmetic, confusing the signs (+, −, ÷ and ×)
- Difficulty with everyday tasks like checking their change and reading analogue clocks (with hands and face)
- Difficulty with naming the days of the week, months of the year, seasons
- Inability to understand financial planning or budgeting, e.g. estimating the cost of the items in a shopping basket
- Difficulty with multiplication, subtraction, addition and division tables, mental arithmetic, etc.
- May transpose numbers, e.g. turn 56 into 65. If a phone number was called out to them, they may write numbers down in an incorrect sequence or leave some out
- Difficulty keeping scores in games
- Difficulty reading timetables, e.g. for buses or trains
- May have difficulty with logical sequencing, e.g. may put vegetables on before meat when cooking dinner
- Difficulty estimating time and judging the passing of time. May be chronically late.
- May have difficulties differentiating left from right
- Difficulty with map reading and may have a poor sense of direction
- May have particular difficulty mentally estimating the measurement of an object or distance, e.g. whether the room is about three or six metres long
- Often unable to grasp and remember mathematical concepts, rules, formulae and sequences
- May have difficulty imputing figures accurately into a calculator
- Will have an intense fear or anxiety about mathematics
- May have a sensitivity to noise or smells

Diagnosis

Dyscalculia is usually diagnosed through teacher observation and later formal assessments. The teacher may note that the child is having an unusual level of difficulty with mathematics when compared to other subjects in class and when doing homework. Parents may have come into the school expressing concern. Some may mention their own difficulties with mathematics to the teacher.

Results from end of year mathematics assessment tests, e.g. Drumcondra mathematics or Sigma-T tests, will be very low (below the 10th percentile), especially when compared to results from end of year reading tests, e.g. Drumcondra reading or Micra-T tests (results above the 50th percentile). On foot of these results and in discussion with parents and special needs support staff in the school, further assessment may be carried out by an educational psychologist, who will conduct interviews and also use a test instrument such as the WISC-IV described above to investigate further. This process will pinpoint more accurately where the child's difficulties lie.

Treatment

Dyscalculia is a special educational need and requires diagnosis, support and special methods of teaching. Maths has a number of basic concepts or skills that must be understood and mastered before proceeding with anything more complex. These skills are normally mastered in junior and senior infants and first class and are part of the Irish primary school mathematics curriculum for these classes. Children with dyscalculia will have an inadequate understanding of one or more of these basic concepts and will therefore become 'stuck'. These basic concepts/skills are as follows.

Early mathematics skills:

- Classifying: Ability to group similar items together.
- Matching: Ability to match similar items with each other and similar sets of items, e.g. a child with dyscalculia may have difficulty setting the table because he or she would find it difficult to match one place setting to the next. The concepts of more than, less than and equal to come into play here as well.
- Comparing: Ability to compare objects according to length, width, weight, quantity, thickness or size.
- Ordering: Ability to order objects according to length, width, height.

Number:
- Counting.
- Comparing and ordering (later, place value, i.e. the idea that the number 5 can have different values depending on where it is placed within a number, e.g. 135 and 351).
- Combining numbers: Numbers can be combined together to make different numbers, e.g. 3 combined with 4 makes a new number, 7.
- Partitioning numbers: A number can be divided up to make different numbers, e.g. 5 can be divided into 3 and 2.
- Read and write numbers.
- Understand the number 0 and how it combines with other numbers, e.g. $4 \times 0 = 0$.
- Estimate (subitise) amounts, e.g. length of something, weight of something, number of items.
- Carry out number operations, e.g. adding and subtracting.

Algebra:
- Recognise and continue patterns and sequences.
- Understand odd and even numbers.
- Understand that patterns emerge when numbers are added, subtracted, etc., such as $9 + 1 = 10$, $8 + 2 = 10$, $7 + 3 = 10$.
- Understand the use of a frame to show the presence of an unknown number, e.g. $3 + 5 = \square$.

Shape and space:
- Understand position, e.g. over, under, up, down, on, beside, in, between.
- Understand direction, e.g. left, right, straight ahead.
- Be able to give and understand directions, e.g. describe how you would get to the office or your house from here.
- Name, sort, describe and compare regular and irregular shapes (both 2-D and 3-D).
- Understand the concept of symmetry and asymmetry.

Measures:
- Length: Understand long/short, tall/short, wide/narrow, etc. Estimate and compare objects in terms of length, use non-standard (e.g. hand spans) and standard (the metre) units of measurement, practical use of measurement for length.

- Area: Understand basic concept of areas, e.g. how many playing cards will fit on the top of your desk.
- Weight: Understand heavy/light, heavier/lighter, balance, weight, etc. Estimate and compare objects in terms of weight, use of weighing scales.
- Capacity: Understand pour/fill, full/nearly full/empty, holds more than/less than/the same amount as. Estimate, compare, measure and record capacity using both non-standard (e.g. mug fulls) and standard (litres) units.
- Time: Develop concepts of time, e.g. morning/evening, night/day, lunchtime, home time, days of the week, school days, weekends, months of the year, seasons, day before, day after. Sequence events, e.g. events in a story, record time, e.g. using egg timer, or later stopwatch or clock. Read time on a clock. Read and use a calendar.
- Money: Recognise coins and notes, practise tendering and receiving money, giving change. Estimate and calculate the cost.

Data:
- Represent and interpret data, e.g. pictograms.

A child with dyscalculia needs to be taught these concepts in real-life situations, e.g. baking a cake or going shopping. This is important because the child is likely to be disheartened in relation to mathematics and therefore needs to clearly see its purpose so that they will be more motivated to learn.

Repetition and practice are also needed. Information technology can come in very useful here, as there are many programs on the market that allow the child to practise skills in an interesting and motivating way. One such program is **Numbershark**, which is used extensively in Irish schools.

Prognosis

With good support and tuition, many children with dyscalculia become competent in mathematics. They may continue to struggle with mathematics to the standard expected for state examinations, but will be competent enough to use mathematics as required in everyday life (functional mathematics). In Ireland, students are permitted to take maths for Junior and Leaving Certificate at foundation level. At this level, mathematics is quite concrete in nature and the courses are aimed at equipping students with skills for life. All of the Irish universities accept foundation mathematics for the purposes of matriculation (a requirement for entry into some), but not for CAO points and not for courses with a mathematics component. This essentially means that a student with dyscalculia can gain entry into universities even if their mathematics skills remain at a basic level. In contrast, most of the Institutes of Technology do not accept foundation-level mathematics as part of their minimum entry requirement (although some do for particular courses). This is due to the fact that many of their courses have a strong mathematics component.

Role of the SNA

An SNA could provide invaluable support in the classroom setting for a child with dyscalculia. He or she could assist and scaffold the child's learning while they are carrying out tasks as set by their class teacher. In addition, an SNA could work with a child using mathematics computer programs, providing assistance if necessary and plenty of praise and encouragement. On a practical level, because many children with dyscalculia tend to have difficulty organising themselves, an SNA could help train and assist the child with this, e.g. packing their bag in an ordered way.

CASE STUDY

Ronan went to school at age five and seemed to be progressing well in most areas. He was making friends and was already well on his way to reading. His teacher did notice, however, that he was having difficulty compared to many of his peers with a number of mathematical concepts. He found it difficult to consistently identify numbers and understand their value. Unlike many of his peers, he also had difficulty with sequencing activities, e.g. the children are given a series of six pictures and they have to arrange them in the correct order to tell the story, like a comic strip. He didn't know the days of the week or months of the year, he didn't know what month his birthday is in or whether it was coming up soon or not. He couldn't tell right from left and frequently put his shoes on the wrong feet. At the end of first class, his results in the Drumcondra test were unusual – he scored in the 96th percentile for reading, but in the 8th percentile for maths. The teacher had never seen such a huge discrepancy between the two results with any child before. On foot of these results, Ronan got one and a half hours of learning support per week.

Ronan was clearly an intelligent child, but there were many concepts that he just simply could not seem to grasp. For example, he mixed numbers up when he was writing them down and would forget which symbol to use if he was asked to add two numbers. If he was asked to add 6 + 2 and 2 + 6, for example, he would frequently get a different answer, not seeming to notice the similarities between the two sums. Perhaps most significant of all, he began to feel like a failure at maths. The teacher would notice him going quiet as soon as she began this part of the day. He wouldn't trust his own judgement on anything. He would just copy down answers from whoever was beside him.

Doing maths homework at home was very difficult – he would cry in frustration and shame. He felt humiliated, given that his younger brother was able to do the maths he couldn't and he was almost two years younger. His mum would try to drill the tables into him, but no sooner would he have 'learned' them than he would have forgotten them again. He began to hate maths and wouldn't participate in anything that even remotely involved maths, e.g. his mum used to try to get him to bake at home, getting him to weigh ingredients, etc. He began to refuse to do this, claiming it was stupid and for girls, even though he'd previously loved baking.

Towards the end of second class, Ronan completed an individual assessment with a psychologist. The results concluded that Ronan had dyscalculia. As a result, Ronan got extra help from a resource teacher as well as the extra learning support he was already getting. The school also received funding for computer software to allow Ronan (and other children experiencing difficulties with maths) to practise basic skills. While at the computer, the school's SNA would help him if he got stuck and offer him encouragement and reassurance. The resource teacher sometimes worked in the classroom with the class teacher, supporting Ronan's learning, while other times she worked with him on a one-to-one basis.

Today, Ronan is in fourth class and doing much better. He still has serious difficulties with maths, but doesn't feel as anxious or fearful about it. He accepts that it is just one of those things that he will have to work at.

chapter six

Special Needs Affecting Language and Communication

CHAPTER OUTLINE

▶ Hearing impairment
▶ Specific speech and language impairment
▶ Dyslexia
▶ Newcomer children whose first language is not English

HEARING IMPAIRMENT

For the purpose of special needs provision, the Department of Education and Skills describes students with a hearing impairment thus:

> Such pupils have a hearing disability that is so serious to impair significantly their capacity to hear and understand human speech, thus preventing them from participating fully in classroom interaction and from benefiting adequately from school instruction. The great majority of them have prescribed hearing aids and are availing of the services of a visiting teacher (this category is not meant to include pupils with mild hearing loss).

> Schools that have a pupil that has been assessed as having hearing impairment and no other assessed disability may be allocated a maximum of 4 hours teaching support per week from a resources teacher, or from a visiting teacher and resource teacher combined. Where a pupil with a hearing impairment also meets the criterion for another low-incidence disability category, provision is allocated as for multiple disabilities (5 hours). (Circular SPED02/05)

Prevalence

About 100 children are born deaf in Ireland each year, with greater numbers having lesser degrees of hearing impairment. Currently, there are over 2,000 hearing-impaired children attending mainstream schools in Ireland, with a further 180 attending Ireland's three schools for the deaf. In addition, there are also significant numbers of deaf children with multiple disabilities attending other special schools.

How we hear sound

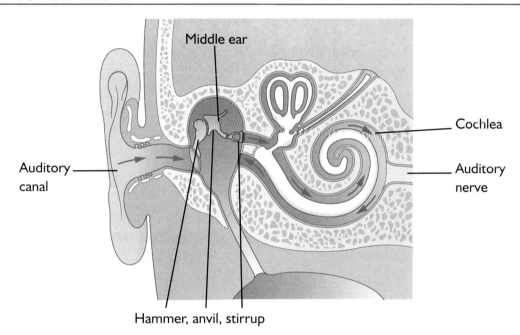

Structure of the ear

Sound waves are picked up from the atmosphere around us by the pinna (the part of the ear attached to the outside of your head). These sound waves travel along the external auditory canal (ear canal) to the tympanic membrane (eardrum), causing it to vibrate.

Three small bones are then activated by the eardrum – the malleus (commonly called the hammer), incus (commonly called the anvil) and stapes (commonly called the stirrup). The malleus is the bone touching the eardrum – it vibrates, amplifying the sound and passing the vibrations on to the incus and finally the stapes.

The stapes is attached to the cochlea, which is a snail shell-shaped structure filled with fluid. The vibrations cause this fluid to move, stimulating millions of tiny hair cells present on the inside of the cochlea. This causes an electrical message to be passed to the cochlear nerve, which travels to the brain to be interpreted as sound.

Causes

There are two basic categories of hearing impairment, both of which have different causes:

1. Conductive impairment
2. Sensorineural impairment

Sometimes children can have a mixture of the two – this is called mixed impairment.

Conductive impairment

Conductive impairment occurs when sound is blocked from entering the inner ear. The cause of the blockage occurs either in the outer or middle ear and loss may be temporary.

Causes:

- Middle-ear infections
- A perforated eardrum
- Earwax or other obstructions, e.g. beads in the ear canal
- Unusual bone growth (otosclerosis) in the ear
- Thick fluid builds up in the middle ear as a result of persistent ear infections, sometimes called glue ear
- Head injury damaging the outer or middle ear

Sensorineural impairment

Sensorineural hearing impairment is caused by problems with the nerves connecting the inner ear to the brain (vestibulocochlear nerve or cranial nerve VIII), the inner ear itself or the areas of the brain that process sound. Sensorineural hearing loss can be mild, moderate or severe, including total deafness.

The main reason for sensorineural hearing loss is abnormal hair cells in the cochlea of the ear. These tiny hair cells pick up vibrations caused by sound entering the inner ear and a sensory message is sent to the brain via the vestibulocochlear nerve. The brain then interprets this as a particular sound. If the hair cells are not functioning properly, the vibrations will not be sensed properly and an inadequate message is sent to the brain. Hair cells may be abnormal at birth or become damaged after birth.

The most common causes of sensorineural hearing loss are as follows.

- Genetic: Some forms of deafness can be inherited from parents. The most common inherited form of deafness is called DFNB1, also known as Connexin 26 deafness or GJB2-related deafness.
- Infections such as meningitis, measles or mumps in infants and children.
- Rubella, herpes, syphilis, HIV/AIDS and chlamydia can be passed to the foetus during pregnancy or to newborns during the birthing process. All of these can cause deafness (among other things).
- Approximately 60 per cent of children with foetal alcohol syndrome have some degree of hearing loss resulting from their mother's drinking.
- Trauma at birth and premature birth (approximately 5 per cent of premature babies experience hearing loss).
- Head injuries after birth, e.g. falls, accidents.
- Prolonged exposure to noise.
- Brain tumours.
- Ototoxic drugs (drugs that can cause damage to the ear) These include some antibiotics, e.g. Gentamicin and Tobramycin, loop diuretics (used to treat patients with kidney problems), some chemotherapy drugs, e.g. cisplatin, and aspirin.

Symptoms

In babies, the symptoms of hearing loss will normally be that he or she does not reach his or her expected milestones for language and social development. Below are listed the expected milestones from birth to two years. A profoundly deaf baby will not reach these milestones. Babies with mild or moderate hearing loss may reach many of these milestones, but will generally have less distinctive speech, which is why their hearing loss sometimes goes undetected.

- **Zero to four months:** Stops movement or quiets in response to speech or unfamiliar noises. Startles to loud sounds. Moves eyes towards sound source. Rouses from light sleep to sudden loud noises. Imitates gurgling or cooing sounds and shows a response to noise-making toys. At three months, the child should soothe or show responses to the mother's voice.
- **Four to seven months:** Begins turning head towards sounds and voices out of sight (four months) and turns head directly towards the sound source (seven months). Smiles in response to speech. Looks in response to own name. Babbling begins.
- **Seven to nine months:** Turns to find a sound source out of sight. Gurgles or coos to sounds out of sight. Tuneful babbling. Understands 'no'. Babbles in

multiple syllables. Responds to his or her own name. Responds to household sounds such as the bath filling – may get excited. At nine months, the child should engage in loud shrieking and sustained production of vowels.

- **Nine to 12 months:** Acquires first true word, usually Dada. Imitates sounds. Looks at a familiar object when named, e.g. 'Where's Daddy?' Responds to music. Understands simple commands or requests, e.g. 'Give Mammy the spoon.' Uses his or her own voice to get attention.
- **Thirteen to 18 months:** Uses sentence-like intonation – voice goes up and down as if they are speaking real sentences. Perceives emotions of others. Uses three to 20 words. Uses all vowels and consonants in jargon.
- **Nineteen to 24 months:** Uses more words than jargon. Asks questions by rising intonation at end of phrase. Comprehends about 300 words and uses about 50 words. Produces animal sounds. May combine two words into phrases, e.g. 'Doggy bold.' Listens to simple stories.

An older child may show some of the following symptoms.

- People have to raise their voice consistently to get the child's attention.
- The child frequently says 'huh?' or 'what?' when somebody is speaking.
- The child has a history of ear infections, often getting earaches or runny ears.
- The child complains of their ears hurting and about certain pitches of sound.
- The child watches the speaker's face carefully. The child turns his or her head so that one ear is facing the direction of the sound source.
- The child speaks very loudly.
- The child turns the TV up very loudly and sits very close to it.
- The child does not consistently look when called.
- He or she confuses sounds that are alike, e.g. if a parent asks 'What about the bread?', the child responds, 'I made my bed.'
- The child's speech is unclear and poorer than you would expect for his or her age.
- The child is very quiet, using little verbal language.
- The child seems inattentive, frequently daydreaming.
- The child may become disruptive at preschool or school, especially at times when children are involved in listening activities, e.g. story time.

Diagnosis

It is possible to screen for hearing loss almost immediately after birth. In some countries (not Ireland), all newborns are screened before they leave the hospital.

This is very good practice given that the earlier a hearing impairment is detected, the less impact there tends to be on the child's ability to communicate effectively as they grow up. Some countries screen only at-risk infants, e.g. premature infants, those with other conditions known to cause hearing loss, babies that have been exposed to various infections, babies of deaf parents and babies with severe jaundice.

Two principal forms of testing are used.

- **Auditory brainstem response test (ABR):** This test involves attaching electrodes to the baby's head to record electrical activity from the auditory nerve (the hearing nerve) and other parts of the brain.

- **Otoacoustic emission test (OAE):** This test is performed by placing a small probe that contains a microphone and speaker into the infant's ear. As the infant rests quietly, sounds are generated in the probe and responses that come back from the cochlea are recorded.

If a baby fails one of these screening tests, it will normally be repeated once more before the child is sent for further diagnostic testing. The purpose of this further testing is to determine the nature of the hearing loss with a view to identifying the best treatment option for an individual child.

Distraction tests

In countries (including Ireland) where this form of infant screening is not the norm, other types of screening exist. In Ireland, at six weeks babies normally go for a check-up with their GP. It is standard at these check-ups for the GP to ask the parents questions about the baby's hearing, e.g. if he or she responds to loud noises or if he or she gets startled. Soon after the baby comes home and again at approximately three months, a public health nurse visits mothers and their newborns. Like the GP, the nurse will ask questions regarding the baby's hearing. However, it is not until the baby's seven month check-up that the baby's hearing is formally screened.

With distraction tests, the baby's attention is gained by a tester (or parent) playing with a toy in front of him or her. A second tester then makes a variety of sounds behind the infant's head using a number of different devices, such as bells. The infant's reactions are noted. If babies have colds that may affect results, then they will be brought back for testing another day. The accuracy of distraction tests have been criticised and are not being used in many countries any more as the primary screening method.

Co-operative and performance tests

From about 18 months, children can be involved in testing that requires them to respond to specific instructions, e.g. a child may be asked to put a toy brick in a bucket every time they hear a sound. These tests are sometimes carried out with primary school children where the child puts on headphones and is asked to raise their hand when they hear a sound. The tester inputs various sound frequencies into the headphones.

Treatment

Treatment depends on the type and degree of hearing loss.

Hearing aids

Hearing aids have three basic parts: a microphone, amplifier and speaker. The hearing aid receives sound through a microphone, which converts the sound waves to electrical signals and sends them to an amplifier. The amplifier increases the power of the signals and then sends them to the ear through a speaker. Hearing aids are primarily useful in improving the hearing and speech comprehension of people who have sensorineural hearing loss resulting from damage to the small hair cells in the inner ear. A hearing aid magnifies sound vibrations entering the ear. Surviving hair cells detect the larger vibrations and convert them into neural signals that are passed along to the brain.

The greater the damage to a person's hair cells, the more severe the hearing loss and the greater the hearing aid amplification needed to make up the difference. However, there are practical limits to the amount of amplification a hearing aid can provide. In addition, if the inner ear is too damaged, even large vibrations will not be converted into neural signals. In this situation, a hearing aid would be ineffective.

Child with a modern hearing aid

Modern hearing aids can be either behind the ear, in the ear or deep in the ear canal. Modern digital hearing aids are fitted with many extra functions, e.g. speech-understanding technology (which cuts down on background noise, thus amplifying speech sounds more), Bluetooth technology for answering mobile phones and direct audio input from TV and radio. Many are now manufactured in different colours to make them less severe looking than the traditional beige.

Radio hearing aids have two parts and are sometimes worn during times in school when background noise is great. The teacher wears a transmitter that is connected to the child's hearing aid. The teacher's voice is then transmitted to the child's hearing aid without all the background noise.

Cochlear implants

A cochlear implant is a small, complex electronic device that allows someone who is severely or profoundly deaf to hear sound. The principle behind the implant is that if someone's cochlear is so damaged that it cannot be stimulated and in turn stimulate the auditory nerve naturally by sound, the auditory nerve must be stimulated directly. Implants are composed of four parts – three of them are outside the body (external) and one is under the skin near the auditory nerve (internal):

- A microphone, which picks up sound from the environment (external).
- A speech processor is a little box normally held in a small backpack or pouch. The processor selects and arranges sounds picked up by the microphone.
- A transmitter and receiver/stimulator, which receive signals from the speech processor and convert them into electric impulses (external).
- An electrode array (surgically placed under the skin in the cochlea) collects the impulses from the stimulator and sends them to different regions of the auditory nerve.

When the child has recovered from surgery, the implant will be turned on and the child begins the process of learning how to understand and use the new sounds. It is vital that the child receives the implant as early as possible in their lives, as the brain is most receptive to sound and language learning at this time. Since Ireland's first implant in 1995, all cochlear implants have been carried out at Beaumont Hospital, Dublin, by their specialist implant team. To date, they have carried out 400 implants on all age groups, ranging from a few months old to late adulthood. Adults and older children who have lost their hearing benefit from implants, whereas those who have been deaf since childhood and have had no memory of sound are unlikely to do so. As of 2010, the Beaumont Hospital website states that children requiring an implant should have to wait no longer than three months for an appointment and that surgery should be completed within a nine-month period. For adults (where time is not so important), the wait time is two years.

Sign language

See also Chapter 14.

Irish Sign Language (ISL) is the first and preferred language of deaf people in Ireland. As other languages exist – French, German, etc. – so do other sign languages, e.g. British and American sign. As with all language, sign language is best learned at as young an age as possible. In fact, many parents are teaching their hearing children simple sign language so that they can communicate their needs before they are able to speak. Sign language is used extensively within the deaf community in Ireland, but very few hearing people can use sign, which has the effect of isolating the deaf community. Sign language classes are widely available throughout the country, however, with most VECs offering it as a night class.

Finger spelling (where words are spelled out – the Irish sign alphabet uses only one hand) and Lámh (a more limited signing system) are also sometimes used.

Lip reading

Lip reading is the technique of understanding speech by visually interpreting the movements of the lips, face and tongue along with information provided by the context and any residual hearing. Because some words have similar lip movements, sometimes lip reading is accompanied by **cued speech**, where words that are similar to others are accompanied by a hand sign to show which word is being said. When speaking, it is not advised to exaggerate lip movements, as this distorts what is being said, since the lip reader has been trained to read normal movements. Lip reading is extremely tiring, so most deaf people supplement it with gesture, mime and writing.

Prognosis

Prognosis will depend on the nature and severity of the hearing impairment together with the nature and effectiveness of the interventions put in place to help the child with the hearing impairment communicate.

Medical advances such as improved hearing aids and cochlear implants have meant that many children who would have gone a lifetime without hearing any sound or developing any speech now do so. Many deaf children now attend mainstream schools side by side with their hearing peers.

There is debate within the deaf community, however, about this medical model of deafness. Some members of the deaf community believe that instead of money being spent on 'fixing' the child's deafness, it should be spent on teaching the hearing world to communicate with the deaf community through sign language. Deafness is only a problem because hearing people don't speak the language.

Deaf children are taught sign language from an early age and some are taught to lip read. In addition, more hearing people are now learning sign.

Role of the SNA

Most deaf children in mainstream schools will have some level of hearing, be it as a result of their own residual hearing, implants or through hearing aids. They will therefore be able to communicate and should be given every opportunity to do so. Like all school staff, SNAs should:

- Sit in front of the child when talking at face-to-face level with light in front of you rather than behind so that the child can see your face clearly. This aids communication.
- Keep background noise low.
- Do not shout or make exaggerated mouth patterns – it may be preferable to just speak more slowly.
- Accompany speech with visual clues and check that the child is understanding as you talk.
- Do not cover your face while you talk; moustaches and beards hide the lips.
- If an older child gets frustrated, write things down.
- Allow the child time to speak.
- It is a good idea to learn sign language. Courses are readily available and are relatively inexpensive.
- Take part in music activities with the child – percussion instruments (drums, bodhráns, etc.) can be particularly effective, as the child can feel the sound as well as hear it.
- As an SNA, you may be asked to accompany the child to the safety of their parent's car at home time.
- Be vigilant that the child's hearing aid is working and that batteries are OK. Inform parents if you suspect something is wrong.
- At times in a busy classroom, an SNA may be asked to help the child with a particular task by wearing a radio transmitter so that the child can hear the SNA over the general classroom bustle.

Molly was the first child born to Sally and David, who both have normal hearing. She was a large full-term baby with no apparent difficulties. Sally and David did suspect that there might be something wrong with Molly's hearing when she was about six months old and mentioned it to the public health nurse, who said that Molly was babbling normally and that her hearing was perfect. As Sally and David had no other children at this stage, they didn't have anyone to compare Molly to and therefore didn't pursue their suspicions any further at this stage.

When Molly was about a year old, Sally and David noticed that Molly had become very quiet. Before this she had babbled, but had recently just stopped. They did nothing about it for a few months, but because she continued to stay silent they decided to bring it to the attention of their GP. Their GP examined Molly's ears and agreed that she was not hearing properly, finding that she had an ear infection for which he prescribed a course of antibiotics. After the ear infection cleared up, Molly remained silent, so Sally and David brought her back to the GP. He did some very basic tests on her hearing and said that there might be another problem apart from the infection. He referred Molly to Beaumont Hospital in Dublin, where she was given a series of diagnostic tests. Molly was diagnosed as profoundly deaf by Beaumont. She was now almost two years old.

The team at Beaumont decided that Molly was a good candidate for a cochlear ear implant, although they would have liked to have given her the implant even earlier, as she had already missed out on two years of language learning. Sally and David were understandably livid, given that they had brought their concerns to the attention of the public health nurse when Molly was only six months old. They were angry because if she had had the implants at that stage, she would most likely be making speech sounds by now like any normal two-year-old.

As the day of the surgery drew near, Sally and David were understandably nervous but also glad that their daughter was getting treatment now and would have a good chance of learning to speak and lead a normal life. Molly had her surgery, which lasted just under three hours. They were the longest three hours of Sally and David's life, and when she came out they cried with relief. Molly was given six weeks to recover from the surgery before the implant was turned on. It was done slowly, bit by bit, to give Molly's brain time to adjust to hearing sound. Little by little, and with the help of her speech therapist, Molly began to speak – one of her first words was ice cream!

Today, Molly is almost five years old. Her speech is not as distinct as other children her age, but it is intelligible even to strangers if they listen carefully. She is beginning primary school in September, which she is really looking forward to. Sally and David are happy with Molly's progress, but feel that Ireland should have a better deafness screening system, like other countries do. They believe that a more specialist approach should be taken and that screening should not be based on error-prone distraction tests at seven or eight months of age.

SPECIFIC SPEECH AND LANGUAGE IMPAIRMENT

Note: The Irish Department of Education and Skills refers to this as specific speech and language **disorder**.

Specific speech and language impairment (SLI) is a developmental language impairment that can affect either expressive (spoken) and receptive (understanding) language or both (this is called a global impairment). SLI is defined as a pure language impairment, meaning that it is not related to or caused by other developmental impairments, e.g. cognitive, hearing loss or acquired brain injury.

Prevalence

It is difficult to get an accurate figure for the numbers of children with specific speech and language impairment because speech is often affected by other issues, e.g. hearing. Leonard (1997) estimates that 5 per cent of children have specific language impairment. Like other language-based difficulties, it is more common in boys than girls.

Causes

The cause of specific language impairment is not known. It tends to run in families (although not always), so there seems to be a strong genetic link.

Symptoms

Expressive language impairment

Expressive language impairment is characterised by limited vocabulary and a poor grasp of grammar. The child's understanding of language is likely to be far superior to his or her ability to communicate using the spoken word. The child will be reluctant to talk and may resort to pointing or gesturing to get their message across. What the child does say often lacks variation in intonation or volume – it may sound flat.

Imaginative play and social use of language may be further impaired. Children often only speak when asked a specific, direct question, replying in very short, basic sentences. Children will have difficulties in describing, defining and explaining and in retelling stories/events. Limited vocabulary may result in the children using empty repetitive phrases and non-specific words.

At school, expressive language difficulties may impact on the student's abilities in relation to writing, spelling, composing sentences/compositions and answering all but the most straightforward of questions. Almost 50 per cent of children with SLI also have dyslexia. There may be evidence of omission of function words such as 'the' and 'is' and grammatical markers such as tense endings, e.g. knowing that 'ed' is usually used to express a verb in the past tense. Difficulties may be noted in the formulation of full sentences and in the understanding of multiple word meanings, e.g. knowing that 'sea' and 'see' have different meanings. Because of their specific expressive language difficulties, many children can have difficulty establishing and maintaining peer relationships.

Receptive language impairment

Students with a receptive language impairment have problems understanding oral language or in listening. They may have difficulty processing and retaining information they hear and in following instructions and directions. Difficulties in understanding what is said will be worse in group situations, e.g. discussions, or where there is a lot of background noise, which is a normal feature of school classrooms. Children will have difficulty answering questions because they may not hear the question asked. Verbal reasoning will be particularly challenging for children with SLI. For example, if the following verbal problem was put to a child with SLI, it is likely that they would find it difficult: *If Anne has more money than John and John has more money than Patty, who has the most money?*

Poor sound discrimination may also be evidenced, whereby the child will not hear the differences between similar-sounding words. Pragmatics involves understanding the subtleties of language. A child with SLI will sometimes have difficulty using language in a socially appropriate way, e.g. tone of voice, eye contact, turn-taking and maintaining a shared topic. As a result, the child may experience problems establishing and maintaining peer relationships.

Global specific language impairment

A child with global SLI will have problems with both expressive and receptive language.

Diagnosis

Early identification is important for the success of interventions for SLI. The disorder is usually diagnosed by comparing a child's linguistic abilities to those that are expected for children of the same age. If the child is significantly behind his or her same-age peers in terms of language development, SLI is considered a likely possibility. One procedure for diagnosing children aged 24 to 36 months asks parents to complete a standardised questionnaire in which they check off the vocabulary the child knows and write down examples of the child's two-word sentences. If the child's vocabulary contains fewer than 50 words and the child does not use any two-word sentences, it is an indication of SLI or another language disorder and further investigation will be required.

Children of school-going age will normally be assessed by a psychologist and a speech and language therapist. The Department of Education and Skills requires this before extra supports are granted for any particular child. The psychologist will assess the child's overall cognitive ability (see the section on assessment in Chapter 5, pp. 130–4), comparing his or her verbal and non-verbal skills. If the child's non-verbal or performance IQ is 90 or above and their verbal IQ is significantly below this, then the child will be referred to a speech and language therapist for further investigation, who will carry out further assessments and advise the school on what to do next.

Treatment

Treatment usually focuses on directly teaching the child the specific skills that he or she is having difficulty with. This work will be led by a speech and language therapist and will be supported by parents and in school by both the child's class teacher, their resource teacher and any other learning support staff, e.g. an SNA. Normally children learn language almost automatically without any direct teaching. Children with SLI will have to be taught language more directly.

- **Phonology:** Sounds of language.
- **Morphology:** Grammar of the language, e.g. cat means one, cats means more than one.
- **Syntax:** Word order in sentences, e.g. John hit the cat, the cat hit John – word order changes meaning.
- **Semantics:** The meaning of words and sentences.
- **Pragmatics:** Knowing how to use language appropriately, e.g. turn taking, tone and volume of voice in different situations, eye contact, knowing when it is appropriate to change topic (for example, if a person was telling you about their beloved dog dying, it would be inappropriate to interrupt to tell them about how you got a new coat for Christmas).

The Department of Education and Skills will allocate a maximum of four extra resource hours per week to children with SLI. As with other special needs, the resource teacher may use these hours to work on a one-to-one basis with the child outside the mainstream classroom or work within the classroom with the class teacher through co-operative teaching.

Throughout the country there are special speech and language classes attached to both primary and post-primary schools (mainly primary). The National Council for Special Education website lists all of these schools (www.ncse.ie). These classes, of which there are 65 distributed over 24 counties, cater for children with specific speech and language disorders and also children with more severe cases of dyslexia (see the next section).

Circular 0038/2007 deals with the criteria for enrolment in special classes for pupils with speech and language disorders in national schools. A complete copy of this circular can be downloaded from www.education.ie.

Prognosis

As with so many other special needs, the prognosis for specific language impairment depends on a number of factors:

- The severity of the impairment
- The age at which interventions began
- The quality of the interventions
- The motivation of the child and his or her family

Generally prognosis is good in that the child learns sufficient language skills to manage effectively, both educationally and socially. It is rare, however, for the child to overcome their difficulties entirely.

Role of the SNA

An SNA will be an invaluable resource for children with specific language impairment in the classroom. An SNA may be asked to sit beside the child, ensuring that the teacher's instructions are understood, and if not, explaining them to the child. Always speak clearly and do not use language that is more elaborate than necessary. Offer the child plenty of encouragement and praise their efforts.

An SNA may be asked to work with the child using specific computer software or on specific language tasks, e.g. naming picture flashcards. Children with SLI should not be corrected on pronunciation too often, as they may lose confidence and avoid speaking altogether. Instead, use the correct pronunciation yourself as soon as possible in the conversation. An SNA may be asked to listen to children's reading; if so, be careful not to jump in too soon to correct errors. Allow the child (this includes all children) time to pronounce the words themselves before helping them.

Ciarán was diagnosed at two years and six months of age with specific language impairment. His parents knew what they were looking for because his elder brother and his father each had the same impairment. He was diagnosed as having a global impairment, although Elaine, his mum, felt that his expressive language was much worse than his receptive language.

At two years nine months, Ciarán began working with a speech therapist, and at three he started preschool. He continued with speech therapy, attending once a fortnight, and his mother practised with him every day. His language improved little by little, but by age five, when he was due to start in his local primary school, his speech was still significantly behind that of his peers. Luckily, Ciarán lives relatively close to a primary school with a special class for children with specific language disorders. There were only six other children in the room. He attended this class for Junior and senior infants and was taught by a teacher who had trained specially in the area. Because he was in this class, he also had additional supports from a speech and language therapist.

At the beginning of first class, Ciarán's language had sufficiently improved for him to move back to his local primary school. This was a big culture shock for him, as there were over 35 children in his class, but he fit in well and adapted. Ciarán does still have difficulties with language and is currently receiving two resource hours, mainly for his reading, but he is progressing well in all subject areas.

Elaine feels that Ciarán is very fortunate. She is fully aware that his progress is largely due to the fact that she and her husband were aware of the condition and knew what to look out for. In addition, because Ciarán was diagnosed early and got early interventions, his language is not as severely affected as others with the condition. She is also glad that she happens to live in an area with a special class for children with specific language impairment. She feels sorry for children who live in areas where no such help is available and believes that whether you get adequate help or not should have nothing to do with where you live.

DYSLEXIA

There are many definitions of dyslexia. A very simple one would be that dyslexia is a specific learning difficulty that makes it more difficult for people to learn to read, write and spell correctly. The Task Force on Dyslexia suggests the following definition (Department of Education and Science 2002):

Dyslexia is manifested in a continuum of specific learning difficulties related to the acquisition of basic skills in reading, spelling and/or writing, such difficulties being unexplained in relation to an individual's other abilities and educational experiences. Dyslexia can be described at the neurological, cognitive and behavioural levels. It is typically characterised by inefficient information processing, including difficulties in phonological processing, working memory, rapid naming and automaticity of basic skills. Difficulties in organisation, sequencing and motor skills may also be present.

Prevalence

There is debate among professionals as to how prevalent dyslexia actually is. Approximately 20 per cent of children in Irish schools have literacy difficulties (10 per cent are judged to have serious difficulties). This figure rises to 50 per cent in areas of poverty and social disadvantage (with 25 to 30 per cent of children in these areas having serious reading difficulties). How many of these children have dyslexia and how many of them have literacy difficulties because of other reasons? Estimates for the prevalence of dyslexia (both mild and more severe) vary widely at between 4 and 10 per cent.

Advocates of programmes such as the Reading Recovery programme believe that if more children were targeted at a younger age, before the child develops negative beliefs and attitudes about their own literacy ability, then figures for literacy problems and indeed dyslexia would decrease. Some professionals believe that dyslexia is actually quite rare and that many children with a diagnosis of dyslexia do not actually have the condition, but rather got off to a bad start with reading, which has escalated into a severe literacy problem over the subsequent years.

Causes

Since dyslexia was first diagnosed in 1886, there has been a huge volume of research conducted internationally as to what causes it. Nicholson (2001), however, argues that the term 'dyslexia' is actually misleading, as it implies a single uniform syndrome, which, of course, it is not. Since the 1980s, educationalists in the US have been using the term 'reading disability' instead of dyslexia to reflect the variations between individuals.

Morton and Frith (1995) and Frith (1997) propose that dyslexia can be described at three different levels:

- A biological level (in terms of brain structure, what causes dyslexia?)
- A cognitive level (in terms of brain functioning, what causes dyslexia?)
- A behavioural level (symptoms of dyslexia, which will be dealt with in the next section)

Biological

Genetic

There is a growing body of evidence indicating a strong genetic link with dyslexia. Grigorenko (2001) provides an overview of this research. Many studies indicate that if at least one member of a family has developmental dyslexia, there is a higher than normal chance that other members will also have reading problems. Evidence from studies of twins reared apart has shown that at least some proportion of developmental dyslexia has a genetic basis, even if it is not yet clear how exactly dyslexia is transmitted. It is believed that dyslexia involves a cluster of different genes, hence the variations between individuals with the condition.

Cerebellum

Research with children with dyslexia indicates deficits in the functioning of the cerebellum (the area of the brain associated with the automatisation of skills). Nicholson and Fawcett (1990) found that children with dyslexia require significantly more time both to acquire a new skill and for it to become automatic. In one of their experiments, children were given a task requiring them to walk along a straight line. There was no significant difference in the performance of dyslexic and non-dyslexic children (control group). However, when the children were asked to count backwards at the same time as walking the line, the balance of the dyslexic group became much poorer. Nicholson and Fawcett argue that their need to concentrate on the new task (counting backwards) required the balance task to be done automatically. Deficits in the functioning of their cerebellum meant that they were unable to do so, causing their balance to deteriorate. In the control group, the ability to balance was more instinctive, allowing them to concentrate fully on the new task.

Now apply this information to reading, writing and spelling – after a few short years, these skills become automatic to someone with normal reading ability. Take the word 'smudge' – if you are a fluent reader, you can read this word automatically; in fact, you cannot see anything other than the word 'smudge'. Not so with the dyslexic reader – reading, like other tasks (influenced by the cerebellum), is not automatic, hence the difficulty. This is also why when people with dyslexia read aloud, their reading is often described as 'laboured'. This is actually an accurate description, because for someone with dyslexia, reading does take conscious effort.

Visual magnocellular system

Some people with dyslexia report what is called visual discomfort. They often experience headaches and eyestrain and report that words seem to move around on the page in front of them. This is thought to be due to a deficit in an area of the brain called the visual magnocellular system. Wearing coloured glasses or having work photocopied onto coloured paper (anything except white) sometimes helps this problem.

Cognitive

Much of the research on the causes of dyslexia has focused on two aspects of cognitive functioning – phonological processing and short-term memory skills.

Phonological processing is the ability to translate letters and words into sounds. Children with dyslexia are not able to naturally do this and must learn to do so in a very deliberate way. Studies of short-term memory skills where children are required to remember number and letter strings show that children with dyslexia tend to have poorer short-term memories.

Symptoms of dyslexia at a behavioural level

While the symptoms of dyslexia vary from individual to individual, some common characteristics are evident. In general, children with dyslexia may:

- Have experienced early speech and language problems
- Confuse directions like left and right
- Have difficulty remembering common sequences such as the days of the week, tables and the alphabet
- Have poor pencil control and awkward handwriting
- Mix up the sounds of words and order of numbers
- Be unable to pair speech sounds with letters and vice versa
- Confuse letters and words that look somewhat alike, such as b/d, p/q, m/w, n/u, was/saw, cat/act, from/form
- Have difficulty copying words and numbers from a book or blackboard
- Have specific difficulties in arithmetic, such as place value, e.g. what value has 5 in each of the following numbers: 521, 251
- Have problems recalling the names of people, words or objects
- Find second or third language learning difficult – this is why children with dyslexia are normally exempt from learning Irish
- Persistent spelling problems
- Reading aloud may be difficult or embarrassing
- There is often a marked difference between verbal and written ability
- May be prone to spoonerisms, i.e. slips of the tongue
- Some children may be prone to clumsiness and untidiness

Diagnosis

Parents and/or teachers who suspect a child is having a problem with reading, writing and spelling should not hesitate to take action. If left undiagnosed and untreated, a specific learning disability such as dyslexia can stop a child from mastering the basics of reading, writing and arithmetic, damage self-esteem and self-confidence and have negative long-term effects. Psycho-educational assessment by a qualified educational psychologist is the only reliable means of diagnosis.

A sample of dyslexic writing. This is the translation: Ellen must drink her milk. Stephen had a picnic of ham sandwiches. What are you two doing here? The flowers have many buds on them. Some people come here every day.

Treatment

If a diagnosis of dyslexia has been made, the child is likely to need extra tuition. The options available fall into two categories: school-based supports and supports outside of school.

School-based supports

- **Support from the class teacher:** The class teacher has an important role to play in being aware and considerate of each student's strengths and weaknesses. There are many things the class teacher can do to help teach a child with dyslexia more effectively (see the section below on general supports).

- **Learning support teacher:** Students with dyslexia, which is not severe enough to qualify for resource teaching or a special reading school/unit, may receive additional support in their school from the learning support teacher (formerly called the remedial teacher). This help is usually in a small group setting and is organised on a withdrawal basis from the regular class. Generally, students whose reading and spelling fall below the 12th percentile but above the 2nd percentile are entitled to help from the learning support teacher.

▸ **Resource teacher:** Resource teaching is specialised tuition for those who have been diagnosed with dyslexia by a psychologist and who have average or above average intelligence but are at or below the 2nd percentile for reading and writing. The maximum number of hours of resource teaching available to such students is 2.5 hours per week, i.e. one 30-minute class per day.

▸ **Enrolment in a special reading school:** Special reading schools are full-time Department of Education and Skills-funded primary schools. However, there are only four of them nationwide (see below). The regular school curriculum is followed, with the exception of Irish. The current pupil to teacher ratio is 9:1 and children usually attend for one to two years, depending on their progress, and then return to their own school. Application must be made by the psychologist who assessed the child, supported by a recommendation from the child's own school, before March of the year of entry. The usual criterion for admission to a special reading school is average/above average intelligence and a significant discrepancy between intellectual ability and literacy levels. The pupil should have completed second class or be at least eight years old and not more than 12 years old. The four reading schools currently in Ireland are:

   – Catherine McAuley NS, Baggott Street, Dublin 2. Tel. (01) 661 5645; www.catherinemcauleyns.ie.
   – Oliver Plunkett School, Alma Place, Monkstown, Co. Dublin. Tel. (01) 280 8824; www.stoliverplunkett.ie.
   – St Rose's NS, Balrothery, Tallaght, Dublin 24. Tel. (01) 451 7933; www.stroses.net.
   – St Killian's School, Evergreen Street, Cork. Tel. (021) 507 131.

▸ **Enrolment in a special reading class attached to a mainstream primary school:** There are a total of 23 special reading classes attached to mainstream primary schools in Ireland (as of March 2010). As with the four reading schools, children attend the reading class for one to two years, depending on need. They then return to their own primary school or to the mainstream part of the primary school to which the reading class is attached. Visit the Dyslexia Association of Ireland website (www.dyslexia.ie) for a list of primary schools with special reading classes attached.

Supports outside of school

The Dyslexia Association of Ireland (DAI) provides out-of-school support for children with dyslexia. This support takes two forms:

- Support on a one-to-one basis from a DAI-trained tutor
- Enrolment in a DAI workshop, exam class and summer schools

Parents of children diagnosed with dyslexia pay an annual membership subscription (currently €40) to the DAI. In return, the DAI sends them information on the supports available outside of school for their child. The DAI has branches throughout the country. Parents should contact the DAI headquarters on (01) 679 0276 or consult their website (www.dyslexia.ie) for further information on dyslexia generally and on their services specifically.

Support on a one-to-one basis from a DAI-trained tutor

The DAI provides members with a list of tutors who are qualified teachers and who have also done additional training in the area of working with children and adults with dyslexia. Tuition is arranged privately between the tutor and parent and normally costs €35 per hour. Most children who attend one-to-one tuition attend for one hour each week.

DAI workshops, exam classes and summer schools

- **Workshops:** The DAI currently runs special out-of-school facilities called workshops for students with dyslexia in 32 locations around the country. To attend a workshop, you must be a member of the DAI. Workshops provide appropriate specialist tuition in small groups. Each session lasts two hours and children normally attend one session a week after school hours. There are two terms in the year and the cost of tuition works out at approximately €400 per term. However, each workshop has its own requirements regarding payment of fees. Each student must have been assessed by a psychologist (and diagnosed with dyslexia) before enrolling and a copy of the assessment report must be made available to the programme co-ordinator at the time of application.

- **Exam classes:** The DAI also runs exam preparation classes to help students sitting state exams (Junior and Leaving Certificate). These classes are offered by some branches and also in the national office in Suffolk Street in Dublin. The course generally consists of weekly sessions of two hours. The course covers the English syllabus as well as ongoing development of efficient reading, revision, note-taking and writing skills. This course runs from September to April of the exam year.

- **Summer schools:** Several DAI branches run summer schools for students with dyslexia, usually in July. These summer classes are similar to workshops in that they offer small group tutorials in various aspects of literacy. Other activities are also offered, e.g. arts and crafts, drama and computers.

- **Assessment service:** DAI provides a private assessment service based in their national office in Dublin. They have a number of educational psychologists available for assessment of both children and adults and referrals are taken from individuals themselves or parents. Assessment includes testing of cognitive abilities as well as literacy skills (and sometimes numeracy skills if mathematics difficulties are reported). The psychologist will also get relevant background information from parents, individuals themselves, schools or colleges. A diagnosis is made based on a combination of the reported history and the performance on the tests. The assessment normally takes between three and three and a half hours and usually costs in the region of €450, although a subsidised rate may be available for people on low incomes or in receipt of social welfare payments. Unfortunately, there is often a waiting list for assessments.

What sort of specialist tuition is offered for children with dyslexia?

Generally speaking, specialist tuition (whether it is inside or outside school) to help children with dyslexia to learn to read, write and spell centres around two things:

- Phonics programmes where the child is taught to 'decode' and 'recode' language, enabling them to read, write and spell more effectively.

- Reading practice: Many children with dyslexia dislike reading and avoid it as much as they can. This makes the problem worse, because not only do they have a specific learning disability that makes it difficult for them to learn to read, but they also get no practice reading. Children are encouraged to read by presenting them with material that is of interest to them as an individual. Children may also use audio books, where they simultaneously read and listen to the book they are reading on tape or CD. This way, their reading is supported by the tape, so the child can enjoy the age-appropriate stories rather then labouring over every word or reading books that are too childish in terms of content for them.

General supports

- Class teachers and SNAs should be well informed about dyslexia. There are various publications available on the subject. (See the Dyslexia Association of Ireland and the British Dyslexia Association websites for book lists.)

- The DAI organises regular five-day courses (on Saturdays) for teachers. Teachers should consider taking this or another similar course to become better informed about this very common special need.

- A structured multisensory programme may be used to teach reading and spelling, e.g. Alpha to Omega by Hornsby and Shear.

- Teachers should avoid asking a dyslexic student to read aloud in front of the class. If the child wants to try to read aloud, however, they should be told the day before what it is they will be asked to read so that they can prepare beforehand.

- When teaching spelling, the child with dyslexia should be given shorter lists of words from the same word family, e.g. mice, rice, twice. Many of the spelling workbooks available today do this anyway, e.g. the My Spelling Workbook series from Prime-Ed.

- For children with dyslexia, over-learning is essential. Information will have to be presented a number of times, not just once or twice.

- Teachers should not correct every error, but instead concentrate on a small number of errors and set manageable targets. The focus should be on content rather than presentation. Teachers should correct in pencil – red pen corrections can be very demoralising for the student to look at, making the page look like a battlefield.

- Dyslexic students should not be asked to copy out spelling corrections.

- Dyslexic students should be encouraged to write in a cursive (joined) handwriting style, as it aids spelling, neatness and fluency.

- Note-taking can be difficult for children with dyslexia, so notes should be photocopied. Teachers should avoid tasks where students are asked to copy large amounts of text from the blackboard. Worksheets should be provided instead.

- Any worksheets given to students with dyslexia should be typed and carefully presented. A large, clear font size such as 12 or 14 should be used. Sans serif fonts are best, e.g. Arial, Comic Sans, Verdana, Helvetica and Tahoma. Headings should be added in bold.

- Provision of visual information can be very beneficial for some learners; include pictures, diagrams, charts and mind maps.

- Information should be photocopied onto coloured paper. If printing information, a coloured font, e.g. green, onto cream-coloured paper is best. Some people with dyslexia find that they get less glare or experience less visual stress, e.g. word movement, when using colours. Some individuals use coloured overlays that they place over the textbook. Others use glasses with tinted lenses.

- Students should be asked to repeat back instructions given, e.g. in a home economics cookery class. This can be a useful memory aid. Instructions given should be clear, concise and not too elaborate.

- Careful consideration needs to be given to lesson planning to ensure that the interest level is high, but that the literacy levels are adapted to suit the student's needs.

- The dyslexic student should sit near the teacher so that the teacher can monitor progress and be available to provide any necessary assistance.

- Encourage the use of word processors, computers, calculators and tape recorders (see the use of ICT below).

- Teachers and other support staff should reward students for effort.

- Self-esteem can be affected by dyslexia. Students should be encouraged and given the opportunity to develop and use their other talents as well.

- Schools should work very closely with parents, taking what they say on board. They know their own child best and can be an invaluable source of help and information.

- If the student is going to receive special arrangements (reasonable accommodations) in state exams, then allow the same accommodations for homework, class tests and mock exams.

- As many students with dyslexia have difficulty organising their work, help should be given to them to establish systems and routines in this regard.

Use of information and communications technology (ICT)

In recent years, the usefulness of ICT in teaching and learning has been recognised. Computers and other assistive technologies are invaluable to all children, but particularly to those with dyslexia and other special learning needs.

- A simple word processor with a spell checker is very useful for children with dyslexia. Children can type work and use the spell checker to check spelling independently without having to constantly ask someone else.

- It is vital for a child who is going to use a word processor for much of their written work that they learn to type. There are many typing programs on the market today that teach tying in an interesting and engaging way. Examples include Mavis Beacon, Type to Learn, Englishtype Junior and Senior and Touch-type Read Spell.

- Materials can be provided on tape or CD, e.g. English novels. In addition, if a teacher spoke class notes or textbook onto a tape, this would be invaluable for students. The National Council for the Blind in Ireland has a talking educational books service for blind children. Every year, their talking books library produces an audio recording of textbooks from the primary and second-level curriculum. If a fee was paid, perhaps these books could be bought for children with dyslexia.

- Electronic dictionaries are a relatively cheap, quick and portable tool for children with dyslexia. Franklin Spellmaster is an example of one such dictionary. These can be particularly useful in that they are programmed to recognise words from their phonetic spelling.
- There are many excellent programs on the market that support the development of basic skills in reading, phonics and spelling. Of course, these are not a substitute for one-to-one or whole class tuition, but are nevertheless useful. Examples include Wordshark, Fast ForWord, Lexia, Starspell, Gamz Player, My Reading Coach and Nessy.
- Some children with dyslexia also have difficulties in maths. Programs such as Numbershark, Math Mania and Math Circus are useful. Indeed, these programs would actually be useful for any child, regardless of whether or not they had a learning disability.
- For students who can read relatively competently but do come across words that they cannot manage, a reading pen is a good solution, e.g. Quicktionary Reading Pen II. These handheld pens contain software that enables them to scan and read words and phrases. They also include a dictionary to explain what a word means.
- Screen-reading software is also available that will read any text on the computer screen, whether it is text the student has just typed, an email or webpage, or pages of a textbook that have been scanned into the computer. Examples of this software are ClaroRead, Kurzweil and TextHelp.
- For students who have to produce larger amounts of written work, e.g. essays, good voice recognition software is now available. One of the most common and accurate is called Dragon Naturally Speaking. After an initial period of training, the program types as you speak. All commands are given via voice, e.g. you say 'new paragraph', 'next line', 'bold', 'comma', 'full stop'. While the program is rarely 100 per cent accurate, the software is getting better all the time.

Reasonable accommodation in examinations

The **State Examinations Commission** (**SEC**) is the body responsible for second-level examinations in Ireland. At the beginning of the examination year, the school principal (or the individual themselves or their parent if they are not attending a school) will usually apply to the SEC for reasonable accommodations. Reasonable accommodations may include the provision of a reader, use of a word processor, use of a tape recorder or a spelling waiver. The accommodations are intended to limit the impact of the candidate's disability on their exam performance while not giving the candidate any unfair advantage.

Department of Education circular S76/00 deals with applications for reasonable accommodation. At Junior Certificate level, it is enough for the school to deem the student to be in need of reasonable accommodation for it to be granted by the SEC. At Leaving Certificate level, however, a psychologist's report is required. Students' certificates will indicate that they have received reasonable accommodations.

Prognosis

In general, how well a child with dyslexia progresses depends on:
- The severity of their dyslexia
- How soon they receive proper supports and interventions
- The quality of these supports and interventions
- Their own general levels of motivation
- How much encouragement and support they receive from home and school
- How well their other talents and abilities are recognised and encouraged

If children's problems are picked up at a young age and they receive good-quality support from their class teacher, learning support teacher, resource teacher, SNA and from outside agencies such as the Dyslexic Association of Ireland, then they should do very well in education. Dyslexia does not go away, but through hard work, children can learn to be competent readers and also learn to use technology and other techniques to overcome their difficulties. Today, there are significant numbers of young people with dyslexia in colleges and universities around the country studying towards certificates, diplomas and degrees. Perhaps you are one such student.

Role of the SNA

Children with dyslexia will not be entitled to an SNA in their own right because they do not have a significant care need and because dyslexia is considered a high incidence, relatively mild special need. However, under the system of general allocation, an SNA may be working with children with dyslexia on a daily basis. He or she can provide invaluable support by:
- Being informed about dyslexia
- Helping the class teacher prepare class work for the child, e.g. photocopying onto coloured paper, typing out class notes, speaking notes onto tape
- Helping the child take down work off the board
- Working with the child while they are engaged with computer programs, e.g. Wordshark

- Helping the child organise themselves and their books and copies
- Helping the child use assistive technologies, e.g. Dragon Naturally Speaking
- Listening to the child reading aloud in a less public place than the classroom
- Offering plenty of praise and encouragement

CASE STUDY

Adam is an only child. His mum, Eileen, works part time in a bookie's shop and his father works as a fork lift driver at a local engineering works. Adam's father, Derek, cannot himself read, but he always put this down to the fact that he hated school, hardly ever attending and leaving at age 13. He has never been diagnosed with dyslexia.

When Adam began primary school, all seemed to be going well at first. Eileen, not really knowing what other children were like, was therefore somewhat taken aback when his junior infants teacher asked her to come in to meet her, as she was not happy with the progress that Adam was making in school. Adam's teacher was very experienced and had had many hundreds of children in her care over the years.

She explained to Eileen that Adam was having trouble with letter naming, holding a pencil correctly, basic sequencing, e.g. naming the days of the week, telling left from right and copying letters or shapes. In addition, his teacher said that she felt his speech was limited and somewhat unclear when compared to his peers and that this sometimes is an early indicator of a specific learning difficulty like dyslexia. She would just like to keep a special eye on him over the coming year. Adam would have this same teacher for senior infants.

When Eileen went home, she felt very upset. She hadn't seen this coming and actually felt a bit angry towards the teacher – how would you know a child had reading difficulties in junior infants? She was very anxious that Adam would be labelled as slow and that that would stick with him throughout his schooling. Derek was also anxious. He knew only too well what it was like to be behind at school, but he took a different attitude. He felt that if Adam needed extra help as he went through school, then so be it. It was good that his teacher was identifying it early and that she was going to keep a close eye on him.

About halfway through senior infants, Adam was still not making much progress, so his teacher recommended he attend learning support. He went out three times a week for one-to-one work, though he continued to make little progress. At the end of this year, this teacher retired.

Adam moved into first class; he was now just turning seven. This year saw a large influx of children into the area and the class grew. First, second and third class were all in the same room, for a total of 38 pupils. Their new teacher, Ms Hynes, was a new teacher and had difficulty controlling such a large class. It wasn't that the children were very badly behaved, just noisy in the overcrowded conditions. Adam began to go downhill over the course of this year. He began resisting homework and became the class clown. The teacher would become very frustrated with him, sometimes yelling at him or sending him to the headmaster's room. He continued to attend learning support, but was falling further and further behind his peers. By the end of first class, he still could read very little. He could copy letters and words but could write very little independently. His behaviour while in class began to get more and more disruptive. The teacher began giving him different work to occupy him, work that would keep him quiet and that he was able to do.

At the end of first class, his Drumcondra test results showed that his literacy was below the 2nd percentile, while his maths was at the 48th percentile. As a result, Adam got extra resource hours – one half-hour every day. His resource teacher generally withdrew him from class, much like the learning support teacher. She tried to make the work she did with him as interesting as possible, but Eileen felt that both the learning support and resource hours were just patching things up and not getting to the root of the problem.

By the end of second class, Adam was resisting school more and more. He would frequently complain about being sick – anything to get out of going. Homework became a battle, especially when work had to be written or learned off. Eileen and Derek asked for a meeting with the school principal. They had heard about a special reading class attached to a school in a nearby town and wondered if the principal thought it would be a better option for Adam. The principal agreed that Adam was making little progress where he was and that the special class was worth looking into. Meetings were set up, and at the beginning of third class, Adam changed school. This was a big step for him as he knew nobody in this new school and he would have to be bussed the 14 miles in and out every day.

Today, Adam is in fifth class in the special reading class. His reading and writing are still well behind his peers in mainstream school, but on a par with others in his reading class. This has done wonders for his self-esteem. In his old school, everyone seemed to pick things up so much more quickly than him and he often felt stupid. Here in his new class, the teachers have more time to explain things and everything isn't done in such a hurry. He has made a lot of good friends there. They have computers and other types of technology where he is now and he enjoys using them. They do plenty of arts and crafts, which he loves.

NEWCOMER CHILDREN WHOSE FIRST LANGUAGE IS NOT ENGLISH

The 2011 census found that there are currently 544,357 residents in Ireland who declared themselves as of non-Irish origin. Many of these people have come to Ireland from the 10 EU accession countries, mostly from Poland, Lithuania and Latvia. Others have come from countries outside the EU, mainly Nigeria, Somalia, Romania, Afghanistan and the Sudan. By law, all children between the ages of six and 16 must attend school in Ireland, and this includes newcomer children. Irish primary and post-primary schools have had to put mechanisms in place to assist children coming into Ireland, particularly for those who have English as an additional language.

Supports

The principal additional support provided by the Department of Education and Skills for newcomer children is English language support teaching. Full details of this are outlined in the DES circular 15/2009 – meeting the needs of pupils learning English as an additional language (EAL) – and can be downloaded in full from www.education.ie.

Allocation of English as an additional language (EAL) support posts

Number of posts	Number of pupils that require EAL support
1	14–30
2	31–90
3	91–120
4	121 and over

Schools with between three and 13 such pupils receive grant aid to fund part-time teaching. Schools with fewer than three pupils must make provision for these children from within existing resources. Children are entitled to English language teaching for not more than two years. Where a school is located beside an asylum accommodation centre, school transport is provided if the school is not within walking distance. Information on the Irish education system is made available to parents in many different languages.

In addition, the NCCA published *Guidelines on Intercultural Education in the Primary School* (NCCA 2005). These guidelines aim to support teachers, school management and other members of the school community in developing a more inclusive classroom environment and to provide children with the knowledge and skills they need to participate in the multicultural Ireland of today.

Difficult issues have arisen for primary schools trying to accommodate and educate newcomer children with English as an additional language.

- Many newcomer children are living in poverty. Contrary to the beliefs of some Irish people, refugees and asylum seekers receive very little from the Irish state. Refugee and asylum seekers receive accommodation and three meals per day plus an allowance (€19.10 per adult and €9.60 per child per week). Since May 2004, no child benefit is paid. This means that many children have insufficient money for books, copies and other school supplies together with money for extras such as school trips, etc.

- While language support teachers have been provided with assessment kits for determining English language proficiency, it is difficult to assess for other special education needs in children who have little English. Currently, all testing for special education needs is carried out through English, making it impossible to judge whether or not a child has a special educational need in addition to their English language need.

- Sometimes parents have no English, meaning that children can receive no help or guidance with homework.

- There is a lack of age-appropriate English language materials for use with newcomer children.

- Children who are sitting in class all day, understanding little of what is going on, may become frustrated and thus disruptive in class.

Role of the SNA

Newcomer children with English as an additional language will not be allocated an SNA unless they have another qualifying special need. Having said this, SNAs employed to help another child in the school may be asked to help newcomer children in the classroom situation.

chapter seven

Special Needs Affecting Emotional and Social Development

ATTENTION DEFICIT HYPERACTIVITY DISORDER

Attention deficit hyperactivity disorder (ADHD) is one of the most common childhood disorders and can continue through adolescence and adulthood. Symptoms include difficulty staying focused and paying attention, difficulty controlling behaviour and hyperactivity (overactivity).

Parents, teachers and others who work and live with children know that *all* children:

▷ Sometimes have difficulty controlling their behaviour
▷ Sometimes have difficulty paying attention
▷ Can be hyperactive and noisy from time to time
▷ Can be impulsive

However, the difference is that children with ADHD have these problems all the time. Behaviours are so intense that they interfere with the child's ability to function in many environments, e.g. the classroom, and with his or her ability to get along with other children.

Prevalence

As yet, there are no reliable estimates for the prevalence of ADHD in Ireland, though studies in Canada and the United States indicate that up to 5 per cent of children may have the condition. ADHD is three to four times more common in boys than girls and also tends to be more severe in boys.

Causes

While the precise cause of ADHD is not completely clear, it is now known that it is a predominantly genetically inherited condition. In terms of biological causes, magnetic resonance imaging (MRI) scans of the brain show differences between the brains of people with ADHD and the rest of the population. In people with ADHD, the right side of the brain is often smaller. Another type of brain scan, positron emission tomography (PET), has been used to obtain pictures of brain activity during tasks requiring concentration. Again, these show differences between those with ADHD and others. ADHD can also be influenced by environmental factors such as alcohol, drug use or smoking during pregnancy, which causes toxins to build up, thus harming the baby's brain.

Most people are able to concentrate on important stimuli in their environment and ignore unimportant stimuli by **inhibiting** their response to less important stimuli. Children with ADHD are not able to inhibit their response to unimportant stimuli and therefore respond to everything. So for example, if a child with ADHD is doing homework in their room and someone decides to run a bath in the room next door, the child with ADHD is likely to go into the bathroom and run their hand under the tap instead of staying with the homework, which is why homework can take hours to complete.

While factors such as poor parenting, a disruptive home life, too much TV or computer games and poor schools cannot cause ADHD, they may cause the symptoms to worsen.

Symptoms

The three major symptoms of ADHD are inattention, hyperactivity and impulsivity.

Children who are inattentive:
- Find it hard to keep their mind on what they are doing
- Get bored or distracted with a task after a few minutes
- Find it hard to get started on tasks, such as homework, that require mental effort
- Make careless mistakes and don't seem to care about details

- Don't seem to listen when you talk to them
- Don't follow through when given instructions
- Don't get things finished
- Are disorganised
- Are always losing things
- However, they may be able to give effortless, automatic attention to something they enjoy, such as computer games or art activities

Children who are hyperactive:

- Are moving all the time
- Can't sit still
- Squirm in their seat, swing their legs, tap their fingers or pens on the table
- Talk too much and often very quickly, jumping from one topic to the next
- Run, jump and climb, even when this is not allowed, e.g. in a church or at school
- Cannot play quietly

Children who are impulsive:

- Do things without thinking, e.g. they may run out into the street without checking for traffic
- Blurt out inappropriate comments
- Shout out answers in class before the teacher has finished the question
- Interrupt other people
- Find it hard to wait their turn

As a result of these behaviours, children with ADHD can often develop social and emotional problems and can often feel depressed and angry. Many find it difficult to make friends because of their frequent disruptive and socially inappropriate behaviour.

ADHD has three subtypes:
1. Predominantly hyperactive-impulsive.
2. Predominantly inattentive. Children who are in this category are often described as having attention deficit disorder (ADD). In the main they will not be hyperactive; in fact, the opposite can be the case.
3. Combined hyperactive-impulsive and inattentive. This subtype is the most common. These children will have many of the symptoms described above in all three categories.

In addition to ADHD, many children have other conditions as well. Conditions that commonly occur with ADHD are:

- Dyslexia (see Chapter 6)
- Dyscalculia (see Chapter 5)
- Dysgraphia (see Chapter 4)
- Dyspraxia (see Chapter 4)
- Difficulty with auditory perception
- Specific language difficulties (see Chapter 6)
- Oppositional defiant disorder (see below)
- Conduct disorder (see below)
- Anxiety, depression and obsessive compulsive disorder

Occasionally, children with Asperger's or Tourette syndrome are falsely diagnosed with ADHD.

Diagnosis

ADHD will be diagnosed by a qualified psychologist. Generally, the psychologist will obtain information from parents and teachers about the child's behaviour, often using questionnaires and interviews. The psychologist will also observe the child him or herself and give the child various tasks to complete, closely observing the child's attention span, activity level and impulse control with regard to his or her age.

In order to diagnose ADHD, the child must have a sufficient number of difficulties with concentration, activity level and impulse control. The behaviours must be present in at least two settings, usually school and home, and the behaviours must be causing significant difficulty with learning and/or socialisation. The evaluation process will also determine the type of ADHD a child has. The psychologist evaluating the child should have extensive knowledge and experience of children with the condition.

Treatment

ADHD is usually treated using a combination of stimulant medication and behavioural therapy.

Medication

Several stimulant medications are available which calm the child, allowing them to bring their behaviour under better control. Many people are surprised to learn that stimulants are given to children with ADHD, as these children seem to be overly stimulated already, but they do work. Ritalin, perhaps the best-known ADHD medication, has been widely used since its release in 1954. Other trade names include Adderall, Dexedrine and Metadate.

Stimulants work by increasing dopamine levels in the brain, and one of the functions of dopamine is to control attention. It also controls motivation, pleasure and movement. By regulating the dopamine levels, doctors can regulate the attention spans and energy levels of those they are treating.

Medication for ADHD can be either short or long acting. Short-acting drugs need to be taken several times a day, whereas the long-acting versions only need to be taken once daily. As with all medications, there may be side effects such as mood swings, restlessness, headaches or loss of appetite.

For some children who cannot take stimulant medication such as Ritalin because of side effects or for whom stimulant medications are not having any effect, non-stimulant medications are available, e.g. Strattera. There would not be many children on non-stimulant medication.

Behavioural therapy

Behavioural therapy can be used alone or with medication, as described above. Basically, behavioural therapy is designed to teach or train children to control their hyperactivity, impulsiveness and lack of attention. Based on the work of B.F. Skinner, desirable behaviour is rewarded (positively reinforced) and undesirable behaviour is not reinforced or is punished in the hope that this will discourage its repetition. For example, a child is rewarded with a trip to the playground for getting their homework done within a one-hour timeframe.

Teaching social skills

Children with ADHD often lack basic social skills, which can frequently alienate them from peers and cause the child to feel rejected. They tend to experience great difficulty picking up others' social cues, act impulsively, have limited self-awareness of their effect on others, display delayed turn-taking ability and over-personalise others' actions as being criticism. They tend to play better with younger or older children, where their roles are more clearly defined. Children tend to repeat these problematic social behaviour patterns and find it difficult to learn from experience. In conversation, they may ramble and say embarrassing things to peers. Unstructured times such as playtime can be particularly difficult. Some children with ADHD have to be taught these skills directly.

In Irish schools, children with ADHD may be entitled to resource teaching hours and an SNA, depending on need.

Prognosis

There is no cure for ADHD and children with the disorder seldom grow out of it. However, many find ways of adapting to and coping with their ADHD as they mature. Many adults have ADHD and do not even know it. They may have difficulty getting organised for work, getting to work on time, staying on task and completing jobs at work, getting along with colleagues and maintaining personal relationships. Some may be accident prone or have multiple traffic accidents. Others become unemployed and there is a higher then average incidence of drug and alcohol addiction among adults with ADHD.

In the past in Ireland, very few children were diagnosed and treated for ADHD. They were usually just expelled from school and given little, if any, help. Nowadays, if a child is having difficulty in school, the school cannot just say the child has broken the school's rules and must therefore be expelled. Instead, they must try to find out what the underlying cause of the child's behaviour is and put a plan in place for him or her. This will mean that in the future, many more children with ADHD will have their condition recognised and measures put in place to help them manage their condition in order to reach their true potential.

Role of the SNA

Some children with ADHD are entitled to care support from an SNA. The Department of Education and Skills circular SPED02/05 allows for the allocation of an SNA where the pupil's behaviour is a danger to him or herself or where it seriously interferes with the learning opportunities of other pupils. Many SNAs currently working in Irish schools are working with children with ADHD.

One of the principal functions of an SNA working with a child with ADHD is to keep the child focused on the tasks at hand and to try to prevent him or her from becoming distracted and interfering with other children's learning in the class. It is vital that the SNA builds up a positive relationship with the child, as the child will then be much more likely to comply with the SNA's requests. Usually the SNA sits beside the child, helping them organise themselves. For example, if the teacher asks the class to take out their English reader, the SNA will ensure that the child with ADHD does so. The SNA should offer plenty of praise and encouragement to the child and he or she may be involved in the child's specific behavioural management programme. The SNA may have to escort the child to the resource teacher, to their parents at home time or anywhere else the child must go unsupervised. If the child is on short-acting medication, the SNA may help him or her manage this.

Alex was born a healthy eight pounds and had no complications at birth. From the outset, his parents would describe him as a difficult baby compared to their other two children. He didn't sleep very much and as a result was frequently tired and cranky. He had colic and cried a lot. As he grew into a toddler, he could be described as hyper, constantly running around, climbing and exploring, and he never seemed to rest. He was quite accident prone and didn't appear to think before acting. He caught his fingers in doors, ran into things, constantly bumped his head and fell off furniture. He wouldn't stay at one thing for any length of time, and bringing him out anywhere could be quite difficult. One Sunday, the family decided to go out for lunch in a nice restaurant. They put Alex in a high chair to keep him quiet, even though he was almost three years old and very big for his age. He squirmed and protested, but eventually they got him to sit. About halfway through the meal, somehow Alex released himself and stood up on the high chair, belly flopping down on top of the table. Luckily Maureen, his mother, was there to half catch him, avoiding scattering everything off the table. The family had to finish the meal quickly and leave, as they were afraid that Alex was disturbing other diners.

Alex started playschool when he was three and a half years old. The staff there did their best, but when Alex arrived at nine o'clock, it was as if a whirlwind swept through the place. He would pull down toys and abandon them a few seconds later. He would throw water and sand, shout and sometimes kick and punch other children. Other parents began to complain about Alex, so the playschool had to arrange with Maureen that Alex only came to the playschool in the afternoons, when it was quieter and they had the staff to supervise him more closely. Maureen and her partner, Paul, split up just after Alex turned three. She felt that perhaps the difficulties herself and Paul had been having since shortly after Alex was born, and now the split, could be a factor in Alex's behaviour. She hoped that as things settled down at home, Alex would settle down as well. She had never even heard of ADHD and just thought Alex, being the youngest, was spoiled and difficult to control.

When Alex went to school at age four and a half, things really began to get worse. In a class with 25 other children and one teacher, Alex was forever in trouble. He couldn't sit still at his desk and was always getting up and running around, shouting at other children, kicking them and scribbling on their work. The class teacher would send him out to the master's room. Alex would cry with fear at being sent out. The master would shout at him and have him sit at a desk at the side of the class, giving him something to do. For the time he was in the master's room, Alex would be able to sit relatively quietly, watching what the sixth class students were doing.

In the yard at break time, the children were forever coming up to the teacher on duty to complain about something Alex had done. He would often try to disrupt the games the other children were playing, e.g. throwing the football out on the road or running away with the skipping rope. He would often physically fight with other children or shout at them. Generally he was not liked and was avoided by his peers. This caused him great anguish, but he didn't seem to have any idea why the children disliked him. His work suffered greatly as well. He spent little time on task and was therefore learning very little at school. Homework was a nightmare, with Maureen fighting with him to do something that should only take 10 minutes. Maureen suspected that the school thought that Alex's behaviour had a lot to do with the fact that he came from a broken home and that she just had no manners on him.

In the middle of senior infants, just after Christmas, Alex's new class teacher suggested to Maureen that she have him assessed for ADHD. This was the first time this was mentioned to her. Maureen made an appointment with the local child and family centre to see an HSE clinical psychologist. She was dismayed to find that there was a waiting list of nine months for assessment and she couldn't afford to have an assessment carried out privately. While waiting for the assessment, Alex continued in much the same way at school, getting into trouble several times every day with both the teachers and his peers. He began to dislike school intensely and often complained of illness in the mornings in the hope of not having to go.

Outside of school, Alex joined the local football club on the under-sevens team. The coaches had to ask Maureen to stay while the training was on because of Alex's behaviour, as they wouldn't be able to keep a close enough eye on him. The pitch runs alongside a busy road and Alex dashed out one day to fetch the ball without even thinking about the traffic going up and down. Luckily, no cars were coming at the time.

The parish runs a disco in the local hall for the school children every Christmas. It was at the disco that Maureen saw just how alienated Alex was because of his behaviour. She noticed how all the kids danced or ran around in groups, arms round each other's necks. When Alex approached any group, he normally charged into them and the group invariably pulled back from him. He seemed to spend the entire time charging into groups and them rejecting him, which really upset Maureen.

In the October of Alex's third year at school, he went for his assessment. The psychologist requested a detailed report from Alex's school and also interviewed Maureen extensively about his behaviour. The psychologist also observed Alex while engaged in a number of different activities. The psychologist's report came back about two weeks later with the diagnosis of ADHD. On foot of this report, Alex was put on Ritalin, which he must take every morning. Within a very short period of time on Ritalin, Alex began to show signs of improvement. He was still fidgety and somewhat hyperactive, but nothing like what he'd been before. The school applied for and received a total of two weekly resource hours for Alex. During this time, the resource teacher works with him on development of social skills, e.g. how to join a group, and also on behavioural management. The child and family centre also advised Maureen on how best to help Alex in the home environment. TV and video games are limited, as are sugary sweets and drinks. He takes omega-3 capsules every day and Maureen has learned to become consistent with discipline. All of these things have made a big improvement to Alex's behaviour and he is much happier as a result.

OPPOSITIONAL DEFIANT DISORDER

Oppositional defiant disorder (ODD) is characterised by an ongoing pattern of disobedient, hostile and defiant behaviour toward authority figures that goes beyond the bounds of normal childhood behaviour. For a child to be diagnosed with ODD, certain factors must be taken into account. Firstly, the defiance must be interfering with the child's ability to function in school, home or the community. Second, the defiance cannot be the result of another disorder, such as the more serious conduct disorder, depression or anxiety. Third, the child's problem behaviours must have been happening for at least six months.

Prevalence

There are no figures available for the prevalence of ODD in Ireland, though figures from other countries estimate it affects 2 per cent of all children.

Causes

The exact cause of ODD is not known, but it is believed that a combination of biological, genetic and environmental factors may contribute to the condition.

Biological factors

Some studies suggest that defects in or injuries to certain areas of the brain can lead to serious behavioural problems in children. In addition, ODD has been linked to abnormal amounts of chemicals in the brain called neurotransmitters. Neurotransmitters are chemicals that allow messages to be transmitted along the nerve cells or neurons of the body's nervous system. If these chemicals are out of balance or not working properly, messages may not make it through the brain correctly, leading to symptoms of ODD and other mental illnesses. Many children and teenagers with ODD also have other conditions, such as ADHD, learning disorders, depression or an anxiety disorder, which may contribute to their behavioural problems.

Genetic factors

Many children and teenagers with ODD have close family members with either ODD, ADHD or other conditions, including mood disorders, anxiety disorders and personality disorders. This suggests that a tendency to develop ODD may be inherited.

Environmental factors

Factors such as a dysfunctional family life, a family history of mental illnesses and/ or substance abuse and inconsistent discipline by parents may contribute to the development of behavioural disorders, although this is not always the case.

Symptoms

Symptoms include a pattern of negative, hostile and defiant behaviour lasting at least six months, during which four (or more) of the following are present. (Note: A criterion is met only if the behaviour occurs more frequently than is typically observed in individuals of comparable age and developmental level.)

- Often loses temper, throws repeated temper tantrums
- Excessively argues with adults
- Often actively defies or refuses to comply with adults' requests or rules
- Often deliberately annoys people
- Often blames others for his or her mistakes or misbehaviour
- Is often touchy or easily annoyed by others
- Is often angry and resentful
- Is often spiteful or vindictive
- Swears or uses obscene language
- Says mean and hateful things when upset

For a child's behaviour to be considered indicative of ODD, there must be a significant impairment in social, academic or occupational functioning.

Diagnosis

Like ADHD, there is no blood test or brain scan that can be taken to diagnose ODD. Instead, parent and teacher interviews and reports are complied and studied by a qualified psychologist. The psychologist will also observe the child themselves, perhaps over the course of a number of sessions, before making a diagnosis.

Treatment

As ODD is accompanied by ADHD in 60 per cent of cases, the drugs Ritalin and Strattera are often used. For children with ODD alone, the drug Risperdal may be used, or Divalproex, which is a mood stabiliser. There have been studies conducted examining the use of omega-3 oils and vitamin E in children with ODD, both of which have been shown to help the problem behaviour to some degree.

In addition to medical treatment using drugs, children and their families often engage in various types of therapy designed to help everyone deal with the challenges caused by ODD. Work will be done with the child on effective anger management. His or her parents and siblings may be involved in cognitive behavioural therapy to help improve communication and decrease negativity in the home. The child might also be engaged in social skills training to teach the child how to be more flexible and to improve frustration tolerance with peers.

Therapy can help children and adolescents to effectively deal with ODD and help them learn how to do the following:

- Use self time-outs
- Identify what increases anxiety and avoid it
- Talk about feelings instead of acting on them
- Find and use ways to calm themselves, e.g. breathing exercises
- Frequently remind themselves of their goals
- Get involved in tasks and physical activities that provide a healthy outlet for energy, e.g. running
- Learn how to talk with others
- Develop a predictable, consistent, daily schedule of activity
- Develop ways to obtain pleasure and feel good
- Learn how to get along with other people
- Find ways to limit stimulation
- Learn to admit mistakes in a matter-of-fact way

Prognosis

The prognosis for many children with ODD is good. They learn strategies to cope with their own behaviour and can often do very well in school, at home and later in the workplace. Other children, however, do not fare so well. In some children,

ODD evolves into the more serious condition, conduct disorder. In fact, if left untreated, ODD has about an 80 per cent chance of turning into conduct disorder as a child ages. Later in life, ODD can develop into passive-aggressive personality disorder or antisocial personality disorder. ODD can cause significant social, academic and/or occupational impairment, so it is vital that it is diagnosed and treated sooner rather than later. Significant numbers of early school leavers have undiagnosed ODD.

Role of the SNA

As with ADHD and conduct disorder (see below), children with ODD may be entitled to an SNA and perhaps resource teaching hours. Children with ODD frequently spend a lot of time outside of class, on restricted timetables or in other rooms, e.g. the principal's classroom or office. An SNA who has built up a good rapport with a child with ODD may not be seen as an authority figure to be defied, but rather as someone who is there to support the child. This can be invaluable in the classroom situation, as the child may co-operate better with classroom activities while their SNA is with them and supporting them. This means that the child misses less class time and is excluded less often. If the child does do something wrong, the SNA can discuss what has happened and make a plan for what would be best to do next time.

CASE STUDY

Living with a child with ODD is a constant battle for any parent or guardian. There are many things that the child does that are a normal part of growing up and maturing. However, their methods of dealing with these things are far from normal. It isn't so much the big things that the child has tantrums over that cause the problems, but rather their refusal to do the most basic, everyday things that are most wearing and cause the greatest arguments and difficulties. Anyone can cope with the odd big row, but when they occur many times a day, every day, then that's a different matter.

For a family living with a child with ODD, even the most basic, undemanding things that need to be done every day can cause uproar. From the time Jenny wakes up in the morning, she refuses to do anything that she is asked to do. Jenny's mother, Andrea, has tried using written lists, notes, reminders and routines to try to stop the verbal nagging, asking, questioning and reminding that goes along with simple everyday tasks such as getting up, getting dressed, eating breakfast or brushing teeth and hair. To ask Jenny to do any of these things is a precursor to an argument. Getting up and out in the morning, even now at ten and a half years of age, is a battle. Downright refusal, followed by raised voices and eventually screaming, will follow.

Even if Andrea keeps her tone flat and non-threatening, it still escalates Jenny's behaviour. She will scream and shout and throw things in the room rather than just get up and get ready.

Andrea always makes sure that Jenny's uniform is ready from the night before (after a lot of discussion, persuasion and reminding before bed). Invariably, there will be an issue with some part of the uniform. The children in Jenny's school wear a school tracksuit. However, there is no set T-shirt with the tracksuit, which causes difficulty probably three mornings out of five if Andrea hasn't set out the correct T-shirt for Jenny. There is no rhyme or reason to which T-shirt is the right or wrong one – one day a particular T-shirt could be OK, while the next it would be all wrong and cause a row. The same applies to socks – one day a particular pair of socks will cause no row, but they might the next day. This behaviour is not just a phase and certainly doesn't have anything to do with the actual clothes. It is Jenny's way of telling Andrea that she has her own mind and is perfectly entitled to change it whenever she wants and to do whatever she wants.

Andrea has two laundry baskets on the landing, a different one for whites and colours. Jenny has been asked to divide her clothes between these two baskets at the end of the day for washing, and even this causes defiance. Jenny will refuse to take the clothes out of her room, put them beside the basket, put them into the wrong basket or throw them round her room rather than put them in the correct place.

Jenny doesn't see that some people are in positions of authority. As far as she is concerned, everyone is equal and no one has a right to tell anyone else what to do. No one is any 'higher' than anyone else, nor have they the right to give instructions (which she automatically sees as orders) or to tell anyone else what to do. She has absolutely no respect for anyone – not her elders, teachers, law or instructors in any extracurricular classes she attends. She speaks to everyone in the same sullen manner if things are not going her way. In her first year in school, Jenny sent a sixth class boy home crying because she boxed him in the stomach and winded him. It didn't even register with her that he was so much older – he was annoying her and that was all that mattered. It's like there is no scale – in Jenny's eyes, the President is equal to a four-year-old, which is true to an extent, but life doesn't work like that and Jenny won't accept that. Andrea tries to explain to Jenny that it is fine to believe that everyone is equal, but at the same time, everyone has to be respected.

Andrea has been called into school many times because Jenny has become abusive both physically and verbally to teachers and classmates. One day while she was fighting with another student, a teacher approached them telling them to stop fighting. Jenny told the teacher that it was none of her business, that she was only a sub teacher anyway. Jenny speaks disdainfully to everyone, and the more comfortable she becomes around a person or situation, the more comfortable she is being defiant and aggressive. She is a lot more oppositional with her mum and her new partner than she is with her father and his wife. She only sees them for a short space of time and rarely displays defiance. However, by the time she comes home, she has built up so much anger and frustration at having to behave that she can be extra difficult for a few days afterwards. It's like the more comfortable and confident she is around someone, the more oppositional and defiant she becomes.

Temper tantrums erupt constantly over tiny things – what is cooked for dinner, what went into the lunchbox, what is on the TV, how long her mum is spending in the shop – you name it and Jenny can argue about it. Andrea finds that Jenny procrastinates constantly rather than doing what she should be doing and can come up with every reason in the book for not doing something she has been asked to do. Tantrums range from shouting, to slamming doors, to breaking things, to threatening to kill herself by standing on the window ledge upstairs and saying that she is going to jump, all of which could stem from telling her she needs to brush her teeth. The cause of the tantrum means nothing. Ignoring tantrums frustrates her, answering her escalates the situation, trying to placate her infuriates her and trying to comfort her annoys and angers her.

Jenny only has one friend and they are constantly fighting and being stopped from seeing each other. Every time she goes over to her house, she does something that she's not allowed to do, e.g. walking down the road, which is in a rural area with a very narrow, winding road, or going onto YouTube and watching inappropriate material. The minute Jenny gets home she tells her mum everything she did. It's like she can't wait to tell Andrea to get a reaction and she knows that there will be consequences.

Jenny also has ADHD and is therefore on Ritalin, which does calm some of her symptoms down. Andrea does her best to be consistent and fair, but worries about how Jenny is going to manage in the workplace, etc., where things don't always go as one wishes them to.

CONDUCT DISORDER

Conduct disorder (CD) is sometimes initially mistaken for oppositional defiant disorder (ODD). However, it is more severe and has more socially disruptive and disturbing characteristics. While students with CD may share characteristics similar to students with ODD, they are more physically aggressive and threatening and appear to lack empathy (the ability to feel for another human being or animal). Behaviour in which the rights of others or age-appropriate societal norms are violated is persistent and repetitive. CD is one of the most disruptive and difficult conditions to affect the behaviour of students, and those with CD have great difficulty following rules and behaving in a socially acceptable way. Typically, CD is not diagnosed until the student is at post-primary level.

Prevalence

The prevalence of CD in Ireland is not known, although other countries, such as the US, estimate that it may be as high as 4 per cent in children aged nine to 18 years old.

Causes

Studies have suggested that the disorder has both biological (including genetic) and psychosocial causes. Social risk factors that may predispose a child to CD include socio-economic deprivation; harsh, punitive or inconsistent parenting with verbal or physical aggression; separation from parents; early institutionalisation; family neglect, abuse or violence; frequent verbal abuse from parents, teachers or other authority figures; parental psychiatric illness, substance abuse or marital discord; large family size, crowding and poverty; and divorce with persistent hostility between the parents. Other risk factors include child abuse and neglect; neurological damage caused by low birth weight or birth complications; under-arousal of the autonomic nervous system (causing children with the condition to be more likely to be thrill seekers); learning impairments; insensitivity to physical pain and punishment; and impaired functioning of the noradrenergic system (this is the system that restores the body to normal after it has been aroused by the fight-or-flight hormone, adrenalin).

Symptoms

Symptoms include a repetitive and persistent pattern of behaviour in which the basic rights of others or major age-appropriate societal norms or rules are violated, as manifested by the presence of three (or more) of the following criteria in the past 12 months, with at least one criterion present in the past six months. (The list has been sourced from *The Diagnostic and Statistical Manual of Mental Disorders* (American Psychiatric Association 2000).)

Aggression to people and animals:
- Often bullies people, threatens or intimidates others
- Often initiates physical fights
- Has used a weapon that can cause serious physical harm to others, e.g. a bat, brick, broken bottle, knife

- Has been physically cruel to people
- Has been physically cruel to animals
- Has stolen while confronting a victim, e.g. mugging, purse snatching
- Has forced someone into sexual activity

Destruction of property:

- Has deliberately engaged in setting a fire with the intention of causing serious damage
- Has deliberately destroyed others' property (other than by fire)
- Deceitfulness or theft
- Has broken into someone else's house, building or car
- Often lies to obtain goods or favours or to avoid obligations, i.e. cons others
- Has stolen items without confronting a victim, e.g. shoplifting, but without breaking and entering, or forgery, such as cashing other people's cheques

Serious violations of rules:

- Often stays out at night despite parental prohibitions, beginning before 13 years of age
- Has run away from home overnight at least twice while living with parents or while in care (or once without returning for a lengthy period of time)
- Is often truant from school, beginning before the age of 13

Conduct disorder rarely occurs alone. It is often accompanied by ADHD, depression or bipolar disorder. Students with CD may also have Tourette syndrome, learning difficulties, mood disorders, obsessive compulsive disorder (OCD) or other special educational needs.

Diagnosis

As stated earlier, conduct disorder is not normally diagnosed until the child enters post-primary school, where the child often begins to display extremes of behaviour inside and outside of school. He or she will often bully others and be extremely disruptive in class, often becoming abusive towards teachers. He or she will come across as having no fear of authority figures or fear of punishment. Outside of school, he or she is frequently in trouble with the law, often for a number of different offences, and generally will show little remorse for what they have done. As with ADHD and ADD, a psychologist will interview significant people in the child's life – parents or foster parents, social workers, teachers, juvenile liaison officers or probation officers if the child has been involved with the justice system. They will also interview the child in order to get a picture of what is happening in the child's life.

Treatment

Children with CD often have very complex problems. Their family life is often chaotic, with many children with the disorder in care. Children will be involved with a number of different agencies and professionals – school management, guidance counsellors and home-school liaison officers, HSE psychologists, behavioural therapists and perhaps addiction counsellors. Department of Justice probation officers and juvenile liaison officers will be involved if the child has been in trouble with the law. It is essential that all these agencies work together to put together a comprehensive plan for the child. Treatment often involves some or all of the following.

- Family counselling.
- Parenting skills courses are arranged for parents who need to be taught better, more consistent parenting skills themselves.
- Sometimes children who are very out of control are accommodated in temporary foster homes for short periods or as respite for their families.
- Substance abuse counselling if the child is abusing street drugs and/or alcohol.
- Curfews are often put in place so that the child is less likely to get into trouble.
- Children are often encouraged to get involved in activities, e.g. youth clubs.
- If children are out of mainstream school, they may be enrolled in a service such as Youthreach that is specially tailored to meet the needs of early school leavers.
- The child may be given extra learning support or resource hours – many children with CD struggle academically in school, in part because they can be taught so little as a result of their disruptive behaviour.
- Children may be put on medication, e.g. Ritalin (if the child also has ADHD).
- Children may participate in anger management or reality therapy courses in order to find better ways of dealing with challenging situations.
- If they have committed offences, some children with conduct disorder will be sent to children's detention schools such as Trinity House, Oberstown Boys School or Oberstown Girls School, all in Lusk, Co. Dublin, or the Finglas Child and Adolescent Centre. These schools seek to provide training and education for these young people, together with counselling and other therapies.

Prognosis

The prognosis for children with CD, particularly if it appears before adolescence, can be poor if the proper interventions are not put in place. Many of the violent criminals we read about every day in the papers likely had CD as children and adolescents. Untreated, their condition has escalated over the years into violent antisocial personality disorder and chronic criminal behaviour, and so the cycle begins again with their children.

Role of the SNA

Children are rarely diagnosed with CD in Irish schools, so many do not receive additional resources on account of having CD. Most who do have extra resources, e.g. an SNA or resource hours, will have them as a result of other co-existing conditions, e.g. ADHD or learning disabilities. The principal role of an SNA caring for a child with CD is to try to keep the child on task and stop them from carrying out dangerous acts or interfering with the learning of other children. An SNA may have to escort the child to the learning support or resource room. It is important that an SNA has a positive relationship with the child and is consistent with discipline. If this is the case, this can often have a very positive effect on the child's behaviour. If the child is involved in practical classes, e.g. home economics or woodwork, the SNA needs to help ensure that the child does not do anything that would cause danger to themselves or others. Sometimes children with CD are excluded from such classes for health and safety reasons.

CASE STUDY

Julie was expelled from school at the end of first year, aged 13. In her one year at the school, she had caused chaos for teachers, management and fellow students alike. Every day there was something, e.g. she would set off the fire alarm, resulting in the entire school being evacuated. She bullied other students, particularly those she saw as being weak or vulnerable. She was aggressive and abusive towards teachers, throwing a stool at one and only narrowly missing her. She smoked cigarettes and often marijuana at the back of the school along with a group of older students. On one occasion, she took in a small bottle of vodka in her bag and drank most of it. The list goes on and on.

Julie has a really tough home life. She lives on an estate that has enormous levels of poverty, unemployment, substance abuse and violence. Her mother is a lone parent and an alcoholic. She has little control over what Julie does. Occasionally her mother goes mad if Julie is caught for something, but she no longer goes up to the school and avoids their calls. Julie's father left years ago when she was very small and she has no recollection of him. She has a younger brother, eight years old, who has a different father. Julie is often left to mind him while her mother goes out drinking.

Julie frequently shoplifts and has been caught a good few times. She doesn't really care, as she knows they can do very little about it because of her age. In September, Julie was referred by her school to the local Youthreach centre. She only went there because her juvenile liaison officer said she had to. In the beginning, she hated it. She felt the staff were really nosy, trying to find out about her home life and what she got up to outside of the centre.

She was in a class with eight other students, doing her Junior Certificate in just six subjects. After a while she began to enjoy the relaxed atmosphere. Things were not all plain sailing, though – some of the teachers still got on her nerves, as did a lot of the students, but unlike before, the staff had more time to talk to her and sort out problems as they arose in a calmer way. She began to trust them a bit.

Outside of the centre, though, things were still the same. She began drinking a lot at weekends and began hanging out with older people. She also became very promiscuous. Julie was just 14 years and six months old when she first became pregnant. She did not know that she was pregnant and continued drinking and smoking marijuana. After 10 weeks she had a miscarriage, which really shook her up. She felt such a sense of loss that she actively began to try to become pregnant again, this time with a fella from the centre who is 16. He didn't know what she was up to, as she told him she was on the Pill. After about two months her plan worked and she became pregnant again. Julie is now four months pregnant and hopes that the baby will force her to calm down. She has stopped drinking but continues to smoke. Her boyfriend is pretty happy about the prospect of becoming a dad.

EMOTIONAL AND BEHAVIOURAL PROBLEMS

Severe emotional and behavioural problems in children and adolescents can be caused by a large range of factors. While there are a small number of children in Irish schools that have psychiatric illnesses such as schizophrenia or bipolar disorder, it is unusual for a child to have such a definite diagnosis at this stage. The majority of young people who experience severe emotional and behavioural problems in childhood and adolescence do so as a result of extreme environmental factors such as abuse, neglect and drug and alcohol misuse.

Schizophrenia in children and adolescents

A definite diagnosis of schizophrenia is very unusual in childhood and adolescence. Some children may exhibit schizophrenic-type behaviours and will be observed closely by the child and adolescent psychiatric services. Symptoms that would cause concern include the following.

- Changes in sleep patterns – may sleep very little
- Extremely withdrawn; the child does not want to see or talk to anyone and may isolate themselves in their room, refusing to go to school or meet friends
- May hoard items
- May wear inappropriate combinations of clothes
- Have severely diminished motivation to do anything, including keeping themselves clean despite being told they have hygiene problems
- Severely reduced ability to concentrate
- Erratic behaviour, paranoia and severe anxiety
- Children and adolescents with schizophrenic symptoms are much more likely to internalise anxious thoughts, paranoia and suspiciousness rather than externalise them in an aggressive manner
- Schizophrenic-type behaviour may be induced by misuse of street drugs
- May begin to talk about strange fears and ideas

Bipolar disorder in children and adolescents

As with schizophrenia, a definite diagnosis of bipolar disorder is very unusual in childhood and adolescence. Some children may exhibit bipolar-type behaviour and will be observed closely by the child and adolescent psychiatric services. The child may alternate between being in an excessively energetic state with racing thoughts and speech, confused and irrational behaviour, speaking of special powers and grandiose ideas, and being very quiet, withdrawn and inactive.

Children and adolescents exhibiting symptoms of schizophrenia and bipolar disorder will be under the care of the HSE child and adolescent psychiatric services. Many will also be availing of the supports listed below for children and adolescents experiencing severe emotional and behavioural problems resulting from negative environmental factors.

There is only one acute adolescent day hospital service in Ireland: St Joseph's Adolescent Centre attached to St Vincent's Psychiatric Hospital in Fairview, Dublin 3. This service caters for young people with significant mental health needs requiring a level of therapeutic intervention that cannot be provided by community mental health services.

Severe emotional and behavioural problems resulting from negative environmental factors

Some children exhibit severe emotional and behavioural problems as a reaction to negative environmental factors. Children suffer physical, emotional and sexual abuse as well as physical and emotional neglect. They may witness drug and alcohol misuse, violence and other extremes of negative behaviour. They may misuse alcohol and street drugs themselves and/or become sexually promiscuous. Understandably, these factors often result in extremely low self-esteem and poor self-image together with severe emotional and behavioural problems. Some children who live their lives in this type of environment develop conduct disorder (as described above), where they become so wounded by the environment they live in that they can no longer feel empathy or sadness for another's pain.

These children have very complex problems and will often be the responsibility of a number of different agencies within the Department of Health and Children, Department of Education and Skills and perhaps the Department of Justice and Equality Skills.

- Children and adolescents living in harmful environments may be removed from their home environment if it is deemed unsafe. Children and adolescents are normally placed with a foster family or in a residential care home.
- Children and adolescents will be allocated a social worker who will try to co-ordinate all the services needed for them.
- If the home is fundamentally safe but in other ways unsuitable, parent(s) are usually visited in their home by staff from the family support services in an effort to sort out difficulties and improve the quality of the environment for children in the home.
- If adolescents are very out of control or violent in the home, they may sometimes be placed in foster or residential care until such a time as they are emotionally well enough to return home.
- If substance misuse is an issue, there are some drug and alcohol treatment centres that can cater for under-18s, although the number of these nationally is limited.
- Schools have various programmes and services on offer to help encourage children and adolescents at risk of dropping out of school to stay in school. These include the early school leaver initiative targeting children aged eight to 15 years and the stay-in-school retention initiative targeting adolescents at post-primary level.
- Children and adolescents who are considered to be a danger to themselves and/or other children in the classroom situation are entitled to a full-time SNA and a number of resource hours, depending on need.

- Some post-primary schools have a home-school liaison officer, who is a teacher with responsibility for developing and maintaining lines of communication between home and school.

- Post-primary schools also have a guidance counsellor (smaller schools may only have one on a part-time basis). This person will be qualified in guidance and counselling and is therefore in a position to provide counselling to students with emotional and/or behaviour problems or else will know where to refer the child for more specialist help.

- Some schools operate a school-tutor system. This can work very well in that the student has the same tutor throughout their schooling, whom they can build up a trusting relationship with.

- Some schools have a special class within the school for students with emotional and behavioural difficulties. These classes have lower pupil–teacher ratios and students often stay in this class for most of the day with the same teacher (much as in primary school). If students move for subjects such as woodwork or home economics, their class teacher will team teach with the subject teacher.

- Some young people work with a youth advocate. The job of a youth advocate is to act as a voice for young people at risk. They help and support the child in accessing services, etc.

- Some adolescents with emotional and behavioural problems are referred by schools to Youthreach centres. Youthreach centres have smaller numbers and have lower pupil–teacher ratios. They offer guidance and counselling and skills-based training programmes such as FETAC as well as more traditional Junior Certificate and Leaving Certificate applied courses. The ethos of these centres is less formal than in schools and many young people do very well in this environment.

- The Irish Youth Justice Service was established in 2005 to co-ordinate all the organisations involved with youth justice in Ireland, e.g. gardaí and probation services. Some young people with emotional and behavioural problems are involved in criminal activity and will therefore be involved with the Youth Justice Service. Garda juvenile liaison officers (JLOs) are specially trained gardaí who work with young people who have committed and admitted to relatively minor offences. JLOs work with the young people in an effort to prevent them from getting into further trouble. Currently there are about 18,000 young people involved with this scheme.

- The gardaí also run youth diversion projects, usually in the evenings and during school holidays, to give young people at risk something to do at times when they are at most risk of offending.

▶ If young people are charged with and convicted of crimes, then they will be assigned a probation officer who will work with them in an effort to help them stop offending. Probation officers work closely with schools, Youthreach centres, social workers, addiction services and anyone else involved with the young person.

chapter eight

Complex Conditions and Syndromes

AUTISTIC SPECTRUM DISORDERS

Autistic spectrum disorder (ASD) is the term used to describe a collection of developmental disorders primarily affecting the child's ability to communicate and form social relationships.

If a child is described as having **autism**, this means that the child has a significant number of the developmental disorders listed on the autistic spectrum. Autism is considered the most severe of the autistic spectrum disorders. If a child is described as having **Asperger's syndrome**, they will have some of the developmental disorders listed on the autistic spectrum but not others. Asperger's is not considered to be as severe as autism. The symptoms of other conditions such as Tourette syndrome are also listed on the autistic spectrum and thus are examples of an autistic spectrum disorder. Autism and Asperger's syndrome are the two conditions that will be dealt with in this chapter.

AUTISM

Prevalence

While estimates for the prevalence of autism vary considerably, a recent Irish study estimated that the incidence of autism in Ireland is approximately one in 166 (www.autismireland.ie). It is four times more common in males and occurs equally among all racial groups.

Causes

Little is known about the causes of autism. It is believed that genetics plays a part because parents who have family members with autism are more likely to have a child with autism. There are also cases where families have a number of children with autism.

Symptoms

Symptoms of autism centre around four areas:

- Severe communication difficulties
- Difficulty in social relationships
- Repetitive activities and routines
- An obsessive, narrow range of interests

These factors will manifest themselves in different behaviours:

- Delayed or sometimes no speech.
- Difficulty expressing needs, resulting in frustration and severe temper tantrums.
- Unusual accents or speech patterns – some children may speak in voices or accents heard on TV or constantly repeat phrases heard on TV.
- Children will have difficulty with two-way conversations, often not responding at all to questions asked or responding inappropriately. For example, if a child was asked how they got on at school that day, they might reply, 'My teacher's name is Jacinta and she is very nice.'
- Literal speech – the child will have difficulty understanding humour, sarcasm, etc.
- Severe temper tantrums.
- Lack of eye contact.
- Delayed toilet training.
- Insistence on sameness and a very strong resistance to change, e.g. may insist on eating the same dinner every day.
- Repetitive movements such as hand flapping, rocking or spinning.
- Many children with autism sleep very little.
- Some children dislike physical contact, e.g. a cuddle.
- Over-sensitivity or under-sensitivity to pain – a child could break a finger and be almost unaware of it, yet receive a tiny paper cut and react excessively to it.

- Some children may head bang or exhibit other self-injurious behaviours, e.g. hand biting.
- Often hypersensitive to smells, tastes, sounds and light. May refuse to wear certain clothes because they don't like the feel of them, cover ears or eyes to block out sound and light, may have very fussy eating patterns.
- Some children with autism dislike crowded places and will get very agitated if they find themselves in this situation.
- Irrational fears together with no fear of real dangers, e.g. a child could show fear of getting into the bath, yet show no fear of a growling dog.
- Engage in repetitive behaviours and ritualised activities and routines, e.g. feel compelled to tap the door handle five times before opening it.
- Have one or a few passionate interests. Interestingly, large numbers of young children with autism have a fascination with trains, while large numbers of adults with autism have an interest in computers, science, technology and animals.
- Have difficulty in making and keeping multiple friends.
- Prefer activities that require relatively little verbal interaction, e.g. construction toys such as Geomag, Lego, Bionicles and K'nex.
- Will play with toys differently, e.g. instead of colouring with a new set of colouring pencils, they may just roll them back and forth on the table, watching with interest.

Diagnosis

Autism is not normally diagnosed until the child is between 18 months and two years of age or older. This is because the symptoms of autism as described above do not normally appear until then. Parents of children with autism generally report that their child appeared to be developing normally until this age. This is partly why the study by Andrew Wakefield et al. (1998) that linked autism to the MMR vaccine caused such concern. Doctors who discounted Wakefield's work argued that because the symptoms of autism appear at the same time that children are normally given the MMR vaccine, they would have developed autism with or without the vaccine and that their autism was not caused by the vaccine.

There are no medical tests for diagnosing autism. An accurate diagnosis must be based on observation of the individual's communication, behaviour and developmental levels. However, as many of the behaviours associated with autism are shared by other disorders, various tests may be needed to rule out or identify other possible causes of the symptoms being exhibited. There are some early screening instruments that have been developed and are now being used to diagnose autism, e.g. CARS (Childhood Autism Rating Scale).

Treatment

Early diagnosis is very important for a child with autism so that early education and training programmes can begin before the child has become frustrated by their condition.

In Ireland at the moment, there are two options: children are either accommodated within existing mainstream and special schools or in a specialist applied behaviour analysis (ABA) school.

Accommodation within existing mainstream and special schools

- **ASD unit is attached to a primary or post-primary school or to a special needs school:** Typically, these classes have six children with ASD and the educational intervention is delivered by a specially trained teacher who has the assistance of a special needs assistant (SNA). The primary function of the SNA is to assist with issues such as toileting, arranging the child's environment, etc.
- **Special school:** The interventions are the same as outlined above, but children with ASD are educated alongside children with other intellectual difficulties.
- **In a mainstream class in a primary or secondary school, with assistance:** The child is educated in a mainstream school with assistance from a resource teacher and SNA. Typically, this kind of provision only suits children who are functioning at a high level.

In all of the three settings described above, there will be limited access to a speech and language therapist and an occupational therapist. The level of provision seems to vary depending on where the child is living.

Specialist ABA school

As of March 2010, the Department of Education and Skills (DES) also funds 13 other schools that follow the educational philosophy known as applied behaviour analysis (ABA). These schools deliver intensive one-to-one intervention to children. Tutors in these schools have all been trained to use ABA techniques. Children attending these schools have a longer school day and a longer school year to ensure retention of the skills acquired and to prevent regression during the long school holidays.

Children enrol in these schools from as young as two and a half years of age, continuing in some schools until they are 18. In order to gain admittance, the child needs to have had an educational psychological report recommending an ABA placement. ABA schools also have access to speech and language therapists and occupational therapists.

Unfortunately, there are currently over 345 children awaiting placements in the 13 existing ABA schools. There are many parents lobbying for greater numbers of these schools to be opened for children with autistic spectrum disorders.

Education methods recommended for children with autism

In this section, we will examine two approaches commonly taken by teachers working with children with autism:

- Applied behaviour analysis (ABA)
- Treatment and Education of Autistic and Related Communication-handicapped Children (TEACCH)

Applied behaviour analysis (ABA)

At its core, ABA is based on the work of the American psychologist B.F. Skinner (1904–90). Skinner came from the behaviourist school of psychology, which believes in the concept of operant conditioning, whereby learning occurs as a result of what Skinner called reinforcers. Reinforcers could either be positive (rewards) or negative (punishments). Through his research, Skinner found that positive reinforcement is a much stronger tool than negative and results in more learning. ABA uses this principle of positive reinforcement through its system of *discrete trial teaching*, sometimes called the *Lovaas method*.

For example, the objective of the discrete trial illustrated below is that the child reliably recognises the colour red. The teacher is sitting at the child's workstation with the child sitting opposite. The teacher has arranged a number of different coloured cubes on the workstation.

Teacher: 'Paula, show me red.'
The teacher takes Paula's hand, shapes it so the index finger is extended and points to the red cube.
Teacher: 'Yes! That's the red cube. Well done!' The teacher jots on the record sheet that Paula was unable to independently identify the red cube on this trial.
[End of first trial.]

Teacher: 'Paula, show me red.' Paula does not respond. After a few seconds, the teacher places her hand on Paula's, Paula extends her finger herself and the teacher helps her to find the red cube.
Teacher: 'Yes. That's the red cube.' The teacher jots on the record sheet that Paula was unable to independently identify the red cube on this trial.
[End of second trial.]

> Teacher: ' Paula, show me red.' Paula does not respond. After a few seconds, the teacher moves to take Paula's hand, but as she does, Paula points to the red cube.
> Teacher: 'Good job! That's the red cube.' Paula still needed a little prompt (the teacher moving to take her hand), so the teacher jots on the record sheet that Paula was unable to independently identify the red cube on this trial.
> [End of third trial.]
>
> Teacher: 'Paula, show me red.' Paula points to the red cube.
> Teacher: 'Yes! Great job! That's the red cube.' The teacher gives Paula a high five and a jelly sweet. She marks on the record sheet that Paula was able to identify the red cube on this trial.

While this example shows how discrete trial teaching can be used to teach a child to recognise a colour, this method can be used to teach the child virtually anything, e.g. put on their shoes, say thank you after receiving something, use eye contact when answering a question. It is very important that children are helped to transfer skills learned in discrete trial teaching to real-life, natural settings.

Treatment and Education of Autistic and Related Communication-handicapped Children (TEACCH)

TEACCH is a system of structured teaching that was first developed in 1972 by Dr Eric Schopler and his team at the University of North Carolina in the US. The main aim of a TEACCH programme is to help people with autism to live or work more effectively at home, at school and in the community. The programme focuses on reducing or removing autistic behaviours or the 'culture of autism', as listed below.

- Relative strength in and preference for processing visual information (compared to difficulties with auditory processing, particularly of language)
- Frequent attention to details but difficulty understanding the meaning of how those details fit together
- Difficulty combining ideas
- Difficulty with organising ideas, materials and activities
- Difficulties with attention (some individuals are very distractible, while others have difficulty shifting attention when it is time to make transitions)
- Communication problems, which vary by developmental level but always include impairments in the social use of language (called 'pragmatics')
- Difficulty with concepts of time, including moving too quickly or too slowly and having problems recognising the beginning, middle or end of an activity

▷ Tendency to become attached to routines, with the result that activities may be difficult to generalise from the original learning situation and that disruptions in routines can be upsetting, confusing or uncomfortable

▷ Very strong interests and impulses to engage in favoured activities, with difficulties disengaging once engaged

▷ Marked sensory preferences and dislikes

TEACCH does this by a system of structured teaching, the main features of which are as follows.

▷ Understand the culture of autism (as described above).

▷ Develop an individualised person- and family-centred plan for each student, rather than using a standard curriculum.

▷ Structure the physical environment, such as having specific areas of the classroom for specific tasks, e.g. the maths table, a domestic skills area.

▷ Use visual supports to make the sequence of daily activities predictable and understandable, e.g. some teachers lay out the child's work for the day in a series of trays so that the child can see how many trays of work need to be completed (see the photo).

Tray set with sorting tasks

For further information on this method of working with children with autism, there are a number of good websites on the subject, e.g. www.teacch.com.

Children with autism will also be engaged with HSE speech and language therapists, occupational therapists and psychologists, who will all support the work being done daily at school.

A relatively new initiative called Assistance Dogs Programme for Families of Children with Autism has been operated by the Irish Guide Dogs for the Blind since 2005. Parents of children who have received a dog report many benefits, including:

- Increased levels of safety for the child
- Constant companionship improves socialisation and interaction
- Dog calms the child
- Increases independence of child and family
- Reduces stress for child and family in public places

Prognosis

Autism is a lifelong condition that can vary significantly in terms of the severity of its symptoms. Some children with autism are described as high functioning, whereas others may have a much lower level of functioning. This will influence prognosis. In the past in Ireland, children with autism were offered very few services and many ended up in adult psychiatric hospitals because their behaviour became increasingly violent and aggressive due to their frustration. Early diagnosis and intervention with autism is vital. If a child is diagnosed early and has access to good, individualised services such as an ABA preschool, then the prognosis for a child with autism can be very positive, given the severity of the condition. People with autism living in countries that have had services longer than Ireland have benefited greatly from early intervention and training and are now leading semi-independent lives in sheltered or supported accommodation. Autism generally does not affect life expectancy in that autism does not in itself affect physical health, although children with very restricted eating habits may experience nutritional deficiencies.

Role of the SNA

If a child with autism is attending a mainstream school or an ASD unit attached to a mainstream school or special school, they will be entitled to the assistance of an SNA. Children who attend ABA schools have their own individual tutor and therefore do not require an SNA. The principal role of an SNA working with a child with autism is to look after the child's care needs, e.g. toileting, putting on shoes and coats, meal times. In addition, the SNA will be involved in setting up the structured teaching environment, e.g. preparing work trays. He or she will also be involved with encouraging the children to keep the classroom tidy, e.g. putting away materials during tidy up. He or she may also be involved in assisting the teacher with the preparation of class materials. Exact duties will vary from school to school.

CASE STUDY

Peter is a seven-year-old boy with autism. He lives at home with his parents, Joan and Paul, and their three other children – two girls who are both older than Peter and one younger boy. Peter lives in a rural community and travels every morning to a large town 15 miles away to a school for children with special needs.

Joan gets up at quarter to seven every morning. She eats her own breakfast first, because if she doesn't, she will be too busy once the children get up. Paul is self-employed and gets up at the same time, though he is usually gone by seven thirty. She then makes the lunches – Peter will only eat white bread and jam. Joan has tried putting other foods in his lunchbox that she feels would be more nutritious, but this has caused aggressive outbursts at school and a refusal to eat anything.

Joan then calls the children. Peter is now able to dress himself (his school uniform consists of an easy to manage polo shirt and tracksuit) and has been toilet trained for the past year and a half. Unlike many children with autism his age, Peter can communicate quite well. While he rarely makes eye contact and can get very frustrated and aggressive if people around him cannot understand what he is trying to communicate, he has a good, clear vocabulary. Joan and Paul taught him to speak using the PECS system, whereby the child first communicates by pointing to pictures and symbols and eventually, through repetition, begins to use words instead of pointing.

Routine is very important to Peter. If his routine is disturbed even slightly, he does not feel comfortable and will start to act out. There are a lot of rules that Joan knows she must follow to avoid a confrontation at breakfast. Peter must have a certain bowl and spoon and he must not see Joan pouring the cereal or putting the milk on it. He must have cornflakes and the sugar must be visible on top. The spoon cannot be in the bowl when it is presented to him. Nobody can touch any of his food. Joan insists that Peter says please and thank you and will not give him his breakfast until he does this. He must sit in a certain chair and the other children know this and accommodate Peter. Sometimes on a Saturday, when Joan has time, she deliberately tries to break some of Peter's habits. This does cause a tantrum, but she feels that Peter must learn that the world will not always be predictable.

The bus comes for Peter at ten to nine in the morning. Depending on Peter's mood and how well he has slept, Peter will either get onto the bus with no problems or sometimes have a temper tantrum. Peter does not like going to school and would rather stay at home. There have been times when Joan has had to physically carry Peter onto the bus and strap him into his seat. Peter does not like wearing a seatbelt and this has been a long-running battle in the past, especially in the family car. The health board did provide Peter with a special harness that was difficult to get out of, but Peter always seemed to manage to wriggle his way out. The bus driver is very strict on seatbelts and will not allow Peter to travel without one. Peter is not allowed to travel on the bus if he does not co-operate, and once or twice Peter has had to be taken off the bus because he just would not keep the seatbelt on. This has caused problems for Joan, because she works part time. In addition, Joan has to drop the two older children to school and the youngest to playschool for nine twenty, so if Peter is being difficult, this can cause stress for all the family. The eldest two girls hate being late for school.

Peter attends a special school that caters for a wide range of children with different special needs. Approximately six years ago, the school opened a special unit for children with autism. The idea was that children with autism would attend the autism unit for a number of years and would then be integrated into the main school. This goal has not yet been achieved, but Joan hopes Peter will eventually be able to do this because he can communicate so well. The autism unit currently has five students with one teacher and two SNAs. The method used to teach the children in the unit is called TEACCH. Joan did look into other alternatives – there is another school in the town that uses the ABA system of working with autistic children – but she felt that the TEACCH system would be more suitable for Peter.

When Peter reaches the school at nine thirty, his teacher will have laid out his different tasks for the day on a series of trays. Peter will systematically work through all his tasks. Peter is coming on very well at reading and is using the Fuzz Buzz series. He is reading at senior infants level. If Peter does not want to do something, he sometimes throws tantrums and can be quite difficult. There is a timeout room off the unit where Peter or other children are sent to calm down. There is nothing to do in this room. There are no windows but the door is left open. Peter sometimes likes timeout, as it gets him out of having to do something he doesn't want to do – for the time being, anyway.

Like most children with autism, Peter has no sense of danger, hence the unit is very secure. If the opportunity arose, Peter would leave the building and would walk out in front of cars on the road. At lunchtime, Peter leaves the unit and eats with the other students in the lunch room. Sometimes Peter finds this difficult, as the lunchroom is noisy and he dislikes noise – he will often start hand flapping and get very agitated and upset. However, it is felt that it is important for Peter to mix with others outside the unit. Joan tries to introduce a new food at school that he will not eat at home, e.g. a yoghurt drink, because sometimes Peter will try new things at school that he will not try at home and vice versa.

The school communicates with Joan and Paul though a communications copy. Peter's school follows the ordinary school year and so Peter is off during school holidays. This poses difficulties for Joan in that having Peter at home every day with three other children can be very demanding and it takes Peter some time to readjust to school upon returning after holidays. Joan feels holidays should be shorter for Peter than for her other children, as she thinks he loses some of the ground he has made during the school term during the holidays, particularly the summer ones.

Peter finishes school at two and returns home at approximately two forty each day on the school bus. Peter is often hyperactive when he returns after spending the day inside, so Joan usually lets him play outside with his youngest brother before his sisters come home at three o'clock. Joan has an arrangement with a neighbour to drop the older girls home. Peter plays in the back yard. The yard is fully secure, as Peter would go towards the road if he managed to get out. The front door and windows are also kept locked, as are many rooms in the house. Joan makes dinner for Peter and his siblings. Peter insists on having oven chips every day. He also eats chicken nuggets or fish fingers but no vegetables. Like at breakfast, the food must be prepared and presented in a certain way. Peter goes through phases like this where he will eat only one or two types of food. These phases last anywhere from a month upwards.

Robots have been of huge interest to Peter for the past year. He is constantly drawing and making them. He can make or draw up to 20 robots a day. He is very particular about his robots and will scream and shout if bits of them fall off or get lost. Often he will not sleep if he has a particular project in mind, which causes him to be more difficult in the mornings. If Peter is being difficult, Joan always tries to stay calm and kneel down so that she is at his level. Calmness is very important so that Peter realises it is him screaming and not someone else making the noise. Peter is very sensitive to noise and does not like raised voices or loud noises like the toilet flushing.

An SNA comes into Peter's house three hours per week, paid for by the HSE. This is to give Joan a break and give her a chance to do shopping or spend time with the other children. Joan feels that this is not enough and most weeks she pays for extra hours out of her own pocket. Peter also receives limited access to a psychologist, speech therapist and language therapist through the school. Joan also feels that some of the resources prioritised by the HSE are geared towards the needs of autistic children generally and not tailored for Peter as an individual. Joan and Paul feel that the people making the decisions about what assistance Peter gets do not know him personally. The HSE also set up parental support meetings on a monthly basis. They provide the venue and refreshments. Joan finds these meetings hugely informative and supportive and looks forward to them. Once a term there is a sibling support group, and Peter's two older sisters enjoy attending these.

Joan and Paul feel that Peter would benefit from mixing more with other children other than his siblings. This can be problematic, however, as many of the activities available in the area are not adequately supervised for someone with Peter's needs. The local football club has said that Peter was more than welcome. While Joan appreciates that their intentions are good, the pitch is alongside a busy road and she would worry for Peter's safety. Joan feels that she cannot visit friends and neighbours if Peter is with her, as he is very curious and she fears he may damage things in their houses. Also, friends' and neighbours' houses are not generally secure enough and there is therefore a danger element to consider. Joan would like to bring Peter on more outings, e.g. to the cinema, but Paul works long hours and she would need someone with her, because if Peter acts up, she needs someone to stay with the other children while she attends to him. Joan and Paul's family do try to help as much as they can, but they all have their own children and lead very busy lives themselves. Also, Peter does not really like being out of his own familiar environment and so does not like going to other people's houses and would be very upset if he had to stay overnight.

Peter's brother and sisters go to bed between eight and half eight every night. Peter is dressed and ready for bed at that time, but he rarely goes to sleep until twelve or one o'clock in the morning. Joan and Paul find it hard to sleep if they know Peter is still awake, as he could injure himself. Even when he does fall asleep, this is no guarantee that he is asleep for the night. He often wakes up five or six times during the night, leaving his parents really tired the next day.

ASPERGER'S SYNDROME

Asperger's syndrome (AS) is an autism spectrum disorder that was first described by the Austrian paediatrician Hans Asperger in 1944. People with Asperger's syndrome, like other conditions on the autistic spectrum, show significant difficulties in social interaction, along with restricted and repetitive patterns of behaviour and interests. It differs from autism in that language and cognitive development are much less impaired. Also, although not required for diagnosis, physical clumsiness and atypical use of language are frequently reported. People with Asperger's syndrome are often described by their peers as odd or eccentric.

Prevalence

It is very difficult to estimate how frequently Asperger's syndrome occurs in the population, mainly due to the fact that it is very difficult to differentiate between Asperger's syndrome and high-functioning autism. In fact, some practitioners believe that Asperger's syndrome should no longer be classified as a separate condition. In Ireland, it is estimated that several thousand people have the syndrome, with about nine times as many males affected as females (Aspire 2009).

Causes

Asperger's syndrome is believed to have a strong genetic component. Children with AS commonly have other immediate or extended family members with behavioural symptoms similar to AS or a family history of depression or bipolar disorder. It is also associated with oxygen deprivation during the birth process in some cases.

Symptoms

The main symptoms of Asperger's syndrome are as follows.

1. Impaired ability to socially interact

Children with AS often experience difficulties with the basic skills required for social interaction. A child with AS finds it difficult to show empathy, e.g. if another child slipped and fell in the playground, they would be unlikely to help the child up and comfort him or her, often coming across as insensitive. Children with AS find it difficult to make friends. They often use very little eye contact, may have blank or unusual facial expressions and adopt unusual postures and gestures, e.g. some children may have unusual ticks or habits.

Unlike children with autism, children with AS are not usually withdrawn around others. They do approach others and do want to make friends, even if in a socially awkward way. For example, a person with AS may engage in a one-sided, long monologue about a topic of interest to them. They will not pick up clues that the other person is not interested in what they are saying and in fact wants to get away from them.

Children with AS will understand the way society works in a theoretical way, but will not be able to apply this information in a real-life situation, e.g. they understand what a joke is but are unable to tell one in the way it is meant to be told.

2. Restricted and repetitive interests and behaviours

People with AS often display behaviour, interests and activities that are restricted and repetitive and are sometimes abnormally intense or focused. The pursuit of specific and narrow areas of interest is one of the most striking features of AS. Individuals with AS may collect volumes of detailed information on a relatively narrow topic such as dinosaurs or train timetables without necessarily having a genuine understanding of or interest in the broader topic. For example, a child might memorise camera model numbers while caring little about photography. This behaviour is usually apparent by age five or six. Although these special interests may change from time to time, they typically become more unusual and narrowly focused and often dominate social interaction so much that the person will speak of little else.

Stereotyped and repetitive motor behaviours are a core part of the diagnosis of AS and other ASDs such as autism. They include hand movements such as flapping or twisting, and complex whole-body movements such as rocking or spinning.

3. Speech and language abnormalities

Although individuals with Asperger's syndrome acquire language skills without significant general delay and their speech typically lacks major abnormalities, their speech will have certain unusual characteristics that will affect their ability to communicate effectively with others and thus their social development.

One of the most important characteristics (mentioned earlier) is verbosity, also called prolixity. What this means is that the individual uses an excess of words. They will go off on long, wordy monologues, not realising that their listeners are not keeping up or interested in what they are saying.

People with AS also use quite literal speech and have difficulties understanding and using things like metaphor, e.g. the government toppled like a house of cards, or figurative speech, e.g. I nearly died laughing. Children with AS appear to have particular weaknesses in areas of non-literal language that include humor, irony and good-natured teasing.

People with AS may also have what is called **auditory processing deficits**. This means that sometimes the child will have difficulty 'hearing' what is being said to them despite normal physical hearing. For example, a child may hear little of what their teacher is saying to the general class, only hearing what she is saying when she is speaking directly to him or her. Children with AS may use unusually formal speech, e.g. a child wishing to join a group of peers playing cards may ask, 'If none of you mind very much, could I please join your group so I may also play cards?' Children with AS may also be unaware of and use unusual intonation (may be flatter than normal), pitch and loudness while talking.

4. Other symptoms

As with autism, individuals with AS may be unusually sensitive or insensitive to sound, light, touch, texture, taste, smell, pain, temperature and other stimuli. They may exhibit physical clumsiness, an unusual bouncing walk and poor handwriting. Sleep problems are very common, with many experiencing frequent nocturnal and early morning awakenings. Many have difficulty identifying and describing their emotions, resulting in high stress levels.

Diagnosis

Diagnosis will be based on extensive observations of a child in a number of different settings, usually home and school. Standard diagnostic criteria require impairment in social interaction and repetitive and stereotyped patterns of behaviour, activities and interests, without significant delay in language or cognitive development. Diagnosis is commonly made between the ages of four and 12, although it may be done earlier. Tools such as the NEPSY-2 test are used by psychologists together with the observations described above and interviews with parents and teachers to arrive at a diagnosis.

Assessments are usually carried out through the child's school by a Department of Education and Skills psychologist or referred by a GP to a psychologist from the HSE local child and family services. This second route will be usual for a child under school-going age.

Assessments can be carried out privately, which will mean a shorter wait time. Lists of psychologists are available from the Asperger's Syndrome Association of Ireland (Aspire) website (www.aspire-irl.org). Aspire also has a family support officer whose job is to direct people who have received a diagnosis of Asperger's syndrome to services for their child.

Treatment

Treatment for Asperger's syndrome centres around managing the condition's symptoms and teaching age-appropriate social, communication and vocational skills that are not naturally acquired during development. Therapies may include the following.

- Social skills training to teach the child directly what is required in frequently occurring social situations, e.g. how to join a group of peers playing a game
- Drama classes where participants have to act out various situations and dilemmas (Dr Carmel O'Sullivan and her research team in the School of Education, Trinity College Dublin, run such classes weekly for children with AS)

- Stress management techniques such as specific exercises and breathing techniques
- Cognitive behavioural therapy to help the child cut back on obsessive interests and repetitive routines
- Occupational therapy to teach life skills
- Physiotherapy to improve physical co-ordination
- Specialised speech therapy to help with the child's understanding of the give and take of normal conversation
- There may be training and support for parents so that techniques learned may be practised at home
- Medications for co-existing conditions such as depression, anxiety and ADHD
- Children with AS will have an individual education plan (IEP) developed for them by people involved with them in the school setting, e.g. school principal, class teacher and perhaps a resource teacher, learning support teacher and SNA. In post-primary schools, the guidance and counselling teacher may also be involved. IEPs are individually tailored plans that address the specific needs of the individual child. The plan sets specific targets or goals for the child and monitors the child's progress closely.

Prognosis

The prognosis for children with Asperger's syndrome is generally good, provided they have been given therapies to help them with their social and communication skills. Many hold down jobs (they work best in jobs where they can work alone on projects) and have families. However, people with AS are at greater risk of depression than the general population.

Role of the SNA

Most children with AS will have normal levels of intellectual functioning and will have no additional care needs. For this reason, children with AS will not normally have an SNA unless they have significant behavioural or emotional problems. This can occur with some children who become frustrated by their social incompetence, becoming aggressive. If this is the case, then an SNA may be employed to assist the teacher in keeping the child focused and calm. An SNA will sit beside the child, talking to and calming the child or perhaps using distraction techniques. They may be asked to accompany the child to timeout and talk to the child there until such a time as they are able to return to the group. An SNA's specific role will depend on the needs of the individual child and also the requirements of the school.

Aaron didn't talk very much until he was about two and a half years old, but when he did he spoke in a posh accent and quickly developed a sophisticated vocabulary. He was a large and awkward child, often tripping over or bumping into things. His mother put it down to being a bit flat footed. When he went to playschool he began to develop intense interests in a small number of activities. For example, he got a large book on dinosaurs for his third birthday and wrecked his mother's head pestering her and asking her to read out the names of the dinosaurs to him. He loved to memorise the names and to find out if they were carnivores or herbivores and also when they lived, what size they were, etc. Everyone was amazed at how much he could remember about them – over a hundred different ones. Another fascination he had was with Geomag. He loved to create 3-D shapes of all different shapes and sizes. Any money he got from family or friends went towards buying more and more of it. The playschool reported that he was doing well, except that he did not seem to want to mix with other children very much. They reported that he tended to stand on the sidelines and when he did try to join the group, he didn't know how and often just barged into the middle of the group, causing play to halt. Academically, he seemed to be very bright – before he was due to begin school he was already reading and recognising numbers.

It was when Aaron started school at age five that he first talked about wanting to make friends. He complained that at lunchtime nobody wanted to play with him. He did have difficulty in this area and spent the vast majority of lunchtime walking round on his own or making unsuccessful attempts to join groups. He did not seem to know how to talk to his peers in a way that made them want to talk to him. If a child did begin a conversation with him, he would get excited and then try to keep the child talking to him by talking to them about things that interested him – he did not seem to realise that others did not necessarily share his same interests. At this stage, his main interest was space. He loved to talk about the planets and how far away they are from Earth, how many moons they have, etc.

In senior infants, one of the most popular boys in the class, Andrew, began showing him some attention, trying to include him in what was going on. Andrew was asked to do this by the teacher. Aaron responded to this by practically holding this boy up to be a hero. At home, he would constantly talk about Andrew, asking his parents if Andrew could come over. On two occasions Andrew did come over – it was then that Aaron's parents realised just how far behind Aaron was in terms of social skills. The minute they got into the car outside the school, Aaron would begin talking incessantly and excitedly to Andrew. Aaron's mother felt very sorry for her son – he was making such an effort to be liked by Andrew, but was going about it in the wrong way.

After those first two visits, whenever Aaron asked Andrew over he was never able to come – he would have football on or something else. Catherine, Aaron's mother, knew that it was just that the child did not want to come over and was feeling crowded by Aaron. She understood this but did not know how to help her son.

DOWN'S SYNDROME

Prevalence

On average, Down's syndrome appears approximately once in every 700 live births but more frequently as maternal age progresses (see table below). It is not known exactly why this is the case, although it is thought to be because an older woman's eggs have been exposed to more toxins over time than a younger woman. Some women, particularly those over the age of 35, opt to have prenatal diagnostic tests done to detect Down's syndrome and other genetic abnormalities during pregnancy, though this practice is understandably controversial.

Maternal age	Risk
15–19	1 in 1,850
20–25	1 in 1,400
26–30	1 in 800
31–35	1 in 380
36–40	1 in 190
41–45	1 in 110
45+	1 in 30

Causes

Down's syndrome was first diagnosed in 1866 by the English doctor John Langdon Down. He described the symptoms of the condition but it was not understood to be a chromosomal abnormality until 1959, when Professor Jérôme Lejeune, a Parisian geneticist, discovered that Down's syndrome occurred as a result of a trisomy (three) of chromosome 21. Normally every cell of a baby's body (except the sex cells) contains a total of 46 chromosomes: 23 from their mother and 23 from their father. A child with Down's syndrome gains an extra chromosome 21, usually from their mother, resulting in them having a total of 47. This extra chromosome in each body cell causes the symptoms of the most common form of Down's syndrome –

standard trisomy. Standard trisomy is the most severe form of Down's syndrome, occurring in approximately 94 per cent of cases.

Since Lejeune's discovery, other forms of the condition, which are much rarer, have been discovered: **translocation** (where one parent passes on an abnormal rather than an extra chromosome 21 that contains extra material, but not a full chromosome) and **mosaicism** (where some cells in the body have the normal 46 chromosomes, while others have 47). Approximately 4 per cent of people with Down's syndrome have translocation and 2 per cent have mosaic Down's syndrome. Individuals with mosaic Down's syndrome may show fewer or less severe symptoms of the condition, depending on what percentage of their body cells have 47 chromosomes.

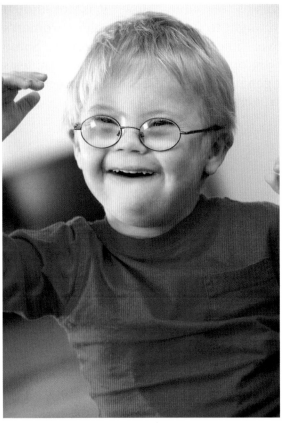

A child with standard trisomy Down's syndrome

A child with mosaic Down's syndrome

Symptoms

Down's syndrome is a complex condition, meaning that its symptoms affect a number of different areas of development.

Physical characteristics

Individuals with Down's syndrome may have some or all of the following physical characteristics.

- Microgenia (abnormally small chin)
- Oblique (slanted) eye fissures with extra skin folds on the inner corner of the eyes
- Poor muscle tone
- A flat nasal bridge
- A single palmar fold on the hand
- Protruding tongue due to a small oral cavity and an enlarged tongue
- A short neck
- White spots on the iris, known as Brushfield spots
- Loose joints; there can also be excess space between the vertebrae of the spine
- Congenital heart defects
- Prone to ongoing respiratory infections
- Excessive space between the big toe and second toe
- Broad head and round face
- Increased incidence of epilepsy
- Hearing deficits sometimes caused by sensorineural factors, other times by chronic serous otitis media, or glue ear
- Short stature with a tendency towards excessive weight gain
- People with Down's syndrome are more prone to certain conditions and diseases, e.g. thyroid disorder, Alzheimer's and leukaemia
- Delayed fine motor skills because of short, chubby fingers
- Delay with gross motor skills, although degree of delay varies, e.g. some children will walk before two years, whereas others will be as old as four years

Effects on cognitive development

Most individuals with Down's syndrome have general learning disabilities in the mild (IQ 50–69) to moderate (IQ 35–49) range, while individuals with mosaic

Down's syndrome typically score 10 to 30 points higher. This is a considerable range, resulting in individuals with Down's syndrome having wide-ranging abilities. In terms of teaching and learning, individuals with Down's syndrome generally benefit most from visual teaching approaches and the use of practical, concrete materials, i.e. doing something rather than talking about it. Most children with Down's syndrome have short attention spans and therefore need short learning sessions. They also benefit from opportunities to rehearse and repeat new skills and learning. Longer tasks should be broken down into smaller chunks, with positive reinforcement after each chunk has been achieved. As mentioned below, most children with Down's syndrome have good social awareness and understanding, so teachers and other staff should be careful about this, as the child will often be very aware of how he or she compares to his or her peers.

Effects on language development

In terms of language development, children with Down's syndrome generally experience speech delay. There is often a larger than normal gap between receptive language (what is understood) and expressive language (what is said). They usually require speech therapy in order to improve their expressive (spoken) language. Many initially use a simple sign language called Lámh (see Chapter 14).

Effects on social and emotional development

Generally, children with Down's syndrome show good social awareness and understanding and therefore are often aware that they are different from their peers. This can lead to feelings of anger, frustration and sadness. Having said this, some children with Down's syndrome do not fully understand some of society's social norms and may, for example, be overly friendly to strangers or people they do not know well. In terms of child protection, this has sometimes put these children in a vulnerable position.

Diagnosis

Down's syndrome can be diagnosed either before or after birth. Before birth, maternal blood screening is usually carried out first, which can indicate that the baby may have a major congenital condition such as spina bifida or Down's syndrome. Blood screening, however, does not give a definite diagnosis. If a definite diagnosis is required, then the two principal tests that will be carried out are chorionic villus sampling or amniocentesis. After birth, the baby will be physically examined and if Down's syndrome is suspected a blood test will be taken to confirm diagnosis.

Maternal blood screening

This test can be conducted on a sample of the mother's blood from the sixteenth week onwards. Unlike chorionic villus sampling and amniocentesis, non-invasive blood tests such as this cannot diagnose a birth defect, they can only indicate that there may be one. Certain conditions such as Down's syndrome and spina bifida in the foetus cause an increase in certain substances in the mother's blood. Detecting these raised amounts is how a positive screen result is obtained.

Chorionic villus sampling

This test is usually conducted between the tenth and twelfth week of pregnancy, when a sample of cells is taken from the placenta and sent away for testing. This is an invasive testing technique and carries with it a small risk of miscarriage (1 per cent). It can detect with a very large degree of accuracy the presence of a range of genetic conditions, e.g. Down's syndrome, cystic fibrosis, PKU and sickle cell anaemia.

Amniocentesis

This test is usually conducted between the fifteenth and eighteenth week of pregnancy, when a sample of the amniotic fluid is withdrawn using a fine needle and sent away for testing. Like chorionic villus sampling, this is an invasive testing technique and carries with it a small risk of miscarriage (0.5 per cent). It too can detect with a very large degree of accuracy the presence of a range of genetic conditions, including Down's syndrome.

Treatment

Down's syndrome is a lifelong condition that impacts all areas of development to a greater or lesser degree. Many of the health issues that frequently accompany Down's syndrome can be treated and children should be given every opportunity to learn the skills they require to lead as independent a life as possible.

Health issues:

- Children may attend physiotherapy to improve muscle tone and also develop motor skills, which may be delayed.
- Children with congenital heart defects often require surgery.
- As a larger proportion of children with Down's syndrome have epilepsy than the general population, many may be on anti-epileptic drugs.

> There is a tendency among children and adults with Down's syndrome to gain weight, partially because of their short stature, so it is important to monitor eating and for the child to take regular exercise.

> Children may have to have grommets fitted for chronic serous otitis media, or glue ear. If the child's hearing difficulties arise from sensorineural factors, hearing aids may be fitted.

Plastic surgery has sometimes been advocated and performed on children with Down's syndrome, based on the assumption that surgery can reduce the facial features associated with the syndrome, therefore decreasing social stigma and leading to a better quality of life. It is as yet uncommon in Ireland.

Speech therapy will prove useful for many children with Down's syndrome to help with expressive speech.

Education

Children with Down's syndrome may be educated in a special school, a special class attached to a mainstream school or within a mainstream classroom with the assistance of the class teacher, a resource teacher and an SNA. Regardless of where the child is being educated, the focus should be on the following:

> Make progress with their cognitive, speech, language and academic skills, with an emphasis on learning skills that will be useful for the future

> Become as independent as possible in their personal care and social lives

> Develop a positive self-identity, self-confidence and self-esteem

> Develop a network of friends, personal relationships and leisure interests

Children with Down's syndrome will follow the curriculum of the school and should also have an ongoing IEP (the provision of education plans for individual students with special needs is mandated by the EPSEN Act 2004). An IEP is a written document that specifies the learning goals that are to be achieved by the student over a set period of time. It should not contain everything to be taught to the student in a period of time, but rather, anything that is **additional or different** to the main class curriculum. The strategies, resources and supports necessary to achieve these goals are also specified in the IEP.

Prognosis

Quality of life for children and adults with Down's syndrome largely depends on how well their health has been monitored and treated and how well their individual strengths have been developed, allowing them to live as independent and fulfilling a life as possible. In the past, many children with Down's were institutionalised from a young age, which severely limited their quality of life.

Currently, the average life expectancy of someone with Down's syndrome is 49 years, with considerable variations between different ethnic and socio-economic groups. This is a significant increase from an average life expectancy of 25 in the 1980s (Young 2002). The causes of death have also changed, with chronic neurodegenerative diseases becoming more common as the population ages. People with Down's syndrome who survive into their forties and fifties commonly suffer from an Alzheimer's-like dementia.

Role of the SNA

Your role as an SNA is to support the class teacher in his or her work with a child with Down's syndrome. You could do this by:

- Assisting the child on a one-to-one basis with tasks set. Do not take over and allow the child to do as much for him or herself as possible. Be patient.
- Helping the child with care needs, e.g. toileting and feeding if necessary.
- Trying to keep the child on task, as attention span is sometimes short.
- Giving plenty of praise and encouragement for effort.
- If a child is on medication, e.g. for epilepsy, you may be involved in this aspect of his or her care.
- You may be asked to escort the child to his or her parents at home time or travel with him or her on school transport.

CASE STUDY

Lucy was only 24 years old when she had Eric, her second child. Lucy had not been offered amniocentesis, probably because she was so young and she didn't really know such a thing existed anyway. Lucy knew from the minute she laid eyes on Eric that he had Down's syndrome. She said it to Alan, her partner, in the delivery room, but he told her in a hushed voice not to be ridiculous, that the baby was perfect. When she asked if everything was OK, her obstetrician said that they needed to check the baby further and would be in to talk to her in a few minutes. She didn't come back for an hour, and that hour was the longest of Lucy's life. Her obstetrician came back and told her that they suspected her baby had Down's syndrome. She said that blood tests would have to be done to confirm the diagnosis, but judging from physical appearance, it seemed pretty certain. Alan asked her if she had ever been wrong with this diagnosis in the past. The obstetrician said not so far, but there have been cases elsewhere. Both Lucy and Alan were dumbstruck. How could this happen? They were in their early twenties – this happened to much older parents, not to their age group. They both felt an unbearable sense of sadness and loss. It was very difficult when people began phoning for news of the birth. Neither of them wanted to talk to anyone.

As the weeks went on, Lucy just got on with the business of caring for Eric. She also had a two-year-old little girl to care for, so life was really busy. Eric had trouble feeding as he had a poor suck, and as a result was very slow to gain weight. He also got a number of ear and chest infections. Lucy never seemed to be long away from the doctor's surgery, but she was back again for something else. Eric's development was much slower than what she remembered from her last baby. His neck muscles were much weaker, resulting in head lag lasting for much longer. He didn't smile at six weeks like her other baby, Ellen. He was slow to sit up and crawl and didn't walk until he was two and a half. Lucy didn't go back to work so that she could care for the children full time. This put the family under severe financial strain. Alan was in the building trade, which had taken a nose dive since the beginning of the economic recession.

When Eric was three, Ellen, his big sister, started school. Lucy decided that this was the right time for her to go back to work part time, so she set about finding a suitable childcare placement for Eric five mornings a week. She found an excellent crèche on the other side of the town that catered for children with special needs. They had a number of childcare staff there specially trained in the area. Lucy began working in a solicitor's office five mornings a week, dropping Ellen and Eric off before going in to work. She was delighted with this arrangement, as she had found herself feeling quite down and isolated at home all day with the children. Sadly, this arrangement didn't last very long. Because of Eric's health problems, she began missing too many days from work and was laid off. This left her back at square one. Without work, she couldn't afford the childcare place for Eric and had to take him out of it. She found this very difficult to do, as he'd been making such good progress. Mixing with other children was excellent for him. Lucy is currently applying to the HSE for a childcare place for Eric. She has not yet had any word back but is very hopeful.

FRAGILE X SYNDROME

Prevalence

Fragile X syndrome is a relatively newly diagnosed genetic condition that affects approximately one in every 4,000 boys and one in every 8,000 girls. The condition primarily causes learning disability, but there are also some physical characteristics.

Causes

Boys have one X and one Y chromosome, whereas girls have two X chromosomes. With fragile X syndrome, the bottom of one X chromosome is 'fragile'. Because girls have two X chromosomes, even if they have the condition they will have one healthy X chromosome to compensate for the 'fragile' one and so normally have less severe symptoms than boys.

Symptoms

- Learning difficulties are usually present in both males and females, with boys being more severely affected. Severity ranges from borderline to moderate general learning disability. Many have short-term memory difficulties.
- Speech and language difficulties will be present in most children with the condition. Language delay is often the first sign picked up by parents and professionals. The child may repeat words and phrases and may have difficulty with comprehension.
- In terms of behaviour and attention, children will often have age-inappropriate tantrums, may sleep very little and be always on the go (hyperactivity). Most are impulsive and lack the ability to concentrate for any length of time. They may avoid eye contact and engage in ritualistic or repetitive behaviour. This is why fragile X is often classified as being on the autistic spectrum.
- Some people with fragile X develop aggressive behaviours.
- In terms of physical characteristics, the child may be late reaching physical milestones such as sitting up or walking, have recurrent middle ear infections and have a long, narrow face with a prominent lower jaw. Adult males with fragile X will have unusually large testes.
- Twenty per cent of children with fragile X also have epilepsy.

Diagnosis

Usually parents seek medical advice because they are concerned about their baby's development – he or she may be slow to smile, sit, walk or talk – and they may have very disturbed sleep patterns. A blood test is required to diagnose fragile X.

Treatment

Treatment interventions will be similar to those for Down's syndrome and other general learning disabilities. There may be some applied behavioural analysis (ABA) work done with the child if they are showing some autistic-like behaviours (see the section on the treatment of autism, pp. 205–9). Generally:

- Provide distraction-free areas for the child to work in at school if possible.
- Keep tasks short, as attention span is short. Tasks should not take any longer than five to 10 minutes.
- Some children benefit from time out between activities.
- Reward positive behaviour and be clear with the child about behaviours that are not acceptable.
- Repeat instructions clearly until the child understands.
- Offer plenty of praise and encouragement.
- Work to the child's strengths.
- Have good routines at home and at school.

Prognosis

While fragile X is a lifelong condition, it does not affect life expectancy unless there are other conditions present. As with autism, Asperger's syndrome, general learning disability and Down's syndrome, prognosis largely depends on both the severity of the condition and the quality of the interventions that have been put in place for the person with fragile X. With good levels of intervention, people with fragile X can lead fulfilling semi-independent lives.

chapter nine

Exceptional Ability/Giftedness

The Education Act 1998 recognises giftedness as a special education condition with a requirement for special teaching and services. The focus of special needs provision in Ireland has, however, been on the provision of services for children with disabilities rather than children with exceptional abilities. This is unfortunate, as it is well established that children with exceptional abilities also need special provision or problems will arise for them.

DEFINITIONS OF GIFTEDNESS

Children who are considered gifted have been assessed by a psychologist and found to have a high level of intelligence, usually an IQ of over 130, or the 98th percentile. However, this is a very narrow view of giftedness. The government-financed *Report of the Special Education Review Committee* (Department of Education and Science 1993) defined giftedness as:

▷ High general intellectual ability
▷ Specific academic aptitude, e.g. for mathematics
▷ Creative or productive thinking
▷ Leadership ability
▷ Visual and performing arts skills

- Mechanical aptitude
- Psychomotor ability, e.g. in athletics

Children who fit into this category have genuine special learning needs, just like the other children with special needs detailed throughout this book. There is a common misconception, however, that children with exceptional abilities will somehow educate themselves and will certainly do OK in school without any special interventions. This is not the case in reality. Many children with exceptional abilities become so bored and frustrated with school that they totally opt out. Others begin to act out in response to their boredom and frustration. At best, the child will do OK in school, but perhaps nowhere near what they could have achieved had they been given more challenging work to do.

The characteristics of gifted children often lead to social and emotional problems that can affect their social and emotional development. Nature often dictates that if there are exceptional strengths in one or more areas, there will be deficits in others. For example, it is not uncommon for a child who is academically exceptionally able to have poor physical co-ordination and therefore be very weak at sports or be a very poor social communicator and therefore have few friends.

While many exceptionally able students are happy, well adjusted and successful in their area(s) of ability, for others, this is not the case. Early identification is therefore important for many students to prevent later underachievement, boredom and perhaps behavioural and emotional problems.

ASSESSMENT AND IDENTIFICATION

Exceptional ability is best assessed and identified using a variety of different methods. Such methods include:

- Observation
- Parent or guardian referral
- Peer referral
- Self-referral
- Referral by other individuals or organisations
- Identification by psychologists
- Teacher referral
- School-wide identification processes (NCCA 2007a)

Observation

- Parents may notice that their child develops skills more quickly in comparison to children of similar age.
- Rapid development in early childhood may be noted and recorded at developmental check-ups by health personnel.
- Friends may draw attention to the child's development of early speech, physical development and/or his or her use of a wide vocabulary.
- Teachers at playgroup/foundation level may find that the newly enrolled child is able to accomplish tasks far beyond the normal expectation for a similar age cohort.
- Teachers at other levels and in some specific subjects may note that challenging tasks are accomplished with ease, coupled with a demand for further challenge, which if not satisfied is rapidly replaced by boredom.

Referral by a parent or guardian

- Parents or guardians are likely to have a detailed knowledge of their children's abilities and can be a useful source of information in identifying a student with exceptional ability. Some schools that are actively trying to cater for children with exceptional abilities sometimes ask parents to complete questionnaires with regards to their child's early development.
- Parents or guardians can, however, feel vulnerable in claiming that their son or daughter is exceptionally able for fear of being regarded as a parent or guardian who thinks they have a genius.
- Through observation of their child from birth, it is often parents or guardians who commonly spot the ability long before the child goes to school.

Peer referral

This is one form of identification that is often overlooked. Students in the classroom are very good at identifying exceptionally able students.

Self-referral

Students who have good self-awareness and know their capabilities can often self-refer. Each self-referral should be investigated, as it is important to be aware that in some cases underachievement may mask a student's real ability.

Referral by others

Other groups outside of school, e.g. a local brass band, piano teacher, drama groups, can often offer insights into the child's abilities that may not be apparent in school.

Identification by psychologists

Exceptionally able students may be referred and identified by the educational psychological services. These services may also be useful in identifying dual exceptionality (where the child has exceptional ability together with some other special need, e.g. ADHD) or underachieving students. They are also useful in gaining a measure of intelligence and aptitude in different areas.

Teacher referral

Teachers may become aware of an exceptionally able student in their class through his or her performance on assessment tests or exams or through informal observation of the child at work. There are also more structured approaches to observing children. The Nebraska Starry Night: Individual Record Sheet is useful for observing young children. The teacher observes the child over a period of time and puts an X in the relevant area as the behaviour is recorded (see Appendix 6 on www.gillmacmillan.ie/assistingchildrenwithspecialneeds). For older children, general checklists that exist for identifying exceptionally able students across the curriculum could be used. Subject-specific checklists are available for individual subjects such as mathematics, language (mother tongue and modern foreign languages), music, technology, history, religious education, science, geography, art, drama, physical education, social, personal and health education, and information technology (see www.ncca.ie).

School-wide identification processes

Schools should have written policies and procedures on identifying and teaching children with exceptional abilities.

CHARACTERISTICS OF EXCEPTIONALLY ABLE CHILDREN

There can be a perception that students identified as exceptionally able have many special qualities and advantages that will help them to succeed in life. There is a growing recognition, however, that for some students, exceptional ability can bring challenges with it, particularly in the areas of social and emotional development, and that students with exceptional ability need support just as much as students with other special needs.

As exceptionally able students can be vastly different from each other in terms of their characteristics and needs, Betts and Neihart (1988) developed a number of profiles of gifted children to try to better understand this group of children and more accurately address their different needs.

The Successfuls

These students quickly learn what is expected of them from adults, such as parents and teachers, and generally do very well in exams and assessments. However, they are at risk of becoming bored at school and using the system to get by with as little effort as possible. The danger with Successfuls is that they begin to lose their creativity and their desire to engage in independent learning. Most Successfuls will deal very well with primary and secondary school, where learning is often teacher directed, but may struggle in university and later life when they are given much less direction.

The Autonomous Learners

Like the Successfuls, these students have learned to work effectively in the school system. However, unlike the Successfuls, who try to do as little as possible to get by, the Autonomous Learners have learned to use the system to create new learning experiences for themselves and are very enthusiastic about school and learning. They can think for themselves and are intrinsically motivated (from within). They do not just 'work for the tick'. They are well respected by both adults and peers alike and are often given leadership roles in school or within the community, e.g. head prefect.

The Challengings

These students often possess a high degree of creativity but may often get into trouble in school with teachers for questioning authority and consistently challenging the teacher in front of the class. These students do not conform to the system and have not learned how to use it to their own advantage and therefore do not get rewarded by it. Many may struggle with their self-esteem and are sometimes excluded from social groups because they also frequently challenge their peers. Others, however, have a sophisticated sense of humour, which may be appealing to their peers. Challengings are at risk of failing to do well in school or dropping out altogether.

The Undergrounds

These students are usually teenage girls who hide their abilities in order to fit in with less able peers. They may show a marked slump in performance early in secondary school and often feel insecure, anxious, pressurised, confused and guilty. It is very useful if Undergrounds are given opportunities to mix with other students who are also exceptionally able so that they can feel that it is normal and desirable to be good at things.

Dropouts

These students are angry with adults and with themselves because the system has not met their needs for many years and they feel rejected. Many dropouts were once Challengings, but because their needs were not responded to, became frustrated and decided to opt out. These students don't usually come to attention until second level, when they may begin to exhibit certain characteristic behaviours:

- Skipping school or classes
- Failing to complete tasks and doing inconsistent standards of work
- Daydreaming in class
- May become self-abusive
- May become isolated in themselves
- May be very critical of self and others
- Is disruptive
- Functioning at an average or below average level
- Is defensive

The Double Label

These students are exceptionally able but also have another physical, social, emotional or learning disability. Very often, interventions focus exclusively on their disability and their exceptional ability is ignored. This can cause the student to become frustrated, feel powerless and begin to act out as a result.

APPROPRIATE INTERVENTION STRATEGIES

What can schools and individual teachers do?

- Just as there is a staff member in charge of other aspects of school life, there should be a teacher given overall responsibility for children with exceptional abilities.

- Class groupings can be structured in a number of ways.
  - If mixed-ability teaching is the norm in the school, then class and subject teachers need to adapt their teaching to suit the range of abilities in their room.
  - Some schools choose to band students in terms of ability, but the exceptionally able student will still be ahead of most of the students even in the top band, so teachers still need to adapt their teaching accordingly.
  - Some countries, e.g. New Zealand, group exceptionally able students together (top 4 per cent), and even if the group is small they are educated together.
  - Some schools allow exceptionally able students to attend some classes, usually mathematics, with older students, e.g. a second year may attend fifth year mathematics classes.
  - Compacting is another method used in some schools where core work (for examinations) is covered very quickly in order to allow for more advanced study. The pace of these classes can be very fast.
- Teachers of exceptionally able students should give choices about the work being carried out. Choices about subject matter, starting point, learning materials, etc. all promote independent learning and are to be encouraged.
- Teachers should prepare differentiated lesson content. The same topic may be covered using materials requiring different levels of understanding.
- Teachers should make sure students are aware of the high expectations set for them.
- Teachers should try to have a wide variety of learning material available to students, e.g. reference books, internet, etc.
- Set more challenging homework for exceptionally able students so that they can expand on what has been done in class independently.
- Schools sometimes organise extracurricular activities suited to exceptionally able students, e.g. music clubs, chess clubs, debating clubs.

BLOOM'S TAXONOMY OF EDUCATIONAL OBJECTIVES

Bloom's Taxonomy of Educational Objectives, as illustrated below, is made up of six different levels of learning. Objectives closer to the top of the learning pyramid should be set for students with exceptional abilities where possible.

Take the example below of the story *How the Grinch Stole Christmas* – see how the higher objectives from Bloom's taxonomy could be applied to activities based on this story.

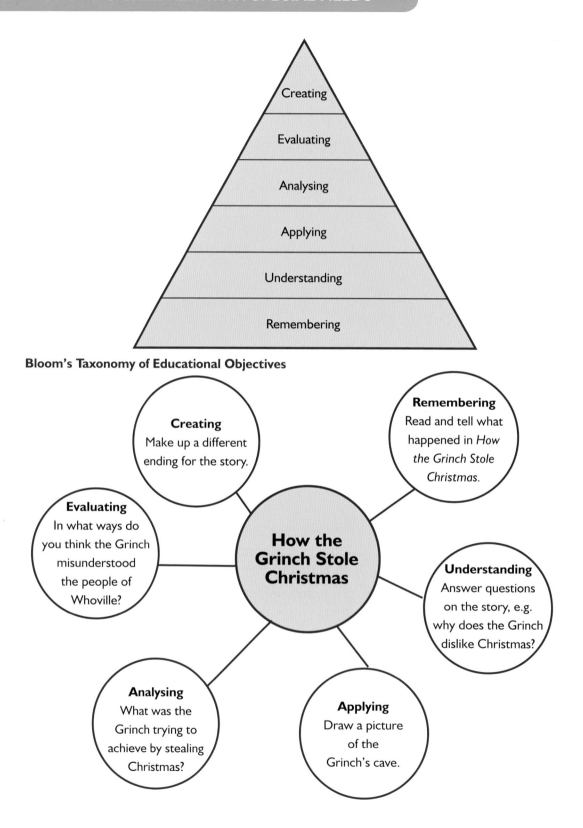

Bloom's Taxonomy of Educational Objectives

Accessibility to the Built Environment

Accessibility to the built environment affects a large number of people in Irish society. The latest census figures indicate that a total of 595,335 people in Ireland have a disability, and of this number, 244,739 have a disability that substantially limits one or more physical activities (Census 2011). The National Disabilities Authority (NDA) was set up under the National Disabilities Authority Act 1999 (see also Chapter 2). The overall function of the NDA is to provide guidance and advice to the government in relation to policies, practices and technical standards with a view to the full inclusion of people with disabilities in all aspects of Irish society, such as employment, housing, support services, transport, ICT and the built environment. This chapter will focus on the built environment.

For many years, inaccessible built environments have restricted the ability of individuals with disabilities to participate fully as citizens in Irish society. In the recent past, however, a number of different Irish policy and legislation documents have been produced and enacted with a view to improving this situation. The **Part M of the Building Regulations (2010) Access and Use** document tries to ensure that buildings are accessible by people with disabilities. There are also a number of pieces of important legislation that provide a legislative framework for organisations to ensure that their premises and services comply with minimum accessibility requirements. The legislation includes the Employment Equality Act 1998, the Equal Status Act 2000 and the Safety and Health and Welfare at Work Act 2005.

While the legislation and the building regulations (2010) cover minimum requirements, the NDA has produced a comprehensive set of best practice guidelines, entitled *Building for Everyone* (NDA 2012). These guidelines are extensive, and while they can be used by everyone, they are primarily aimed at public services and buildings.

THE BUILDING REGULATIONS (2010) – PART M, ACCESS AND USE

The building regulations apply to the construction of new buildings and extensions to buildings. They also apply when the use of a building is being changed, e.g. from a dwelling house into a preschool facility. They do not apply to buildings constructed before 1 June 1992, before the first version of these regulations was published. The latest regulations apply to buildings constructed after 1 January 2012.

Part M of the regulations tries to ensure that:

- Dwelling houses are visitable by people with disabilities
- Buildings other than dwellings are accessible and usable by people with disabilities

To satisfy the requirements of the regulations, all buildings should be designed and constructed so that (a) people with disabilities can safely and independently approach and gain access to the building and (b) elements of the building do not create an undue hazard for people with disabilities, including those who are visually impaired. In addition, non-dwellings should be designed so that (a) people with disabilities can (a) move around within the building and use its facilities, (b) access sanitary accommodation, e.g. toilets, (c) have access to sufficient suitable spectator seating where applicable, and (d) there are suitable aids to communication available for people with a visual or auditory impairment.

The regulations are divided into three sections. The section that applies to a particular building depends on the nature of that building.

- **Section 1:** Buildings other than dwellings and their environs together with common areas of apartment blocks and their environs.
- **Section 2:** Existing buildings other than dwellings and their environs together with common areas of existing apartment blocks and their environs. Section 2 also applies to buildings where there is a reason why some regulations cannot be fully implemented, e.g. change of use of an historic building.
- **Section 3:** Applies to dwellings and their environs. This section deals with individual houses and apartments, but not common areas of apartment blocks.

The rest of this chapter will deal with Section 1 of the regulations only, as these are the requirements applicable to buildings where a special needs assistant is likely to be working, e.g. a school.

Section 1 of the regulations is divided into six sections:

1. Approaches to buildings other than dwellings

2. Access to buildings other than dwellings
3. Circulation within buildings other than dwellings
4. Sanitary facilities for buildings other than dwellings
5. Other facilities in buildings other than dwellings
6. Aids to communication

All six of these sections will now be examined in detail. This information will be useful for completing the access audit part of the assessment requirement for the module Children with Additional Needs (5N2396) (see the section on assessment on www.gillmacmillan.ie/assistingchildrenwithspecialneeds).

I. Approaches to buildings other than dwellings

The aim of this section of the regulations is to ensure that adequate provision is made to enable people with disabilities to safely and independently access and use a building.

- The building should be designed in so far as is possible so that the difference in level between the entrance storey and the site entry point, designated car parking spaces, set down points and assembly points is minimised. Access routes should be as level as possible. A gradient of 1:50 or less is considered level. Changes in level are difficult for many people (wheelchair users, people with walking aids, people pushing buggies or people with a visual impairment) and should be avoided.

- Where a level entrance is not possible, a gently sloping access route is next best. The gradient should be as shallow as possible, generally no steeper than 1:20. This means a rise of 1 metre in height should take 20 metres along the ground.

- Where the gradient is greater than 1:20, an access ramp needs to be provided. The ramp surface should be suitable for wheelchair traffic and should reduce the risk of slipping. Slopes and landings should be at least 1.5 metres wide. Ideally, gradients on the ramp should not be steeper than 1:20. In exceptional circumstances where there are no alternatives, slopes of 1:12 are permitted provided sloped sections are not any longer than 2 metres. These requirements ensure that a wheelchair user does not have to push up steep slopes for long distances without flat sections for rest. Steps should also be provided, as some people find these easier.

- Level landings at the top and bottom of ramps should be at least 1.8 metres long and 1.8 metres wide. Intermediate landings should be at least 1.5 metres long and clear of any door swings or other obstructions. They need to be as big as top and bottom landings if they need to act as passing places or the ramp has three flights or more.

) Any open sides must have a raised kerb 100mm high. Where a gradient is steeper than 1:20, a suitable continuous handrail should be provided.

) An alternative means of access for wheelchair users should be provided, e.g. a platform lift, where the total rise of the ramp gradient is greater than 1:20 and the total rise is greater than 2 metres.

) On circulation routes, e.g. entrances or footpaths around buildings, building features that could present a hazard to people with disabilities, particularly those with a visual impairment, should be avoided. Such hazards include windows or doors that open outwards. If balconies or other protrusions exist, there needs to be 2.2 metres of headroom clearance. If windows do open out (see the diagram below), then guarding, planting or another barrier needs to be in place to prevent someone walking into it.

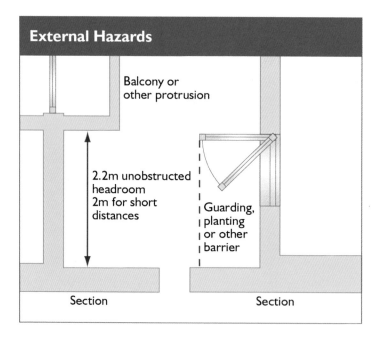

Street furniture, such as lighting columns, signposts, litter bins, seats, etc., should be located on or beyond the boundaries of the access routes, not obstructing them.

) Low-level posts such as bollards should not be located within an access route and should contrast visually with their background. They should not be linked with chains, as this can be hazardous for people who are visually impaired.

⟩ Drainage gratings should be positioned beyond the boundaries of access routes. If this is not possible, they should be flush with the surrounding surface. This is to minimise the risk of trapping canes or wheelchair wheels and to minimise the risk of visually impaired people tripping as a result of them. Dished channels should not be used within access routes to avoid tripping.

⟩ Access routes should be surfaced with firm, reasonably smooth and durable material. Loose pebbles should not be used. The surface should be slip resistant, especially when wet.

⟩ Passing places should be provided along access routes for wheelchair users. These places should be at least 2,000mm long and 1,800mm wide. This allows two wheelchair users to pass one another.

⟩ The danger of walking into a vehicular route should be minimised by providing an additional pedestrian route. Otherwise, tactile paving should be installed to warn people with a visual impairment that they are entering a vehicular route.

⟩ Access routes should be well lit.

⟩ Stepped access routes should have a minimum clear width of 1,200mm or more. Landings of at least 1,200mm should be provided at the top and bottom of each flight. Tactile hazard warning surfaces (e.g. corduroy) should be incorporated into both the top and bottom landings.

⟩ There should be no single steps. The rise in a flight of steps should not exceed 1.5 metres. A single flight can contain up to 18 risers if the going (the part you put your foot on) is 350mm or greater. The wider going allows people with mobility issues to stop and rest with both their feet fully on the step.

⟩ Step nosings (the edge of the step) should incorporate a permanently contrasting continuous material. The surface of threads should be slip resistant, especially when wet. Projecting or overhanging step nosings should be avoided, as should tapered threads and open risers.

⟩ The rise of each step should be the same (between 150mm and 180mm) and the going on each step should be between 300mm and 450mm. There should be a continuous handrail on both sides of flights and on landings.

⟩ Handrails should comply with the following regulations:
  – Handrails on stairs should be at a height of between 900mm and 1,000mm from the pitch line and between 900mm and 1,100mm on landings.
  – Where a second handrail is provided for children or adults of short stature, they should be at a height of between 600mm and 700mm.
  – Where there are two or more flights, handrails should be continuous.
  – Handrails should contrast against their background without being reflective.

Stepped Access – Key dimensions and use of hazard warning surface

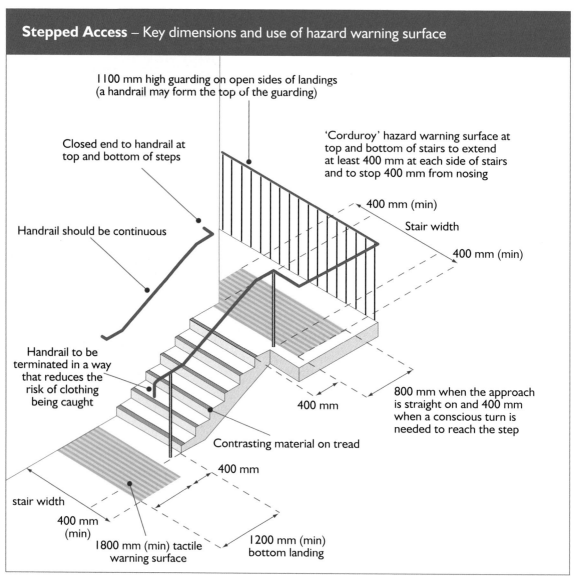

1100 mm high guarding on open sides of landings (a handrail may form the top of the guarding)

Closed end to handrail at top and bottom of steps

'Corduroy' hazard warning surface at top and bottom of stairs to extend at least 400 mm at each side of stairs and to stop 400 mm from nosing

400 mm (min)

Stair width

400 mm (min)

Handrail should be continuous

Handrail to be terminated in a way that reduces the risk of clothing being caught

400 mm

800 mm when the approach is straight on and 400 mm when a conscious turn is needed to reach the step

Contrasting material on tread

400 mm

stair width

400 mm (min)

1800 mm (min) tactile warning surface

1200 mm (min) bottom landing

– Handrails should be circular with a diameter of between 40mm and 50mm. They should not protrude more than 100mm out. There should be a gap of between 50mm and 60mm between the handrail and the wall to which it is fixed.

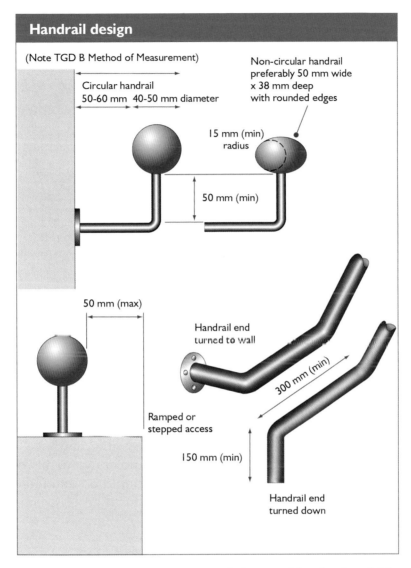

Handrail design

(Note TGD B Method of Measurement)

Circular handrail
50-60 mm 40-50 mm diameter

Non-circular handrail
preferably 50 mm wide
x 38 mm deep
with rounded edges

15 mm (min)
radius

50 mm (min)

50 mm (max)

Handrail end
turned to wall

300 mm (min)

Ramped or
stepped access

150 mm (min)

Handrail end
turned down

- At pedestrian crossings, tactile paving and dropped kerbs should be provided.
- Designated parking spaces should be provided as a percentage of overall parking spaces (5 per cent), with a minimum provision of at least one space. Where designated parking is provided, it should be easily located and clearly marked (on the ground and with additional signage if necessary) The minimum dimensions of designated parking bays are indicated on the diagram below. All bays should be located on firm, level ground and be the bays closest to the entrance. Dropped kerbs should be provided from the bay to the access route. Where ticket machines are present, at least one should be located near the designated parking bay with controls at a level of between 750mm and 1,200mm

above the ground. There should be a clear space in front of the machine 1,850mm x 2,100mm long.

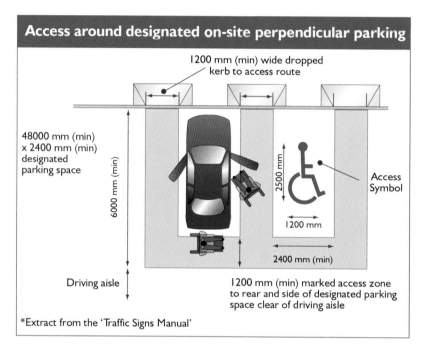

Where there is a road on site leading to a building, there should be a set down area provided at or adjacent to at least one accessible entrance. This allows a person who is a passenger in a vehicle to safely and conveniently alight from the vehicle and enter the building. Set down areas should be marked and should be located on firm, level ground. They should not form an obstruction to through traffic.

2. Access to buildings other than dwellings

The aim of this section of the regulations is to ensure that everyone can independently access entrances to buildings, thus avoiding segregation based on ability.

The regulations state that all of the following entrances should be accessible to people with disabilities except in exceptional circumstances where factors such as steeply sloping sites or planning restrictions do not permit it. This is to avoid segregating entrance to a building based on ability.

- The main entrance that a visitor not familiar with a building would normally expect to approach
- The entrance closest to the designated parking area

⏵ The entrance closest to the designated set down area

⏵ Any entrance with a unique main function, e.g. the entrance to a particular department in a hospital

⏵ Entrances exclusively used by staff

⏵ Exits to assembly points (fire) or to the boundary of the site

Accessible entrances

⏵ Entrances should be clearly signed and easily seen.

⏵ A level landing at least 1,800mm x 1,800mm clear of any door or gate swing should be provided immediately in front of the entrance.

⏵ The door entry system should be accessible to a wide range of abilities. Particular attention should be give to the needs of people with additional mobility, hearing and visual needs.

⏵ Any structural supports, e.g. columns, should not present a hazard to people with a visual impairment.

⏵ The surface of the floor of the entrance should not impede the movement of wheelchairs or mobility aids. It should not present a tripping hazard. Where mat wells are provided, they should be level with the floor they are in. Finish material should be firm.

⏵ Manually operated external doors with a self-closing device can pose difficulties for a wide range of people, including children. If the force required for opening the door is too great and the speed of closing too fast, people with disabilities can be thrown off balance. Revolving doors are not considered suitable either.

Power door manually controlled – with easily seen button

⏵ Entrance doors should have controlled closing devices to allow independent use by everyone, regardless of ability.

- Powered door opening and closing systems are accessible to a wide range of people, as they require little, if any, strength to open. Powered sliding doors, either manually or sensory controlled, are preferred.
- Where powered doors are manually controlled, the control should be operable using a closed fist. Controls should contrast visually with the surrounding background.

Where an accessible entrance door is provided:
- Doorways should have a minimum clear opening width of 800mm. With double doors, at least one leaf should provide this minimum. Doorways used by the general public should be 1,000mm minimum.
- Door handles should be located between 800mm and 1,050mm above floor level.
- Where possible, there should be a glazed vision panel(s) extending within the zone 500mm to 1.5 metres above the finished floor level. This allows for visibility to the opposite side of the door (see the door pictured below).
- There should be at least 300mm of unobstructed space on the side next to the leading edge of a single leaf door.
- Doors that are fully glazed must have permanent markings within two zones from 850mm to 1,000mm and from 1,400mm to 1,600mm above the floor to indicate that they are glazed. This increases the visibility of glass.
- Ironmongery (handles) on doors must be suitable for operation by people with disabilities. They should be operable with one hand and visually contrast with the door.
- Entrance lobbies should be designed and constructed to allow wheelchair users and a person assisting them to move clear of one door before using the next one while allowing space for another person to pass in the opposite direction.

Some entrance lobbies will have an external entrance door, an entrance lobby and then an internal entrance door. This arrangement serves a number of functions, e.g. air infiltration and draught reduction. The main issue with entrance lobbies is their size. Where an entrance lobby is too small, accessibility issues arise for wheelchair users. Floor surfaces of entrance lobbies should help remove rainwater from shoes and wheelchairs. If mat wells are provided, they must be level with the floor so as to prevent them from becoming a tripping hazard and the mats themselves should be firm to prevent wheelchair wheels from sinking into them. Generally, a lobby space should be at least 300mm wide by 1,570mm long.

Glazed vision panel in door

3. Circulation within buildings other than dwellings

The aim of this section of the regulations is to help ensure that people of all abilities can travel horizontally and vertically within a building, making use of all facilities.

Reception area

The reception area should be easily identifiable as such. Concise signs and universally accepted symbols indicating other parts of the building should be provided.

   Reception desks should be designed in such a way as to facilitate everyone.

- In order to facilitate wheelchair users, reception desks should have a clear man-oeuvring space in front of them – 1,200mm x 1,800mm wide if there is a knee recess (at least 500mm deep) and 1,400mm x 2,200mm wide if no recess exists.

- Desks or counters should be designed to suit people standing and sitting. Desks should therefore have two levels: 950mm to 1,100mm for people standing and 760mm maximum for wheelchair users and people of short stature. Knee recesses should be provided on either side of the counter to facilitate customers and staff not less than 700mm above floor level. In cases where there is no necessity to sign or transact business across a desk, then a knee recess on the staff side of the counter only is required.

- A hearing enhancement system should be installed and clear signage provided to indicate its presence.

▷ Glazed screens in front of reception desks should be avoided except for when they are required for security reasons. Reflective patterned surfaces behind reception should be avoided, as this makes signing and lip reading more difficult.

Internal doors

▷ Internal doors, particularly self-closing doors with strong hinges, can create barriers for people with limited upper body strength and should only be used where necessary, e.g. fire barriers.

▷ Where practicable, internal doors should be held open with a specialised device, automatically closing the door in the event of a fire. In terms of width, internal doors must meet the same requirements as external doors described above.

Corridors or passageways

▷ A clear, unobstructed corridor or passageways width of 1,500mm allows a wheelchair user and an ambulant person to pass each other. A width of 1,800mm is required for two wheelchair users to pass. The regulations require a minimum width of 1,200mm and regular passing places should be provided if the wider options are not possible.

▷ Where corners exist on corridors or passageways, a turning circle of 1,800mm minimum is required.

▷ Seating and handrails should be provided in long corridors, i.e. over 20 metres. Minimum clear corridor width should still be maintained.

▷ Floors should be level. If there are gently sloping areas, rest areas should be provided. If the gradient is greater than 1:20, then the area should be considered a ramp and must follow the regulations for these (described in section 1). Floor finishes should be slip resistant.

▷ Any door opening out onto the corridor or passageway should be recessed so that when it is fully open it does not jut out into the corridor. Exceptions are for smaller doors into store cupboards, etc.

▷ Corridors and passageways should be adequately lit.

A suitable passenger lift should be provided to any storey above or below the entrance storey where the net floor area of the building exceeds the following figures: (a) each floor of a two-storey building is more than 280m^2 or (b) 200m^2 in a building of more than two storeys.

▷ In the case of flats, a lift should be provided when the total number of flats above the entrance storey exceeds eight or the number of flats 10 metres or more above the entrance storey exceeds two.

The location of the lift in a building should be clearly indicated. There should be a clear area 1.5 metres x 1.5 metres in front of each entrance to the lift. Lift doors should have a clear opening width of 800mm. The width of a car lift should be at least 1.1 metres wide and 1.4 metres long. Lift controls should be at least 900mm from floor level and not more than 1.2 metres. Controls should not be located in corners. Suitable tactile indictors should be provided to indicate floor numbers, and if the lift serves more than one floor, then floor numbers should be visually and voice indicated. Lift doors should stay open for at least eight seconds. A half-length mirror should be provided on the back wall of the lift so that wheelchair users can safely reverse out.

Where a lift does not have to be provided, internal stairs should be provided that are suitable for the needs of ambulant disabled people. The rise of flight between landings (where the person can rest) should not exceed 1.8 metres. The rise of each step should be uniform and not greater than 175mm and the going (where you put your foot) not less than 250mm. A suitable continuous handrail should be provided.

Where the area beneath the stairs has a height of less than 2,100mm, it needs to be enclosed or guarded to prevent people from walking into it.

Use of facilities in a building

Each storey of a building should be designed and constructed so that people with disabilities can independently circulate and use the services and facilities on that storey. If there is a change of level within a storey, then sloped access, a passenger lift or platform lift should be available. Either this or the same range of services and facilities should be available on both levels.

Ironmongery, taps, light switches, power points, etc. should be located at a level that does not require wheelchair users to stoop or stretch unduly. Light pressure only should be required for their operation.

4. Sanitary facilities for buildings other than dwellings

General provision

Provision of sanitary accommodation for people with disabilities should be made on the same basis as provision made for other users of the building. For example, if an office building provides sanitary accommodation for staff only, then provision for staff with disabilities should be made regardless of whether any member of staff has a disability. Likewise, if sanitary facilities are provided for customers or visitors to the building, then provision should be made for customers or visitors with disabilities.

▶ In primary school classrooms where WC facilities are part of the classroom environment, provision should be made for one WC suitable for an ambulant disabled person within the classroom environment together with at least one wheelchair-accessible unisex WC positioned either as part of the classroom environment or situated in the common areas of the building.

▶ The number and location of sanitary facilities will depend on the nature of the building, the size of the building and the numbers using the building. When wheelchair sanitary accommodation is unisex, it should be approached separately from other sanitary accommodation, i.e. it should not be located in either the male or female toilet block. It should be well signposted.

▶ For a WC cubicle to be suitable for a wheelchair user, it must be big enough for necessary wheelchair manoeuvre and for transfer onto the WC by either the wheelchair user themselves or with assistance from a helper. In buildings with a net square area of over 200m^2, cubicles should be 1,800mm x 2,500mm. In smaller buildings, the required size is 1,500mm x 2,200mm.

▶ Doors into wheelchair-accessible WC facilities should open outwards or slide sideways. The door should have an emergency release mechanism, e.g. lift off hinges in case a user fell behind the door and could not get up. It should have a horizontal rail for pulling the door closed and an easy lock mechanism.

Inside the cubicle

▶ An emergency pull cord is required with visible and audible indicators to show it has been activated.

▶ The fire alarm signal must be both visible and audible from inside the cubicle.

▶ The floor surface of the cubicle must be firm, level and slip resistant. It must also contrast visually with the walls and fittings.

▶ A shelf (or two if the cistern is not suitable for use as a shelf) must be provided for personal effects, e.g. a handbag, and a separate colostomy changing surface.

▶ Two clothes hooks – one at 1,400mm and another at 1,050mm above floor level – should be provided.

▶ Where there is only one WC for use by everyone, a standing height wash basin and a finger rinse basin should be provided.

Wheelchair accessible unisex WC (1800 mm x 1800 mm turning space)

Additional width required for larger washbasin (provide mirror, paper towel dispenser and soap dispenser alongside)

Horizontal pull rail

500 mm (min)

Sanitary dispenser

1800 mm x 1800 mm (min) wheelchair turning space

Disposal bin

Shelf

2500 mm (min) (Refer to Diagram 16 for details of fittings on this wall)

Mirror

Wall A (See Diagram 16)

2 No. clothes hooks fixed at 1050 mm and 1400 mm above floor level

Hand rinse basin*

**(See notes below)

Vertical grab rails

Alarm pull cord

140-180 mm

Horizontal grab rail

750 mm

Drop down rail

50–60 mm

500 mm

Vertical grab rail

150 mm

320 mm

500 mm

200–250 mm

Sanitary disposal unit

970 mm

Alternative position for alarm pull cord

Colostomy changing shelf**

1800 mm (min)

2300 mm (min) for larger washbasin

NOTE:
Example layout shown for right-hand transfer to WC
The overall dimensions should exclude such items as heat emitters, skirting boards tiles and boxing in of pipework. Adjustments in room sizes will be needed to accommodate these items.
*The tap on the hand rinse basin should be positioned on the side closest to the WC.
**Where high or low level cisterns are used, a rail with a padded back rest and a separate colostomy changing shelf 125 mm to 150 mm deep x 400 mm (min) wide with its surface 950 mm above floor level should be provided. Where a flat-topped close-coupled cistern is used, the cistern should be adequate to also act as a back rest. IF the top of the cistern is flat it should be adequate to facilitate a colostomy changing surface for standing users without the extra requirement for a separate shelf.

- WC flush mechanisms and taps on basins should require little strength or dexterity to operate. Spatula-shaped flush handles and taps are preferable. The flush handle must be on the transfer side of the WC.

- Where a building has more than one cubicle suitable for a wheelchair user, the internal layout of the cubicles should provide for both left- and right-hand transfer onto the WC.

- The front of the WC pan should be a minimum of 750mm from the back wall of the cubicle. This allows the wheelchair user to reverse against the wall parallel to the WC pan. The pan should be at a height of 480mm from floor level.

- The distance between the front edge of the WC and the front edge of the finger rinse basin should be between 140mm and 160mm. This is to allow for use of the finger rinse basin while seated on the WC.

- There should be a vertical grab rail at a distance of 200mm from the front of the WC pan so that the wheelchair user does not have to reach backwards for support when transferring back into their wheelchair. The grab rail should be 600mm long and strong enough to withstand the user's weight.

- Where provision for ambulant disabled people is required, suitable grab rails should be provided in conventional WC cubicles.

5. Other facilities in buildings other than dwellings

This section of the regulations deals with the following:

1. Audience and spectator facilities with fixed seating
2. Audience and spectator facilities without fixed seating
3. Refreshment facilities
4. Accessible sleeping accommodation
5. Switches, outlets and controls

- Generally, 1 per cent of audience and spectator seating needs to be wheelchair accessible, with additional space provided as required.

- Passageways to this seating should be clearly signed and totally wheelchair accessible. There should be some standard seating in the location too for a friend or helper to accompany the wheelchair user and to avoid segregation. Wheelchair users should have an unobstructed view of the event.

- Where there is a raised podium, e.g. in a lecture theatre, it should be accessible via a ramp or platform lift.

- A hearing enhancement system should be installed. This does not include classrooms in primary or post-primary schools or offices.

〉 Where refreshment facilities are provided, e.g. bars and restaurants, all areas of the facility should be accessible. A section of the serving area, e.g. a bar counter, should be at a height of 850mm to facilitate someone in a wheelchair requiring service.

〉 Where sleeping accommodation is provided, doorways into the accommodation should be at least 800mm wide with an easy-to-use locking mechanism. Rooms should have a visual and auditory fire alarm system. En-suite facilities should comply with the sanitary regulations above.

〉 Socket outlets should be located between 400mm and 1,200mm above floor level, with a preference for the lower end of the range. Switches for lighting and permanently wired appliances should be located between 400mm and 1,200mm above the floor, unless needed at a higher level for particular appliances. All switches and controls that require precise hand movements should be located between 750mm and 1,200mm above the floor, e.g. controls for heating systems. The majority of controls should be of a push button variety, not requiring manual dexterity.

6. Aids to communication

Signage, visual contrast, lighting and audible aids assist people in accessing a building and fully utilising its relevant facilities.

〉 In terms of signage, important messages may have to be relayed using visual, tactile and auditory means. Signs should be as clear and as short as possible. Text should not be set entirely in capital letters, as this makes letter shapes more difficult to make out. International symbols for important features should be used, e.g. for sanitary accommodation. The presence of a hearing enhancement system should be indicated if it exists.

〉 Visual contrast is very important for people with a visual impairment, e.g. the handle contrasting visually with the door or the nosing on a step contrasting with the rest of the step.

〉 Well-designed lighting can assist people's mobility around a building as well as identify hazards and provide a better environment for lip reading or signing.

〉 Hearing enhancement systems should be installed in important areas, e.g. reception areas.

BUILDING FOR EVERYONE

As noted earlier, the building regulations state the minimum legal requirements regarding access for people with disabilities. The National Disabilities Authority

(NDA) has produced a much more extensive and comprehensive set of best practice guidelines, entitled *Building for Everyone* (NDA 2012). These guidelines can be viewed and downloaded at www.universaldesign.ie/buildingforeveryone. The guidelines are laid out in a series of 10 booklets:

- Booklet 1: External Environment
- Booklet 2: Entrances and Horizontal Circulation
- Booklet 3: Vertical Circulation
- Booklet 4: Internal Environment and Services
- Booklet 5: Sanitary Facilities
- Booklet 6: Facilities
- Booklet 7: Building Types
- Booklet 8: Building Management
- Booklet 9: Planning
- Booklet 10: Index and Terminology

The *Building for Everyone* guidelines are very detailed, extending to almost 1,000 pages. While they may be too detailed to be used in their entirety for the access audit required by the module Children with Additional Needs, they can be referred to for specific requirements, as they contain good diagrams and colour photographs illustrating examples of good practice.

chapter eleven

Responding to Special Needs

RESOURCES, SERVICES AND FACILITIES AVAILABLE TO CHILDREN WITH SPECIAL NEEDS

Generally, resources, services and facilities available to children with special needs are provided by the following government departments along with the voluntary sector.

▷ Department of Education and Skills
▷ Department of Health and Children
▷ Department of Social Protection (allowances and entitlements)
▷ Voluntary sector (generally part government funded and part funded by public donations)

This section outlines the resources, services and facilities available to children with special needs under each of these headings. The list is not exhaustive, but seeks to give a good general overview.

DEPARTMENT OF EDUCATION AND SKILLS (DES)

The resources, services and facilities available to children with special needs through the DES have all been dealt with in previous chapters (Chapter 3 on the structures within Irish special education, and also in Chapters 4 to 9 detailing each individual special need). To summarise here, the following is a list of the resources, services and facilities currently available.

Resources

▸ The main resource offered by the DES is its teaching and support personnel (described below under Services).

▸ Schools can avail of money under a **minor works grant** to make adaptations to their school for children with disabilities, e.g. a wheelchair ramp, automatic doors.

▸ **Grants are available for the purchase of assistive technology** or equipment in schools, e.g. laptops for students with particular special needs. What is covered by these grants and how they may be applied for are explained in circular M14/05, which can be downloaded in full from www.education.ie. Basically, grants are available towards the purchase of equipment for pupils to use in schools who have been diagnosed as having serious physical and/or communicative disabilities of a degree that makes ordinary communication through speech and/or writing impossible for them. Following the establishment of the National Council for Special Education, all applications for special equipment must be submitted by school management authorities to the special educational needs organiser (SENO) with assigned responsibility for the school. The rate of grant in respect of any pupil will be the cost of the equipment, subject in general to a maximum grant of €3,800. In relation to pupils with a visual impairment (VI) and hearing impairment (HI), the Visiting Teacher Service assesses and gives advice to the SENO in relation to equipment commonly used, e.g. technology, large print, tapes, Braillers, audiology equipment. The SENO will take account of the visiting teacher's recommendations when considering applications for equipment for such pupils.

▸ Grants are available to schools for the purchase of test materials by guidance and counselling teachers (dealt with by DES circular 0099/2007).

▸ Schoolbooks grant for students in need – for full details, see DES circular 0049/2008 (primary schools) and 0023/2008 (post-primary).

Services

▸ **National Council for Special Education (NCSE):** Processes applications for additional services and resources in schools.

▸ **Regional Special Educational Needs Organisers (SENOs):** Liaise locally with schools in processing applications for resources and services.

- **National Educational Psychological Service (NEPS):** Provides educational psychologists to schools for assessment of needs and advice on how best to fulfil those needs.

- **School principals:** Are responsible for working with the SENO in order to secure resources, facilities and services for children with special needs attending their school.

- **Class teachers:** Are responsible for adapting their teaching to suit the needs of all children, including those with special needs, and also for bringing the additional needs of some students to the attention of their parents and the school principal so that extra help may be sought.

- **Learning support teachers:** Work with children with high incidence special needs in order to support and help them make better progress in school.

- **Resource teachers:** Work with children with low incidence special needs (up to five hours per week) to support their learning.

- **Language support teachers for children with English as an additional language:** These are available to children for the first two years of being in a school (or for a shorter time if they no longer have a special language need). If a school believes a child needs additional support after a two-year period, then the school has to carry out assessments (using a language assessment kit provided to schools). The number of teachers employed in this capacity in any particular school will depend on the number of children attending. Schools with fewer than 14 children will be allocated part-time hours, schools with 14 to 30 pupils get one full-time teacher and schools with 31 to 90 pupils have two full-time teachers. Schools with greater numbers than this get an allocation calculated on numbers and also how long individual students have been getting the support.

- **Special needs assistants:** Work with children with either significant care needs or severe emotional or behavioural needs in either a mainstream, special class or special school setting.

- Students with special needs can avail of **reasonable accommodations** in state exams to remove the impact of the child's special need on their performance in the examinations but without giving him or her an unfair advantage over those not receiving such accommodations. Examples of reasonable accommodations include exemptions from certain examination components, modified papers, reader, scribe, individual examination centre, etc. For a full description of the reasonable accommodations available, see Chapter 3.

- In addition to the normal **school transport service**, there is also a service for students attending special schools or schools with special classes. A supervised transport service is also available for children who require it as well as harnesses, if needed. In some parts of the country there is a special school transport scheme for Traveller children in an effort to encourage better school attendance among these children. Applications for special school transport schemes should be made through the local SENO.

◗ While individual education plans (IEPs) are recommended by the EPSEN Act 2004 and are standard practice in many nations, e.g. the US, UK, Australia, Canada and New Zealand, they are not legally required in Irish schools for children with special needs. Having said this, most schools will develop education plans for all children in their school with special needs because it is good practice to do so. An IEP sets out a plan of work for the child **in addition to** the normal curriculum-based class work that the child will be doing anyway. For example, a goal for a child with ADHD may be 'to be able to sit and listen to instruction and to manage his or her own behaviour (reduce impulsivity)'. The plan would outline the strategies that would be employed in order to achieve this goal.

Note: The National Council for Special Education has produced a booklet called *Guidelines on the Individual Education Plan Process* (2006). This booklet was sent to all schools in October 2009 but is also available from NCSE, 1–2 Mill Street, Trim, Co. Meath.

Facilities

The DES offers a range of different facilities for children with special needs:

◗ Placement within a mainstream school with additional supports, e.g. learning support, resource teaching and an SNA

◗ Placement within a mainstream school in a special class with a full-time resource teacher and usually an SNA

◗ Placement within a special school, usually with the support of an SNA

◗ Placement within a voluntary sector school (with government funding), e.g. ABA schools for children with autism

Home Tuition Scheme

This scheme is intended to provide a compensatory education service to:

◗ Children with a significant medical condition that is likely to cause major disruption to their attendance on an ongoing basis

◗ Children aged two and a half to five years who have been assessed by the HSE as having an autistic spectrum disorder (ASD) requiring early intervention

- Sometimes this scheme is used as an interim measure for children awaiting an appropriate educational placement

Allocation of hours

- The maximum allocation of home tuition hours for children with a medical ailment is 10 hours per week, with the allocation reflecting the level of attendance.
- The maximum allocation of home tuition hours for children awaiting an appropriate placement is 20 hours per week, subject to the appropriate school calendar.
- The allocation for children with ASD up to three years of age is 10 hours' tuition per week and is intended to provide an individualised early educational intervention programme. This increases to 20 hours per week once the child is three years of age, provided that he or she is not enrolled in an early intervention class. Where a child is attending a Health Service Executive (HSE) early intervention service/preschool, attendance will be taken into consideration in determining allocation. Home tuition ceases in the summer following a child's fifth birthday, or earlier where a place in an ASD class is available.

Qualifications of tutors

It is most desirable if tuition is provided by a qualified teacher. If this is not possible, then other suitably qualified people may be employed, e.g. someone with a BA in psychology.

DEPARTMENT OF HEALTH AND CHILDREN

The HSE organises and administers all resources, services and facilities provided by the Department of Health and Children for children with special needs. Below is a list and brief description of these resources, services and facilities. This list is not exhaustive but includes what is principally available.

Resources

The principal resource provided by the HSE to children with special needs is the time and expertise of the service providers listed below. In addition, the HSE provides medications, medical aids and devices, e.g. hearing aids, electronically controlled wheelchairs, home nursing care and equipment such as nebulizers.

Services

The **family support services** provide a wide range of services to children and their families, including the following.

Family support services for families at risk

This service offers therapeutic work, parent education courses and home-based parent and family support (where a support worker actually offers help in the family home). In terms of special needs, this service could be useful for the family of children with emotional and behavioural problems, as frequently the child's home environment is contributing to their problems in school and other settings. Foster care and residential care are also offered for children who are either at risk themselves or pose a risk to their families because of their behaviour. The family support service also offers various interventions to promote the development and education of children from disadvantaged backgrounds. Interventions include measures such as crèches, nurseries, play groups, preschools, homework clubs, after-school clubs, home–school liaison services, alternative school projects, youth and community work, etc. In terms of special education needs, these interventions can help prevent or reduce the occurrence of particular special needs, e.g. literacy difficulties, behavioural and emotional problems.

Child protection and social work services

These are based at 32 Local Health Offices around the country that help protect children at risk of abuse and/or neglect.

Child and adolescent health services

The **child and adolescent health services** provide a range of different services related to children with special needs.

- **Addiction services:** Some HSE areas provide addiction counselling services to under-18s on an outpatient basis.
- **Dental care:** Good dental care is important for all children, but particularly for some children with special needs. Free dental and orthodontic treatment is available to all children under the age of 18, although there are long waiting lists for some treatments, e.g. orthodontic treatments.

Child and adolescent mental health services

In addition, the **child and adolescent mental health services** operates nationwide, although the extent and type of provision varies considerably and largely depends on the area of the country the child is living in. This service is for children and adolescents up to the age of 16 and their families. This service works with children and their families for a wide variety of reasons. These may include:

- Self-harm and attempted suicides
- Depression
- Fear, phobias or anxiety
- Post-traumatic stress disorder
- Bereavement or separation
- Eating disorders, e.g. anorexia or bulimia
- Difficulties at school
- School refusal
- Behaviour difficulties
- Temper tantrums
- Attention deficit hyperactivity disorder
- Autistic spectrum disorder
- Aggressive behaviour

Therapies offered include:
- Individual counselling and psychotherapy
- Family therapy
- Art and play therapy
- Cognitive behaviour therapy
- Group therapy
- Parenting courses
- In some situations, medication may be suggested or prescribed. This happens only after a full assessment and discussions with parents.

Staff offering these service include consultant child psychiatrists, clinical psychologists, clinical nurse specialists, social workers, family therapists, psychiatric nurses, childcare workers and administrative staff.

Disability services

The disability services provide a range of services to children with special needs, e.g. medical and surgical aids and appliances, such as wheelchairs. They also provide respite care for families caring for a child with certain special needs, e.g. autism. The child is usually cared for by a 'host family' overnight or for a few days in order to give the child's family a break. With some of the more severe special needs, e.g. moderate general learning disability, after the child reaches 18 years of age, the disability services may provide semi-independent living accommodation and care for him or her if required.

Respite care

Respite care may involve providing alternative family or institutional care for a person with a disability in order to enable the carer to take a short break, a holiday or a rest. It can cover very short-term respite, e.g. a babysitter for an evening, or a much longer arrangement for a holiday. Schemes of respite care are sometimes called Breakaway or Friendship schemes. Respite care or temporary care in Ireland may be based in the community or in an institution. In practice, respite care is provided to a varying degree at a number of locations around the country, in some cases by your HSE area and in others by voluntary organisations.

Eye test

The Community Ophthalmology Service is provided if a child is established as having a visual defect. The child is seen approximately every four to six months and undergoes supervision to ensure that the visual acuity is improving with the use of spectacles and/or occlusion therapy (patching).

General practitioner service

The general practitioner (GP) has a critical role in the Child Health Screening and Surveillance and Immunisation Programme. The Maternity and Infant Care Scheme provides an agreed programme of care to all expectant mothers who are ordinarily resident in Ireland free of charge. The GP provides an initial examination, if possible before 12 weeks, and a further six examinations during the pregnancy, which are alternated with visits to the maternity unit/hospital. If an expectant mother suffers from a significant illness, e.g. diabetes or hypertension, up to five additional visits to the GP may be provided. The scheme also provides for two postnatal GP visits. In terms of special needs, the GP is often the first person that worried parents contact in relation to the child. If a special need is suspected, then it is the GP's duty to refer the child on to the appropriate service.

Hearing test

The primary focus of the Paediatric Audiology Service (hearing tests) is to detect children who have permanent hearing loss. All children suspected of having a hearing loss are given a hearing test suited to their developmental age. If a loss is detected, their parents or guardians are given a diagnosis as to the type and severity of the hearing loss, i.e. temporary (conductive) or permanent (sensorineural). Management of cases may involve giving advice and information, onward referral and provision of hearing aids.

Immunisation

Vaccinations under the Childhood Immunisation Programme in Ireland are provided free of charge to all children. The Childhood Immunisation Programme protects children from tuberculosis, diphtheria, tetanus, whooping cough (pertussis), HiB (haemophilus influenzae B), polio, meningitis C, measles, mumps and rubella. In terms of special needs, this programme is vital for the prevention of infections that can cause developmental problems, e.g. deafness because of rubella infection.

Nutrition and dietetics

Hospital dieticians and nutritionists provide advice and guidance to individuals both inside and outside of the hospital setting. This service is particularly important for children with special needs such as cystic fibrosis and diabetes, where dietary factors are vital to good health.

Occupational therapy

The occupational therapy service assesses and treats children who have a range of difficulties, such as dyspraxia, developmental co-ordination disorders, poor fine or gross motor skills, perceptual difficulties, poor concentration and poor eye movement co-ordination. The primary goal for children is to help them develop, restore and maintain skills, behaviours and relationships necessary for independent living. The children who avail of the service typically have difficulties with academic, behavioural and handwriting issues or problems with self-care, including dressing, bathing and eating. The service is engaged in follow-up to initial assessments by occupational therapists, to fit prescribed equipment for clients in their homes and to train and supervise equipment use. The occupational therapy services are increasingly aware of the prevalence of children who have multiple problems who need a holistic therapeutic approach encompassing other disciplines.

Physiotherapy

Physiotherapy services are generally provided in hospitals, usually on an outpatient basis. Physiotherapists work with children with special needs such as cerebral palsy and cystic fibrosis using mainly physical means such as exercise, manipulation and massage. Physiotherapy is free to children and all medical card holders.

Psychology service

The community psychology service has a focus on prevention, assessment, early detection and intervention for children in difficulty who may be out of home and who are identified as being at risk or in need of protection.

Public health nurse

The public health nursing service is responsible for child health monitoring, which involves a programme of screening interventions and support for parents, starting at birth and extending through the preschool years. In total there are nine timed age-related visits offered to children under the Child Health Surveillance Screening Programme (CHSS). Public health nurses are often the first point of contact with the HSE.

Speech and language therapy

Speech and language therapy is specifically concerned with the assessment, diagnosis and management of those who have speech and/or language impairments. Speech and language impairment is one of the most common types of disorders in childhood. Young children who have speech and language difficulties are at risk of continued communication problems as well as for associated cognitive, behavioural, social and psychiatric difficulties. Language-impaired children are also at high risk for learning difficulties and behavioural problems. This service concerns itself with the prevention and early detection of communication problems, the education of other professionals, parents and teachers and the clinical training of undergraduate therapists. The speech and language therapy services see client groups with the following presentations:

- Phonological (speech-sound) impairment
- Developmental language difficulties
- Specific speech and language impairment
- Fluency/stammering
- Autistic spectrum disorder

- Written language disorder
- Cleft palate
- Learning disability
- Hearing impairment
- Dysphonia/voice disorder

Facilities

All the services listed above are delivered from a wide range of different HSE facilities, including hospitals, community health centres, rehabilitation centres, GP surgeries and preschool settings.

ALLOWANCES AND ENTITLEMENTS

The Department of Social Protection, along with certain other organisations such as the HSE and Revenue Commissioners, provide certain allowances and entitlements for people with particular special needs and for those who care for them. Some of the more common allowances and entitlements are outlined below.

Domiciliary Care Allowance

Domiciliary Care Allowance is a monthly payment to the carer of a child with a disability so severe that it requires care and attention and/or supervision substantially in excess of another child of the same age. This care and attention must be provided to allow the child to deal with the activities of daily living. The child must be likely to require this level of care and attention for at least 12 months.

The Domiciliary Care Allowance scheme was administered by the HSE before it was transferred to the Department of Social and Family Affairs. The Domiciliary Care Allowance rate is €309.50 per month (as of 2013).

Carer's Allowance

Carer's Allowance is a payment to people living in Ireland who are looking after someone who is in need of support because of age, physical or learning disability or illness, including mental illness. The rate of payment is €218.90 for a carer living with a partner caring for a child. The Carer's Allowance is not payable to everyone – it is mainly aimed at carers on low incomes who live with and look after certain people who need full-time care and attention. Those on Carer's Allowance will also qualify for free household benefits such as free electricity/natural gas/bottled gas refill allowance, free television license, free telephone rental allowance and a free travel pass.

Respite Care Grant

The Respite Care Grant is an annual cash payment made by the Department of Social Protection to certain carers for use as they wish. The Respite Care Grant is currently €1,375 and is paid in respect of each person being cared for.

Carer's Benefit

Carer's Benefit is a payment made to insured persons (who have been paying PRSI – a stamp) in Ireland who leave the workforce to care for a person(s) in need of full-time care and attention. Carer's Benefit is payable for a total period of 104 weeks for each person being cared for and can be taken in one or more blocks. Payment is currently €221.20 per week.

Disability Allowance

Disability Allowance is a weekly allowance paid to people with a disability who are between 16 and 65 years of age (as of 2013, the current rate is €188 per week). To qualify for Disability Allowance, a person must:

- Have an injury, disease or physical or mental disability that has continued or may be expected to continue for at least one year
- As a result of this disability be *substantially restricted* in undertaking work that would otherwise be suitable for a person of this age, experience and qualifications
- Be aged between 16 and 65
- Satisfy a means test
- Satisfy the habitual residence condition (Ireland must be where you live)

Homemaker's Scheme

The Homemaker's Scheme makes it easier for a homemaker to qualify for the state pension (contributory). A homemaker is a person (male or female) who gives up work on or after 6 April 1994 to care for a child (under 12) or someone who has a disability.

Medical card

A medical card may be issued by the HSE to the parents of children with special needs or to the child themselves if they are over 16. A medical card allows the holder to receive certain health services free of charge:

- Free GP (family doctor) services
- Prescribed drugs and medicines (with some exceptions)
- Inpatient public hospital services, outpatient services and medical appliances
- Dental, optical and aural services
- Maternity and infant care services
- Some personal and social care services, e.g. public health nursing, social work services and other community care services
- A maternity cash grant of €10.16 upon the birth of each child

Incapacitated child tax credit

Tax credits can be claimed by a parent or guardian in respect of a child who is permanently incapacitated, either physically or mentally, from maintaining him or herself.

Revenue allowances and VAT refunds

Various tax and VAT refunds are available to the parents of children with special needs, e.g. if necessary modifications are made to the house to accommodate the child or if a specific vehicle had to be purchased to accommodate a wheelchair.

VOLUNTARY SECTOR

For many of the special needs outlined in Chapters 4 to 9, voluntary organisations have been set up providing support for the person with the special need and their families. Some of these organisations are run on a completely voluntary basis and rely totally on the public for donations, while others do receive substantial government funding, but usually need to raise money themselves in addition to this funding. Most organisations have a website outlining their role and the services they provide.

Voluntary organisations involved with special needs provision

Special need	Voluntary organisations
Epilepsy	• Brainwave
Sickle cell anaemia	• No voluntary organisation in Ireland
Dyspraxia	• The Dyspraxia Association of Ireland
Dysgraphia	• No voluntary organisation in Ireland
Visual impairment	• National Council for the Blind of Ireland • Irish Guide Dogs for the Blind
Cystic fibrosis	• Cystic Fibrosis Association of Ireland
Spina bifida and hydrocephalus	• The Irish Association for Spina Bifida and Hydrocephalus • Irish Wheelchair Association • Jack and Jill Children's Foundation
Muscular dystrophy	• Muscular Dystrophy Ireland • Irish Wheelchair Association • Jack and Jill Children's Foundation
Cerebral palsy	• Enable Ireland (formerly Cerebral Palsy Ireland) • Irish Wheelchair Association • Jack and Jill Children's Foundation
HIV and AIDS	• AIDS West • ACET (AIDS Care Education and Training)
General learning disabilities	• Order of Malta (some regions have centres of education)
Hearing impairment	• Irish Deaf Society • Irishdeaf.com
Dyslexia	• Dyslexia Association of Ireland
ADHD	• HADD Family Support Group for ADHD in Ireland • www.adhd.ie
Autistic spectrum disorders	• Irish Autism Action • Aspire: Asperger Syndrome Association of Ireland
Down's syndrome	• Down's Syndrome Ireland
Fragile X syndrome	• Irish Fragile X Society

There are also a number of registered charities in Ireland that help children with a wide variety of special needs.

- **The Bubblegum Club:** An Irish registered charity whose mission is to provide outings for children, many of whom suffer from life-threatening illness, long-term debilitating illness or are disadvantaged in some other way.

- **Camphill Communities of Ireland:** This group is part of an international charitable trust working with people with intellectual disabilities and other kinds of special needs. There are currently 18 communities around Ireland providing education, training and accommodation to approximately 500 people. There are also a number of day attendees.

- **Carers Association:** The national voluntary organisation of family carers in the home who provide high levels of care to frail older people, those with severe disabilities, the terminally ill and children with special needs. Established in 1987, it is owned and controlled by carers and represents their interests as well as providing a range of supports and services.

- **CARI:** Provides professional, child-centred therapy and counselling services to children, families and groups affected by child sexual abuse.

- **Cheeverstown House:** Based in Dublin, this is a voluntary organisation providing a wide range of residential, respite and day services to almost 400 children and adults with an intellectual disability.

- **Children to Lapland Appeal:** Every year, the Children to Lapland Appeal takes long-term and terminally ill patients and deserving children from hospitals countrywide to Lapland.

- **COPE Foundation:** Provides services to persons with intellectual disabilities in Cork city and county.

- **Fight for Sight:** An Irish charity promoting eye care awareness and the prevention of sight loss, with information on eye diseases including AMD, cataracts, diabetic retinopathy and retinitis pigmentosa.

- **Fighting Blindness:** A voluntary organisation that promotes research into retinal degenerative diseases.

- **Headway:** Works with people affected by acquired brain injuries. It provides services to carers, families, professionals and people with an acquired brain injury. Services include day services, rehabilitative training, therapy and family support services, community access, supported employment, outreach services, national telephone helpline, publications and a website.

- **ISPCC:** Provides services for children experiencing abuse and neglect.

- **Jack and Jill Children's Foundation:** Provides direct funding to families of children with brain damage who suffer severe intellectual and physical developmental delay, enabling them to purchase home respite care.

- **Special Olympics Ireland:** Year-round sports training and competition programme for people with a learning disability.

THE ROLE OF SNAs IN THE CONTEXT OF SPECIAL NEEDS PROVISION

The role of the SNA has been detailed under each of the special needs outlined in Chapters 4 to 9. This section deals with the role of the SNA in a more general way, but examines the circulars below (particularly 07/02) more closely:

- **Circular SPED07/02:** Applications for full-time or part-time SNA support to address the special care needs of children with disabilities
- **Circular SPED0009/2009:** Review of all SNA posts in primary, special and post-primary schools by the National Council for Special Education
- **Circular 0037/2009:** Notification of transitional arrangements being put in place in relation to the outcome of the review of all SNA posts in primary, special and post-primary schools by the National Council for Special Education

Circular SPED07/02: Applications for full-time or part-time SNA support to address the special care needs of children with disabilities

This circular deals with the circumstances under which a school can employ an SNA and also the role and duties of an appointed SNA. For a full copy of the circular, see Appendix 7 at www.gillmacmillan.ie/assistingchildrenwithspecialneeds.

Criteria for employing an SNA

An SNA may be employed either on a full- or part-time basis in a school if there is a pupil enrolling in the school with a significant **care need** arising from a disability or where their behaviour is such that they are a danger to themselves or to other pupils. Thus, SNAs may be employed to care for children with special needs such as visual impairments, spina bifida, muscular dystrophy, cerebral palsy, autistic spectrum disorders, Down's syndrome, ADHD, oppositional defiant disorder and conduct disorder. An allocation will only be made if it is judged (by the referring psychologist) that such a need exists. For example, there could be one child with Down's syndrome who requires an SNA and another who doesn't because they have no special care needs.

Role of the SNA

The day-to-day job description of individual SNAs will be laid down by the principal (in consultation with the class teacher and resource teacher) of the particular school in which he or she is working. Generally, though, an SNA's role involves the following:

- Prepare and tidy up the classroom(s) in which the pupil(s) with special needs is/ are being taught.
- Help children board and alight from school buses. Where necessary, travelling as an escort on school buses may be required.
- Provide special assistance as necessary for pupils with particular difficulties, e.g. helping physically disabled pupils with typing or writing.
- Assist with clothing, feeding, toileting and general hygiene.
- Assist on out-of-school visits, walks and similar activities.
- Assist the teachers in the supervision of pupils with special needs during assembly (coming into school), recreational (e.g. lunchtime yard duty) and dispersal periods (home time or in secondary schools between classes).
- Accompany individuals or small groups who may have to be withdrawn temporarily from the classroom, e.g. to attend the resource teacher.
- Provide general assistance to the class teachers, under the direction of the principal, with duties of a non-teaching nature. (SNAs may not act either as substitute or temporary teachers. In no circumstances may they be left in sole charge of a class.)
- Where an SNA has been appointed to assist a school in catering for a specific pupil, duties should be modified to support the particular needs of the pupil concerned.

Schools vary in how they interpret these duties. Some schools do not involve the SNA in any academic work whatsoever and the SNA is solely involved in caring physically for the child. In other schools, SNAs are very much involved in the academic work of the classroom, helping children with work that has been assigned by the teacher, e.g. assisting and reinforcing children while they use computer programs such as Wordshark and Numbershark.

In 2009, two DES circulars were issued to schools relating to the recruitment and retention of SNAs (circulars 0009/2009 and 0037/2009). These two circulars led to widespread media reporting that the DES was reducing the numbers of SNAs in schools. This is both true and false. The National Council for Special Education's remit is to carry out audits of all schools with regard to their special needs provision. Cuts were to be made if a particular school had continued to employ an SNA when the child they were looking after had left the school or no longer had care or behavioural needs requiring the assistance of an SNA. SNAs can continue to be employed for children meeting the requirements as outlined in the older circular SPED07/02 (see above).

INTERDISCIPLINARY TEAMS

Many children with special needs are involved with a large number of different professionals, organisations and agencies. The four main service providers and the services they provide are all outlined at the beginning of this chapter. To ensure a good-quality, effective service, all of these organisations should be communicating with each other about the overall service provision for each individual child. This does not always happen, however, and is one of the frustrations reported by parents of children with special needs.

PARENTS AS PARTNERS

Parents should be involved in decisions made about their child from early diagnosis on. In some cases, it is a parent that first suspects that a child has a special need and they should therefore be involved in diagnosing the child, e.g. interview with psychologists. The EPSEN Act recommends that all children with special needs have a regularly updated IEP. Parents should have an important input into this plan, as they know their child best and what their needs are. Professionals should make an effort to communicate effectively with parents and should not use unnecessary jargon and keep the parent informed every step of the way.

Schools should communicate regularly with parents about their child's progress. Some schools have what is sometimes called a communications copy, where teachers can write notes to parents and vice versa. It is important to remember, though, that not all parents can read, not all parents can speak and read English and not all parents have the confidence to communicate their worries and fears to school personnel and may say nothing, even when they are worried.

Preschools and schools should produce a handbook containing essential information for parents. Newsletters and notes can be used to communicate with parents. Some establishments have developed websites containing useful information and news for parents.

Parents should feel supported by all the professionals working with their child. They should be able to talk to them if they have worries or concerns. In turn, it is vital that parents support the work that is being done with children at home, e.g. practising speech or physiotherapy exercises. Children with special needs tend to progress much better if their home and school environment complement each other.

Good communication between parents and preschools and schools gives children a sense of continuity of service between home and school, thus helping their progress.

chapter twelve

Good Practice

CHAPTER OUTLINE

- Health and safety policies and procedures
- Special needs assisting skills
- Principles of good practice

HEALTH AND SAFETY POLICIES AND PROCEDURES

All centres that cater for children, including children with special needs, are required to have certain health and safety policies and procedures in place to help ensure the health, safety and well-being of their participants. Preschools, primary schools, special schools and post-primary schools will generally have policies and procedures for some or all of the following. They should be contained in a staff handbook or displayed for easy access by staff. Parents should also have access to them through a parent information booklet.

- **Child protection:** See Chapter 13.
- **Anti-bullying:** Anti-bullying policies and procedures should include definitions of bullying, procedures for dealing with suspected cases of bullying and an outline of how the organisation intends to provide anti-bullying education to students.
- **Equal opportunities:** Equal opportunities should be emphasised throughout all school policies, e.g. enrolment policy, subject choices.
- **Illness:** Illness policy and procedures should include guidelines for parents regarding when it is not permitted to send a child to school, e.g. if they have a contagious illness, and guidelines and procedures for dealing with a child that becomes ill at school.
- **Medication:** Some schools will not take responsibility for medicating children. However, if schools are to be inclusive of children with certain special needs, they need to develop new sets of policies and procedures in order to facilitate such children. Schools need to develop procedures for medicine storage, e.g.

insulin needs to be refrigerated, and administration. If a member of staff is required to administer medication, they will receive training to do so by HSE personnel.

▸ **Exclusions:** As part of a school's discipline policy, there needs to be clear procedures in place regarding the exclusion (whether temporary or more permanent) of children who consistently and seriously break the school's rules, posing a risk to themselves, fellow students and school staff. These policies have become particularly important since the introduction of the Education Welfare Act 2000. Policies should be written with input from the local education welfare officer, whose job is to deal with students who have been excluded from school. Policies on exclusion are particularly relevant to children with special needs affecting their emotional and social development, such as ADHD, oppositional defiant disorder, conduct disorder and emotional and behavioural problems resulting from environmental abuse and neglect.

▸ **Outings:** Schools and other organisations, particularly those dealing with younger children, should have clear policies and procedures regarding outings. Policies regarding parental permission, supervision levels and safe return to the educational establishment or to the child's parent or guardian after the outing are vital to prevent accidents.

▸ **Resting:** The HSE sets down regulations for crèches and preschools regarding rest and sleep. Sleeping facilities should be away from the play area and should be provided for children under two or for older children if they have a need. Children should be checked regularly and records kept. There are rules on sleep positions and on the physical environment regarding heating and ventilation.

▸ **Child collection:** Crèches, preschools, special schools and primary schools must have policies and procedures in place regarding child collection. Policies and procedures outline who can collect a child and what needs to be done before a new person can collect a child, and where the child must be collected from – this will change the older the child gets, e.g. a parent of a preschool-age child will be required to come into the reception area for the child to be directly handed over, whereas a parent of a primary school child may only have to be standing in the yard where the teacher can see who the child is being collected by. Special arrangements may have to be made for some children with special needs, particularly if safety is an issue, e.g. with autism, where the child will frequently be unobservant of dangers.

▸ **Security:** Educational institutions need to be conscious of security on a number of different levels, including physical security of the school building and its contents. There is also an onus on schools under the Data Protection Acts 1988, 1998 and 2003 that records kept on children in schools are securely kept.

- **Areas to which the child/children have access:** In preschool settings, children should not have access to food preparation areas. In primary schools and post-primary schools, students should not have access to the staff room or office where confidential records are kept. In primary schools, playgrounds are often segregated by age for safety purposes.

- **Sun protection:** Parents are usually requested to put sun protection cream on children, pack additional sun cream and also pack sun hats during the summer months. Children should not remain outside for too long in very hot weather and should be given plenty of fluids. Shaded areas for play should be available for children with particularly sun-sensitive skin.

- **Accidents, incidents and injuries:** Preschools and schools are required to have a suitably equipped first aid box for children. It should be stored safely but accessibly and should be taken on outings. A staff member with up-to-date first aid training should be on the premises at all times. Emergency numbers should be to hand in the case of accidents. Up-to-date numbers for parents or guardians should be readily accessible. Accident and incident report forms should be filled out by a staff witness should an accident or incident occur.

- **Hygiene:** If food is available for children/students, strict food hygiene guidelines must be adhered to. If food is taken in pre-prepared, then it must be purchased from a HSE-registered supplier and stored appropriately after purchase. Clean drinking water must be available for children/students. Toilet and changing facilities (if required) should be clean. Waste, e.g. soiled nappies, should be disposed of safely and hygienically. Toilets and nappy changing areas should not communicate directly with any occupied room. There should be a ventilated space in between, e.g. hall. There should be one toilet and hand basin for every 10 children or 8 adults. Wheelchair-accessible facilities should be available.

- **Disaster/fire plan:** A disaster or fire plan should be developed (in consultation with a fire safety officer). All staff members should be clear on evacuation procedures and their responsibilities regarding procedures. Each room should have an evacuation plan displayed. Regular fire drills should be carried out with children so that they are clear on what to do in an emergency. Emergency numbers should be displayed. Roll calls should be taken early in the morning and altered throughout the day if necessary to ensure accuracy.

- **Non-smoking:** Smoking is not permitted by law in preschools and schools.

- **Discipline policies:** Organisations should have clear discipline policies and procedures for breaches of discipline that pose a danger to the student themselves, fellow students or staff members.

- **Infection control:** Organisations should have policies and procedures in place for infection control.

SPECIAL NEEDS ASSISTING SKILLS

Feeding

Levels of independence regarding feeding vary among children with different special needs. While most children with special feeding needs have physical disabilities, this is not always the case. For example, some children with autism have sensory defensiveness regarding certain tastes and textures and may have special feeding needs. When feeding a child with special needs, there are certain factors that need to be taken into account.

- Medical conditions: Does the child have any allergies or special food requirements? Does the child have difficulty swallowing or a tendency to gag on certain foods?
- Safety: Ensure the child is not being fed too quickly, that they are not being given foods that they cannot chew or swallow easily and that they are strapped into their chair if necessary and are sitting in a comfortable position for feeding.
- Allow plenty of time for meals.
- If the child is able to self-feed, protect clothing if necessary. Children may use adapted feeding equipment to improve grip and strength and to prevent bowls slipping and food spillages.
- If children are eating finger food, they should be closely supervised. Make sure hands are washed especially well before and after feeding.
- Some children do not indicate thirst or hunger and therefore records of their food and fluid intake need to be accurately maintained.

Toileting, clothing and general hygiene

As with feeding, levels of independence regarding toileting vary among children with different special needs. Children with physical disabilities such as cerebral palsy or spina bifida (if they are paralysed) may require help with either getting onto and off the toilet, changing incontinence pads or perhaps with emptying a catheter bag (although this is not common with younger children). Children with learning or social disabilities may only require help with hygiene and require no physical lifting.

- Public buildings such as schools are all now required by law to have a large toilet to accommodate people with disabilities. Keep the door closed to protect the privacy of the individual.
- Before helping someone with their toilet needs, wash your hands and put on plastic disposable gloves and also a plastic apron if required. Wipe down the

toilet seat. Remember, many children with spina bifida are allergic to latex, so schools should not buy gloves with latex in them.

If you are caring for a child who requires moving and handling onto the toilet, you should be given the opportunity to do a manual handling course, either as part of your college training or as part of an on-the-job training course. This is vital so that you can move the child safely (both for your safety and theirs). The information given below is not meant to replace this training, but rather to give a general idea of what is involved in toileting children with various special needs.

- Many wheelchair users have sufficient strength in their upper arms to safely lift themselves up onto the toilet and down again afterwards. Hand rails are often sufficient to help with balance and they will require no help with toileting. Others may only require someone to be there in case they lose their balance and/or to assist them to clean themselves afterwards or to readjust clothing. Others will have a need for greater assistance.

- If a child has to be moved onto the toilet, wheel their chair so that it is positioned alongside the toilet. The sides of the wheelchair will normally slide down. Moving should be done with the person facing you. Bend your knees and move the child by holding them under their arms. Support the child's weight by holding them against you. Tell the child when you are going to move them (one, two, three and up). Stand beside the child while they are on the toilet or support if necessary. Do not hurry the child. When they are finished, help the child lean forward so that they can be cleaned. Support them with your body while you are doing this.

- Some children with paralysis from the waist down have little bowel or bladder sensation. This means that they will not know when their bladder is full or when they are having a bowel movement. For this reason, many children wear incontinence pads or nappies every day. SNAs should be vigilant that the child is clean and fresh at all times during the day.

- By the time a child begins school, his or her parents will usually have worked with him or her to try to train the bowel into moving at the same time every day, usually the morning. This means that the child will be unlikely to soil themselves during the day.

- Even if children do not have a bowel movement, they will wear a pad for urine collection. SNAs will be required to change the child, so there should be suitable changing facilities available. A washable changing couch at the same level as the wheelchair seat is best. Disposable gloves and a protective apron should be worn. Used pads should be disposed of in sanitary bins for collection by a specialist waste management company.

▷ Some teenage boys self-catheterise using a thin tube, e.g. a Ryles tube. This tube is inserted up through the penis and into the bladder. The bladder will then empty into a small urine collection bag. More permanent catheters are not usually used (e.g. Foley catheter) with young people. All catheters carry the risk of infection, so scrupulous hygiene is essential. Some people who use catheters on a regular basis may be on a permanent low-level antibiotic. Most build up a good immunity to urinary tract infections over the years and get fewer and fewer as time goes on.

▷ Generally, catheterisation is not as successful with girls as with boys, as infections are more common. Some older girls opt to have an operation that brings the ureters directly outside through an opening in the side of the abdomen, which is plugged. Urine empties into a bag, which can be easily emptied by the older child themselves.

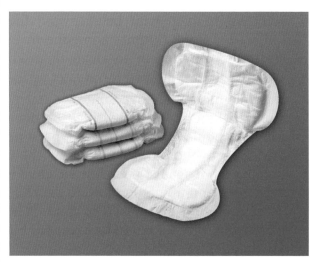

▷ Children with learning or other disabilities such as autism may need help with toileting. Children may wear pads or nappies, which will need to be changed as above, or the children may need to be helped with personal hygiene tasks such as cleaning themselves after using the toilet or washing their hands before returning to class.

Incontinence pads

Boarding and alighting from school transport

As with feeding and toileting, some children with special needs require more assistance than others with boarding and alighting from school transport.

Nowadays, if a child is a wheelchair user, school transport should be wheelchair accessible. The floor at the entrance of the bus should lower to allow the wheelchair to be wheeled in and out. Once the wheelchair is on board, the floor should rise up again to allow the wheelchair to be wheeled into the body of the bus, where the child's chair is securely harnessed in. Make sure the child is securely strapped into their chair, as there is little point in securely fastening the wheelchair if the child is unsecured in the chair.

Sometimes children with special social or behavioural needs, e.g. children with autism, may have to be supervised on their journeys to and from school. SNAs will have the responsibility of ensuring the child keeps his or her seatbelt on and remains seated at all times. If the child keeps removing their seatbelt, then a harness may be supplied, which is more difficult to open. On arrival at school or at the child's home, it is the responsibility of the SNA to accompany the child (perhaps by the hand) into the care of their parents or their teacher.

PRINCIPLES OF GOOD PRACTICE

The principles of good practice include the following.

- The use of appropriate language to describe children with special needs
- Confidentiality
- Access and inclusion
- Independence
- Advocacy and empowerment
- Boundaries

Use of appropriate language to describe children with special needs

The language used when talking about children with a disability is very important. Language has the power to shape attitudes and beliefs within society. The use of inappropriate language when talking about disability is not only insulting and devaluing, but it also contributes to poor self-image and low self-esteem among children with disabilities.

Children copy the language used by the adults around them. It is therefore vitally important that teachers and SNAs use appropriate language when talking about children with special needs. As a general rule, you should always refer to the child first and the disability second. So the term 'a baby with Down's syndrome' should be used, *not* 'a Down's baby', or 'a child with autism', *not* 'an autistic child'. Below is a list of appropriate and inappropriate terms for use when talking about children and people with disabilities. It was developed as a bookmark by the UK-based registered charity SCOPE.

Avoid	Use instead
(The) handicapped	Disabled (people)
Afflicted by, suffers from, victim of …	Has …
Confined to a wheelchair or wheelchair bound	A wheelchair user
Mentally handicapped, retarded, subnormal	Has a learning difficulty
Cripple, invalid	Person with a disability
The disabled	People with disabilities or disabled people
Spastic	Person who has cerebral palsy
Able-bodied	Non-disabled

Sometimes people begin talking to the carer as if the child (or adult) with the disability is not there. This is very offensive and is sometimes called the 'does he take sugar' syndrome, where people speak over disabled people's heads as if they cannot think or make decisions for themselves.

Confidentiality

Confidentiality is very important for staff working with all children, including children with special needs. Staff should never discuss children in their care outside of the work setting and certainly not with friends or family in social situations. If in the course of a classroom discussion you as a student are giving an example of something from your workplace, you should take care not to name the workplace or the child you are talking about. If you are including photographs of children in your workplace as part of your assessment work, permission should be sought from parents and faces should not be shown. It is possible to take photographs of hands only or photograph over a child's shoulder to demonstrate the activity yet protect the child's identity. Faces may also be blacked out. Taping children's voices also requires parental permission. If you are making a video recording of an activity, permission must be sought from the parents of all the children evident in the video.

The Data Protection Act 1988, 1998 and 2003 concerns the holding of both written and electronically kept records. All records should be securely kept.

Access and inclusion

'Access' and 'inclusion' are two terms frequently used in relation to disability. Access means having the freedom or ability to obtain or use something. In education, this usually means physical access to transport and buildings, classrooms and other school facilities. Inclusion, on the other hand, means giving children with and without disabilities opportunities to learn, play and socialise together. Inclusion means equality and the removal of social barriers to enable the full participation of people with disabilities in all aspects of mainstream school life. Inclusion has been a long time coming in Irish schools. For many years, children with disabilities were educated in isolation in special schools, or worse, not given educational opportunities at all. Schools with an inclusive approach will:

- Create an ethos of equality, respect and value for all children.
- Welcome children with special needs into their school.
- Create a physically accessible environment for all children.
- Display books and posters showing positive images of disabled children and adults.
- Provide appropriate care and learning support for children with special needs, e.g. an SNA and resource teacher.
- Seek additional funding for resources, e.g. assistive technology.
- Value parents as partners and make every effort to communicate with parents in an effective way, e.g. if a parent is deaf, learn to use finger spelling to communicate with him or her.
- Listen to what parents are saying about their child – they know them best.
- Each school should have a regularly updated individual education plan (IEP) for each child in the school with special needs. This plan should detail the child's individual educational goals together with information on how these goals are to be achieved.
- Schools should make every effort to liaise with other external agencies working with children with special needs to help ensure that a co-ordinated service is being offered.
- Adapt activities so that all children can take part and ensure that children are not excluded from activities because of their special need.
- Challenge incidences of discrimination, use of inappropriate language and stereotyping.
- Deal with incidences of bullying in accordance with the school's discipline policy and procedures.
- Staff training in various aspects of special needs provision should be provided and availed of.

'Inclusion is the value system which holds that all students are entitled to equal access to learning, achievement and the pursuit of excellence in all aspects of their education. The practice of inclusion transcends the idea of physical location and incorporates basic values that promote participation, friendship and interaction.' (National Council for Special Education 2006)

Independence

Promotion of independence should be one of the main goals of IEPs. Independence is an important factor in the promotion of positive self-image and self-esteem. Children who are overprotected and are not given opportunities to develop independence can begin to believe that they are incapable and that the adults around them do not believe in their abilities. Depending on the level of the child's disability, learning self-help skills such as feeding, dressing, toileting, cooking, cleaning, handling money, shopping and using public transport should all be facilitated. Apart from self-help skills such as these, staff should also be aware of not over-helping children with academic work. Certainly support children's learning, but do not jump in too soon to show the child how to do something correctly – give them time to figure things out for themselves.

Advocacy and empowerment

Those who work with children with special needs, be they teachers, special needs assistants or other professionals, need to act as advocates for the children they support in order to empower them towards reaching their full potential. As a special needs assistant, to be an effective advocate you need to:

- Learn all you can about the child's special need
- Focus on the child's strengths and build on them
- Give the child choices about their learning and their day-to-day decisions, e.g. decisions about which piece of work to do first, second and so on
- Listen very carefully to what the child is saying about their problems, needs and wants
- Relay information about children's problems, needs and wants to others working with the child
- Investigate and learn as much as you can about new equipment, resources or ways of working that could benefit the child
- Listen to the child's parents and liaise effectively with them

Boundaries

Having professional boundaries while working with all children, including children with special needs, is very important. Having professional boundaries does not mean that the adult cannot be warm and caring towards the child, but it does mean that there certain types of behaviour that are not appropriate or helpful for either child or adult. Professional boundaries normally centre around the following.

Communication boundaries:

- Appropriate language should be used at all times.
- Feedback should only be given that comments on what the child has done, not on their personality or abilities.
- Communication should only occur in certain settings, e.g. the child should not be phoning carers at home.
- Carers should not talk about school management decisions with the child, e.g. if a child with ADHD was suspended by management, it would be wrong for an SNA to discuss the fairness of this with the child.

Expectation boundaries:

- Children with special needs may be encouraged to become dependent on carers, expecting carers to be there for them at all times, even outside school. This should be avoided.
- If boundaries become fuzzy, children may begin to view the relationship as a friendship rather than a professional care relationship. This can lead to the child feeling rejected when the carer cannot fulfil the normal role of friend.

Physical contact boundaries:

- It is important that physical contact is kept to the minimum necessary for carrying out a particular task, e.g. helping a child hold a pencil.
- It is important that SNAs that are required to help children with toileting needs are trained to do so and that they will do so in as efficient and respectful a manner as possible.

Location boundaries:

- In general, children should be worked with in group situations only. If one-to-one work needs to be carried out, e.g. a resource teacher, then the teacher should keep the door of the room slightly open (or some schools have glass panels fitted in the doors), a corner of a desk or some other physical barrier should be between the child and the adult and the child should be seated closest to the door.

Child Protection

The issue of child protection is of vital importance for any book aimed at students intending to work with children, particularly children with special needs. The last 10 to 15 years have seen a litany of horrific cases of abuse in families, schools, churches and sports clubs emerge throughout Ireland.

Children with special needs, particularly if they have intimate physical care needs or difficulty communicating, have been targets for perpetrators of abuse in the past. It is therefore vital that every individual working with children in Ireland in any capacity is familiar with the law in relation to child protection, namely **the Child Care Act 1991 and the Children Act 2001**, and are also fully aware of *Children First: National Guidance for the Protection and Welfare of Children* (referred to as the *Children First* guidance for the rest of this chapter).

Child protection is a very important issue in Irish society today. In 2011, for example, there were over 31,000 child welfare and protection referrals made to the HSE (a number of referrals can relate to the same child, so this does not mean 31,000 separate cases). Presently, there are over 6,250 children in care placements throughout the state. Of the 6,155 children in care in 2011, 45 per cent were in care with the voluntary consent of the child's parents. Over 85 per cent of non-voluntary admissions (court ordered) to care in 2011 were due to abuse (physical and sexual), neglect and serious family problems (www.childrensreferendum.ie).

THE CHILD CARE ACT 1991

The legislative basis for dealing with children in need of care and protection is provided by the Child Care Act 1991. The promotion of the welfare of children is the main principle underpinning the Act, together with the protection of children who are at risk of abuse or neglect. The Act differs from older pieces of Irish legislation in that it puts the rights of the individual child to care and protection above all else. The Act puts the onus on the HSE to promote the welfare of children in its area who are not receiving adequate care and protection. The Act recognises that children do best if they can remain with their families, but that the child's safety must always come first. If children are at a real risk of abuse or neglect, it is the role of the HSE to remove them from their families and care for them elsewhere, e.g. in a foster care environment.

The Act is extensive. It is divided into 10 parts, with each part dealing with a different aspect of child protection.

- **Part 1** gives a short title and defines important terms used throughout the Act, e.g. 'child' means a person under the age of 18 years other than a person who is or has been married.

- **Part 2** outlines the functions of the HSE in relation to child protection, the HSE's duties in relation to homeless children and the functions of childcare advisory committees (these committees help the HSE evaluate how well they are carrying out their functions under the Act). This part of the Act also deals with the involvement of voluntary bodies in child protection work and the role of the HSE to support them in this work.

- **Part 3** deals with the duties of An Garda Síochána to take children to safety and also with emergency care orders where children are taken into care because of immediate risk of harm.

- **Part 4** deals with taking children deemed to be at risk of abuse or neglect into care. The Act explains the regulations regarding interim care orders, care orders and supervision orders. Interim care orders are applied for when it is felt that a child cannot remain where they are while a care order is going through the courts. Interim care orders normally last eight days, although extensions may be granted. Care orders are more long term; they are applied for and last for as long as it is felt necessary. With supervision orders, children are not removed into the care of the HSE, but are supervised by HSE personnel. This section of the Act also deals with appeals against care and supervision orders.

- **Part 5** restates the principle underpinning the entire Act – that in all instances, the welfare of the child is paramount. This section also states that the child's wishes should be considered (with consideration for his/her age and level of understanding) in relation to care arrangements. A guardian *ad litem* should be appointed to act on behalf of the child. The section also deals with requests for reports on children and procedures that must be followed if there is a refusal to deliver up a child and they have to be searched for under warrant. This section also deals with the media – that certain matters are prohibited from being broadcast or published. This is to protect the identity of the child.

- **Part 6** deals with rules and regulations regarding children in care, be it foster care, residential care or in the care of relatives. It also deals with access arrangements for parents/guardians of children in care. The latter part of this section deals with children being adopted while in care (see also the Children's Referendum section below) together with children leaving care because they have reached 18 years of age and are going into aftercare. Some children are removed unlawfully from care each year and the Act gives guidance on what should be done in these cases to recover these children.

- **Part 7** deals with preschool services. Before preschools are opened, notification must be given to the HSE. Preschool services must follow certain operational regulations and the HSE has the power under this Act to inspect preschool services, demand improvements if necessary and close down unsatisfactory services.

- **Part 8** deals with children's residential centres. Children's residential centres must be registered and must closely follow the regulations governing residential centres. If a centre is seen not to be compliant, then it can be removed as a registered centre and not permitted to operate. This decision can be appealed in the district court.

- **Parts 9 and 10** of the Act cover regulations regarding the administration of the Act.

THE CHILDREN ACT 2001

This Act and the Child Care Act 1991 (above) are collectively called the Child Care Acts 1991 and 2001. Much of the Children Act 2001 relates to children who are young offenders, and while this issue is closely linked to child protection (children who experience neglect and abuse are more likely to become young offenders), this book will focus on part 2 of the Act, which deals with family welfare conferences.

Under the Act, the Children's Court may request a family welfare conference to be convened in respect of a child whom the court feels may be a child protection risk. A chairperson is appointed and the child's case is investigated. If a child protection issue is found to exist, then a care order or supervision order may be applied for. A number of different people may be asked to attend the family welfare conference so that a balanced view of the child's situation is obtained. The child themselves, their parents/guardians, any guardian *ad litem* appointed for the child, other relatives, HSE personnel and any other person whom it is felt would make a positive contribution to the conference may be asked to attend. If it is later found that a person attending the conference is not acting with the best interests of the conference and the child in mind, they will be asked to leave.

The conference will discuss all the issues relating to the child's welfare and protection and come up with recommendations. The Act stipulates that the conference co-ordinator must notify everyone attending the conference of its recommendations in writing. On receipt of the conference recommendations, the HSE may apply for a care order, supervision order or any other service or support recommended by the conference. Where a conference has been ordered by the Children's Court, the recommendations will be referred to the court too.

Part 3 of the Children Act 2001 makes a specific addition to the Child Care Act 1991 regarding **special care orders**. These orders are applied for when it is believed that the child poses a substantial risk to his or her own safety, health, development and welfare because of his or her own behaviour. This would happen, for instance, if it was found that a child was abusing drugs or alcohol and was at risk of overdose. A special care order could be applied for so that the child could be more closely supervised.

THE CHILDREN'S REFERENDUM

The Children's Referendum was held and passed on 10 November 2012. The referendum sought to amend the Irish Constitution in relation to the specific rights of children whose parents have consistently failed in their duty of care to them. If it is deemed to be in their best interest, children can now be adopted by their foster parents, even if their birth parents do not agree. Children of married parents can now also be adopted (in the past, married parents could not voluntarily place their children up for adoption). The views and wishes of the child are now taken into account, as long as the child is sufficiently mature to make this appropriate.

Of the 6,155 children living in care in 2011, over 91 per cent were living in foster care, with nearly one-third being fostered by a relative. Over 2,000 children have been living with the same foster family for five years or more. With this new referendum, it is possible that some of these children will now be adopted by their foster parents and have the opportunity to lead more stable lives (www.childrens referendum.ie).

CHILDREN FIRST: NATIONAL GUIDANCE FOR THE PROTECTION AND WELFARE OF CHILDREN

The *Children First: National Guidance for the Protection and Welfare of Children* document was published by the Department of Children and Youth Affairs in 2011. This guidance supersedes all others, e.g. *Children First* (1999), and should be the only guidance used by organisations.

One of the main points of the *Children First* guidance is that *everyone* has a duty to protect children – it's not just the job of the gardaí, social workers and other health professionals. For this reason, everyone working with children and young people should be aware of the contents of the *Children First* guidance, and if possible avail of child protection training. A complete copy of the *Children First* guidance can be downloaded at www.dcya.gov.ie.

Structure of the guidance

The guidance is divided into four parts, with additional references and appendices sections. The four parts are as follows:

1. Key Messages: Principles, Aims and Use of the *Children First: National Guidance*
2. Definitions and Recognition of Child Abuse; Basis for Reporting Concerns and Standard Reporting Procedure; Interagency Co-operation [including roles and responsibilities within health and justice]
3. Guidance for HSE Children and Family Services and Other Professionals; Protocol for An Garda Síochána – HSE Liaison
4. Special Considerations [especially vulnerable children, peer abuse, training in protection and welfare]

A summary of parts 1, 2 and 4 will be provided here, but it is best if students download and read a copy of the guidelines in full. The last section of parts 2 and 3 will be dealt with in less detail, as it is not as directly applicable to special needs practitioners as the other sections.

PART I: KEY MESSAGES: PRINCIPLES, AIMS AND USE OF THE *CHILDREN FIRST: NATIONAL GUIDANCE*

Key principles of best practice in child protection

Towards the beginning of the *Children First* guidance document, the 10 key principles that should inform best practice in child protection and welfare are given.

These are very important and underpin everything else, so they are listed in full here:

1. The welfare of children is of paramount importance.
2. Early intervention and support should be available to promote the welfare of children and families, particularly where they are vulnerable or at risk of not receiving adequate care or protection. Family support should form the basis of early intervention and preventative interventions.
3. A proper balance must be struck between protecting children and respecting the rights and needs of parents/carers and families. Where there is conflict, the child's welfare must come first.
4. Children have a right to be heard, listened to and taken seriously. Taking account of their age and understanding, they should be consulted and involved in all matters and decisions that may affect their lives. Where there are concerns about a child's welfare, there should be opportunities provided for their views to be heard independently of their parents/carers.
5. Parents/carers have a right to respect and should be consulted and involved in matters that concern their family.
6. Factors such as the child's family circumstances, gender, age, stage of development, religion, culture and race should be considered when taking protective action. Intervention should not deal with the child in isolation; the child's circumstances must be understood within a family context.
7. The criminal dimension of any action must not be ignored.
8. Children should only be separated from parents/carers when alternative means of protecting them have been exhausted. Re-union should be considered in the context of planning for the child's future.
9. The prevention, detection and treatment of child abuse or neglect requires a coordinated multidisciplinary approach, effective management, clarity of responsibility and training of personnel in organisations working with children.
10. Professionals and agencies working with adults who for a range of reasons may have serious difficulties meeting their children's basic needs for safety and security should always consider the impact of their adult client/patient's behaviour on a child and act in the child's best interests. (*Children First: National Guidance*, p. 4)

Aims of the *Children First: National Guidance*

The *Children First* guidance is intended to assist people in identifying and reporting concerns related to child abuse and neglect. The roles and responsibilities of the HSE and An Garda Síochána are highlighted as well as the importance of inter-agency co-operation and multidisciplinary responses. *Children First* also highlights the importance of training, supervision and support services for children and their families.

Use of the *Children First: National Guidance*

The *Children First* guidance helps ensure best practice in the recruitment of staff or volunteers, which includes garda vetting, taking up of references, good HR practices in interviewing, induction training, probation and ongoing supervision and management. The guidance also helps ensure that staff members or volunteers are aware of how to recognise signs of child abuse or neglect and know what to do if they have reasonable grounds for concern. All organisations must identify a designated person to act as a liaison with outside agencies if a child protection issue arises within their organisation. The designated person is responsible for reporting allegations or suspicions of child abuse to the HSE Children and Family Services or to An Garda Síochána.

PART II: DEFINITIONS AND RECOGNITION OF CHILD ABUSE; BASIS FOR REPORTING CONCERNS AND STANDARD REPORTING PROCEDURE; INTERAGENCY CO-OPERATION

Definition of child abuse

This part of the guidance (and its associated appendices) describes the four principal types of child abuse (neglect, emotional abuse, physical abuse and sexual abuse) and offers guidance on how to recognise such abuse. A child may be subjected to one or more forms of abuse at any given time. In the *Children First* guidance, 'a child' means a person under the age of 18 years, excluding a person who is or has been married.

Neglect can be defined in terms of an omission, where the child suffers significant harm or impairment of development by being deprived of food, clothing, warmth, hygiene, intellectual stimulation, supervision and safety, attachment to and affection from adults, and/or medical care. Neglect generally occurs over a period of time rather than at one specific point in time, e.g. a child whose mother is going into hospital to have a baby is fed crisps and fizzy drinks for the day. As this is a one-off incident, it is not considered neglect; however, if the child was normally fed in this way, it would.

Emotional abuse is normally a feature of the *relationship* between a parent/carer and a child rather than a specific event or pattern of events. It occurs when a child's developmental needs for affection, approval, consistency and security are not met. Children who are constantly criticised, blamed, given too much responsibility, over or underprotected, ignored or given no affection are emotionally abused. Children may be abused in other ways at the same time. If emotional abuse occurs alone, it can be very difficult to recognise if not directly witnessed.

Physical abuse results in actual or potential physical harm from an action or lack of action that is reasonably within the control of a parent/carer. There may be single or repeated incidents. Physical abuse includes the imposition of severe physical punishment: beating, slapping, hitting or kicking, pushing, shaking or throwing, pinching, biting, choking or hair-pulling, terrorising with threats, observing violence, use of excessive force in handling, deliberate poisoning (e.g. with alcohol or medication), suffocation, fabricated/induced illness, or allowing or creating a substantial risk of significant harm to a child.

Sexual abuse occurs when a child is used by another person for his or her gratification or sexual arousal, or for that of others. Examples include exposure of the sexual organs or any sexual act intentionally performed in the presence of the child; intentional touching or molesting of the body of a child; masturbation in the presence of the child or the involvement of the child in an act of masturbation; sexual intercourse with the child, whether oral, vaginal or anal; sexual exploitation of a child, e.g. for prostitution or pornography; and consensual sexual activity involving an adult and an underage person (under 17 years).

Recognition of child abuse

Child neglect or abuse can often be difficult to identify and may present in many forms. A list of indicators of child neglect and abuse is contained in Appendix 1 of the *Children First* document. Because of its importance to childcare practitioners, this list is given in full as Appendix 8 (see www.gillmacmillan.ie/assisting childrenwithspecialneeds). It must be stressed that usually no one indicator can be seen as conclusive evidence of abuse, as it may indicate conditions other than child abuse. All signs and symptoms must be examined in the broader context of the child's situation and family circumstances.

The ability to recognise child abuse can depend as much on a person's willingness to accept the possibility of its existence as it does on their knowledge and information. There are commonly three stages in the identification of child neglect or abuse:

1. Considering the possibility
2. Looking out for signs
3. Recording information

Basis for reporting concerns and standard reporting procedure

Everyone must be alert to the possibility that children with whom they are in contact may be suffering from abuse or neglect. This responsibility is particularly relevant for professionals such as teachers, childcare professionals, health professionals and those working with adults with serious parenting difficulties. It is also an important responsibility for staff and people involved in sports clubs, community activities, youth clubs, religious/faith sectors and other organisations catering for children.

The HSE Children and Family Services should always be informed if a person has a *reasonable concern* that a child is at risk of being abused or neglected. A concern about a potential risk to children posed by a specific person, even if the children are unidentifiable, should also be communicated to the HSE Children and Family Services. Anonymity cannot be guaranteed to people reporting abuse, especially when information is sought as part of legal proceedings.

Designated liaisons for reporting neglect or abuse

Every organisation (both public and private) providing services for children should identify a *designated child protection liaison person* to act as a liaison with outside agencies and as a resource person for staff. He/she is responsible for ensuring that the standard reporting procedure is followed so that suspected cases of child neglect or abuse are referred promptly to the designated person in the HSE Children and Family Services, or in the event of an emergency and the unavailability of the HSE, to An Garda Síochána. He/she should be knowledgeable about child protection, undertaking regular training to remain up to date.

Standard reporting procedure

Any person reporting a child abuse or neglect concern should do so without delay to the HSE Children and Family Services. Reports can be made in person, by telephone or in writing. Contact numbers for all HSE offices nationwide are given in Appendix 2 of the *Children First* document, on the website www.hse.ie/go/socialworkers or by phoning LoCall 1850 241 850.

Before deciding whether or not to make a formal report, you may wish to discuss your concerns with a health professional or directly with the HSE Children and Family Services, but *under no circumstances should a child be left in a situation that exposes him or her to harm or to risk of harm pending HSE intervention.* In the event of an emergency where you think a child is in immediate danger and you cannot get in contact with the HSE, you should contact the gardaí. This may be done through any garda station. A copy of the Standard Report Form is given as Appendix 9 (see www.gillmacmillan.ie/assistingchildrenwithspecialneeds). The HSE must follow up on referrals even if the standard reporting form has not been used.

Relevant legislation

The Protections for Persons Reporting Child Abuse Act 1998 makes provisions for the protection from civil liability of persons who have reported child abuse 'reasonably and in good faith' to designated officers of the HSE or to any member of An Garda Síochána. This protection applies to organisations as well as to individuals. This means that even if a communicated suspicion of child abuse proves unfounded, it would have to be proven that the person/organisation had not acted reasonably and in good faith in making the report.

The Data Protection Acts 1998–2003 and the Freedom of Information Act 1997 are also relevant to child protection (see Chapter 2, p. 15).

Interagency co-operation (including roles and responsibilities)

This section of the guidance outlines in detail the role of different personnel working specifically within the area of child protection and also generally with children. It is important for childcare practitioners to have a good understanding of these roles and of the concept of interagency co-operation.

Interagency co-operation

No one professional has all the skills, knowledge or resources necessary to comprehensively meet all the requirements of an individual child protection case. Therefore, it is essential that all professionals and organisations involved with a child and his or her parents/carers work together to deliver a co-ordinated, comprehensive response.

Roles and responsibilities of the HSE Children and Family Services

Under the Child Care Act 1991, the HSE has certain statutory obligations for the protection and welfare of children:

- The HSE must be open to receiving information from any source about a child who may not be receiving adequate care and protection.
- Having received such information, the HSE must seek to establish whether the child in question is receiving adequate care and protection. It must co-ordinate information from all relevant sources and make an assessment of the situation.
- Having identified a child who is not receiving adequate care and protection, the HSE is obligated to take appropriate action to promote the welfare of the child.

Roles and responsibilities of An Garda Síochána

An Garda Síochána has three primary roles in relation to child protection:

) Thoroughly investigate cases of alleged child abuse and/or neglect and to bring offenders to justice

) Intervene with HSE personnel (or alone where HSE personnel are not on duty) to protect a child or children in immediate risk of harm or abuse

) The Garda Central Vetting Unit (GCVU) provides vetting on behalf of organisations employing personnel to work in a full-time, part-time, voluntary or student placement capacity with children and/or vulnerable adults

Roles and responsibilities of other health sector personnel

While there are HSE personnel specifically employed to work within the area of child protection, as described above, many others also have important roles to play. This section of the guidance provides details on the roles of general practitioners (GPs), primary care teams (e.g. public health nurses, hospitals, mental health and addiction services) and child and adolescent psychiatric services. While each of these services will have their own areas of expertise and skill, all of them have a responsibility to use this expertise and skill while working with children to consider the possibility of abuse, look out for signs and record information.

Roles and responsibilities of other organisations working with children

The guidance refers here to all organisations that work with and care for children, including schools, private companies (e.g. crèches), voluntary organisations (e.g. football clubs) and charities. Some specific guidance is given for particular sectors (e.g. schools), but generally, all organisations must:

) Provide clear guidance for staff, volunteers and students on work placement in relation to child protection (based on *Children First*)

) Appoint a designated person within the organisation with specific responsibility for children protection

) Ensure that all personnel are garda vetted before beginning work within the organisation

For a detailed account of all these roles and responsibilities, see pp. 18–27 of the guidance.

PART III: GUIDANCE FOR HSE CHILDREN AND FAMILY SERVICES AND OTHER PROFESSIONALS; PROTOCOL FOR AN GARDA SÍOCHÁNA – HSE LIAISON

This part offers guidance on the steps to be taken by staff in the HSE Children and Family Services and other professionals in responding to reported child protection and welfare concerns. It describes the assessment process to be followed in order to establish whether reasonable grounds for concern exist, guidance on the effective use of child protection conferences, the development of a child protection plan and protection review conferences.

Again, while the detail of this chapter is not of direct relevance to special needs practitioners, it is helpful for all individuals working with children to have a good general awareness of what happens after a child protection concern is raised with the HSE Children and Family Services.

- If a child protection concern has been raised with the HSE Children and Family Services, it will be followed up without delay by an appointed social worker. The social worker will notify the child/children's parents or guardians that a child protection concern has been raised unless by doing so it would put the child/children further at risk. The gardaí may also be informed at this stage.

- The social worker will then begin preliminary screening and enquiries. He/she will find out if the case is already known to the HSE. If it is, he/she will contact the people previously involved and establish what is already known.

- An initial assessment will then be carried out. This assessment may involve talking to the child and his or her parents/carers to help establish whether grounds for concern exist, a medical examination and treatment, and talking to other people involved with the child (e.g. GP, teachers) to identify the nature and severity of any risks and to identify any strengths and protective factors that appear to lessen the risk, such as supportive extended family.

- If a decision is made to offer services to a child and his or her parents/carers, a key worker will be allocated to the case and a decision made on initial protective action to be taken. Usually a family support plan and a child welfare plan will be compiled.

- If concerns are considered to be *unfounded*, then this must be (a) stated in the case file, (b) gardaí must be informed and (c) the child and family must be supported, e.g. with counselling.

- Family support plans try to support families whose children's welfare is under threat. Supports take a variety of forms and are designed to prevent children from having to enter the care system (sometimes, however, child protection issues are such that children cannot remain with their families and must be taken into the care system). If a family is receiving family support, their needs will be identified and supports targeted accordingly. For example, if children were being neglected due to parental alcohol misuse, family support would involve linking with addiction services. Families are encouraged to identify their own solutions as much as possible.

- Child welfare plans incorporate family support plans (described above) and also actions specific to the child. Both family support plans and child welfare plans are reviewed and evaluated regularly and thoroughly. If they are thought not to be working, a *child protection conference* will be held. This meeting is normally organised and chaired by an HSE social work manager and will involve all the relevant agencies working with the child and their family, such as An Garda Síochána, schools, crèches and preschools, addiction services, etc. The child's parents/carers will also be present, unless doing so would not be in the child's best interests. Agencies may be asked to be present for only part of the conference.

- During the conference, an interagency *child protection plan* will be formulated. The plan will identify current and potential risks to the child. It will identify strategies to protect the child, identify who is responsible for the implementation of named strategies and identify the resources needed to carry out the plan. The conference will consult with the child and his or her parents/carers (if applicable) on the content and feasibility of the plan and will also set a date for a review of the plan. The child's name will be entered on the Child Protection Notification System (CPNS).

- When a child protection plan has been put in place, it is the responsibility of all identified professionals and agencies to implement those parts of the plan that relate to them and to communicate with the key worker.

- The role of the key worker is to distribute the plan to all involved, explain key aspects of the plan to the child and if applicable to his/her family. Key workers should give families a list of all personnel involved in the plan and inform them of any change in personnel.

- A child protection *review* conference will be held six months after the child protection conference, or sooner if appropriate. All agencies involved with the child and their family will normally be asked to submit a written report regarding the case. Progress on the case will be evaluated and further actions planned where necessary. Sometimes no further actions are necessary and the review may ask for the delisting of the child's name from the Child Protection Notification System.

Emergency action to protect a child

If a report made to the HSE Children and Family Services indicates the presence of immediate and serious risk, urgent action must be taken to protect any children in that situation who may be in danger. This may involve securing the co-operation of a protective carer, family member or other responsible adult in the child's home whose capacity to protect the child can be defined and agreed. If this is not possible, then the child may need to be placed in the care of the HSE, preferably with the consent of the parents/carers, but if necessary using legal measures under the Child Care Act 1991. Removal of children from their homes is very stressful and requires sensitive handling. The likely effects of separation must be balanced against the danger of leaving the child at home.

If there is reason to believe that a medical examination will indicate more clearly whether or not a child has been physically abused or seriously deprived or neglected, or if a child appears to require medical treatment, then in consultation with An Garda Síochána, a doctor with appropriate experience should carry out the examination. If there is reason to believe that a specialist assessment will indicate more clearly whether a child has been sexually abused, a referral should be made to the child sexual abuse assessment service for the area where a doctor with appropriate training and experience should carry out a physical examination for sexual abuse. Parents/carers should be asked for permission and given the opportunity to attend. If permission is refused, then parents/carers should be informed of the HSE's option to apply for an emergency care order or supervision order.

Case transfers and serious incident reviews

The HSE Children and Family Services should have a case transfer protocol in place. This protocol explains what must be done if a child about whom there are protection or welfare concerns and/or his or her parents/carers move to another jurisdiction or to another area within the HSE.

Serious incident reviews occur after a serious incident, e.g. a child dies in care or a child dies who is known to the HSE child protection system. The review closely evaluates the circumstances surrounding the serious incident and in this way tries to identify possible deficits in the system.

The remainder of this section of the guidance deals with HSE recordkeeping, supervision and support of HSE child protection staff, guidance on interviewing parents/carers and children, and dealing with conflict between children and their parent/carers. As they are not directly relevant to the work of special needs professionals, they will not be dealt with here. They can be read on pp. 41–5 of the guidance.

Protocol For An Garda Síochána – HSE liaison

This section of the guidance provides detailed information for members of An Garda Síochána involved with child protection cases. Again, while the detail of the guidance is not required by special needs professionals, it is useful to have a broad overview of how a child protection case progresses, the personnel involved and their roles.

The HSE and An Garda Síochána are the two main agencies empowered by law to carry out assessments and investigations of suspected child abuse and neglect. An Garda Síochána has the additional responsibility of preparing an investigation file for the Director of Public Prosecutions (DPP), who decides on and carries out prosecutions. An Garda Síochána has the power to remove a child to safety under Section 12 of the Child Care Act 1991 if there are reasonable grounds for believing that there is an immediate and serious risk to the child. The child shall be delivered into the custody of the HSE as soon as possible. As with the HSE, a member of the gardaí will be appointed as the officer designated to each particular case.

Cases to be formally notified by the HSE to An Garda Síochána and vice versa

Where the HSE suspects that a child is being physically or sexually abused or wilfully neglected, they are obliged to formally inform the local gardaí superintendent using the Standard Notification Form. If a criminal prosecution is not expected, e.g. unintentional neglect, the gardaí do not have to be informed. Where doubt exists, however, the gardaí should be consulted for advice. The garda superintendent appoints a garda and designates him/her to the case. Without delay, this garda must make contact with the HSE social worker connected with the case and begin working together on the case, completing the Record of Garda – HSE Liaison Form. At the same time, the superintendent appoints an inspector/sergeant to manage the investigation of the case. The same process must occur where the gardaí suspect that a child is being physically or sexually abused or wilfully neglected. This must be done without delay. The gardaí do not have to have sufficient evidence to support a criminal prosecution before notifying the HSE.

PART IV: SPECIAL CONSIDERATIONS

This section of the guidance provides additional information on three very important issues relating to child protection:

- Vulnerable children
- Peer abuse
- Training in child protection and welfare

Vulnerable children

While it is possible for any child to be abused or neglected, there are children who may be especially vulnerable and who may have been abused or neglected, or who are at risk of abuse or neglect. These include:

- Children in residential settings
- Children in the care of the state under the Child Care Act 1991 (foster care, relative care and residential care)
- Children who are homeless
- Children with disabilities
- Separated children seeking asylum
- Children being trafficked

The Social Services Inspectorate (SSI) section of the Health Information and Quality Authority (HIQA) has statutory responsibility (under the Health Act 2007) for inspecting HSE children's residential centres, special care, hostels, relative/foster care and children detention schools. All those caring for children in these settings must be alert to the possibility of abuse by other children, visitors and members of staff. Policies and procedures aimed at preventing abuse must be in place. There must be clear written procedures on how to deal with suspected abuse and these must be accessible and fully explained to children and to staff.

Research has shown that children with disabilities are at an increased risk of abuse. The abuser is most likely to be known to the victim. It is therefore vital that parents, teachers and all staff in services for children with disabilities are familiar with the indicators of abuse and be alert for signs of abuse (see Appendix 8 at www.gillmacmillan.ie/assistingchildrenwithspecialneeds). All organisations working with children with disabilities should have clear guidelines for preventing, identifying and reporting child abuse or neglect and should ensure that all staff and volunteers are garda vetted and trained in the use of the *Children First: National Guidance.*

Other very vulnerable children also exist in our society: children who are living here having been separated from their birth parents and whose first language is not English and also children who have been trafficked into this country for the purposes of exploitation/sexual employment. These children sometimes resist HSE intervention because they are afraid.

Occasionally children come to the attention of the HSE who for a variety of reasons are homeless. It is the responsibility of the HSE to work with these young people to investigate why this situation has arisen and work towards a solution. This may involve medical or psychological supports in addition to finding suitable accommodation. The HSE may try to accommodate the young person with a suitable relative, or failing that, in a residential unit or in foster care.

Peer abuse

With some cases of child abuse, the alleged perpetrator will be another child. When this arises it is particularly important to consider how the HSE Children and Family Services and other agencies can provide care for both the child victim and the child abuser. This is particularly important because it has been very well documented that many adult child abusers began abusing as children and many were abused themselves as children.

Sexual abuse

In relation to sexual abuse by children and young people, four categories of behaviour warrant attention: normal sexual exploration, abuse reactive behaviour, sexually obsessive behaviour and abusive behaviour by adolescents and young people.

- **Normal sexual exploration:** This could consist of naive play between two children that involves the exploration of their sexuality. One of the most important aspects of this behaviour is tone. There should be no coercive or dominating aspects to it. There is usually no need for a child protection intervention.

- **Abuse reactive behaviour:** A child who has been abused acts out this abuse behaviour on another child. Both children need to be supported by child protection interventions.

- **Sexually obsessive behaviour:** Children may engage in sexually compulsive behaviour, e.g. excessive masturbation. These children may not have been sexually abused, but may be using this behaviour as a comfort because of other unmet needs, usually emotional needs. These children need specialist help in addressing unmet needs.

- **Abusive behaviour by adolescents and young people:** Behaviour that is abusive will have elements of domination, coercion or bribery, and secrecy. Often there is inequality between victim and abuser, e.g. size, age or intellect. Both children should be supported by child protection interventions.

Bullying

Bullying can be defined as repeated aggression – whether it be verbal, psychological or physical – that is conducted by an individual or group against others. It is behaviour that is intentionally aggravating and intimidating, and occurs mainly among children in social environments such as schools. It includes behaviours such as teasing, taunting, threatening, hitting or extortion by one or more persons against a victim. Bullying can also take the form of racial abuse. With developments in modern technology, children can also be the victims of non-contact bullying, via mobile phones, the Internet and other personal devices. (*Children First*, p. 61)

All organisations working with children should have a well-thought-out policy and set of procedural guidelines for dealing with bullying. Serious instances of bullying behaviour is child abuse and should be referred to the HSE Children and Family Services.

Training in child protection and welfare

All agencies involved with children have a responsibility to ensure that training in child protection and welfare is available on an ongoing basis. The level and type of training required depends on an individual's role within an organisation. All staff working with children should be trained in the recognition of signs of abuse (see Part II and Appendix 1 of the guidance, duplicated as Appendix 8 of this book and available at www.gillmacmillan.ie/assistingchildrenwithspecialneeds) and what immediate action to take (see Part III of the guidance).

The HSE divides training into two levels: basic and advanced. For most special needs practitioners, the basic level of training is sufficient for their work. Basic-level training gives personnel knowledge of the relevant childcare legislation and a working knowledge of policies, procedures and protocols for child protection. The designated child protection liaison person within an organisation would require more advanced training. *Children First* emphasises the need for inter- and intra-agency training, i.e. agencies working together. This type of training is essential, as many failures of child protection have resulted from a breakdown in communication within or between organisations.

chapter fourteen

Communicating Effectively with Children with Special Needs

To relate effectively to children with special needs, communication needs to be a two-way process. The child needs to be able to communicate effectively with the adult and the adult needs to be able understand what the child is communicating. In turn, the adult needs to be able to communicate effectively with the child and the child needs to be able to understand what the adult is communicating. With particular special needs, this process can sometimes be more challenging, both for child and adult.

Some children, such as children with cerebral palsy, moderate or severe general learning difficulties, specific speech and language disorder, autism, Down's syndrome and newcomer children whose first language is not English, may have difficulty with expressive speech (speaking themselves). Some may also have additional difficulty with receptive speech (understanding what has been said to them). Children who are deaf may have difficulty with both expressive and receptive speech. Some children with specific learning difficulties, e.g. dyslexia, will have difficulty communicating, but only on paper. It is the job of an inclusive school to find ways to facilitate communication. This can be done in a number of ways, each of which will be examined in more detail in the rest of the chapter.

▶ Staff should follow general rules for communicating effectively to children

▶ Use of assistive technology

▶ Use of alternative ways of communicating, e.g. Lámh, picture exchange communication system (PECS), Irish Sign Language

GENERAL RULES FOR COMMUNICATING WITH CHILDREN WITH SPECIAL NEEDS

- If you are asking a child a question, ask the child, not his or her carer.
- Kneel down so that you are at the same level as the child when communicating with him or her.
- Do not cover your mouth when talking and avoid having light coming from behind you, as this casts your face in shadow and facial clues will be more difficult for the child to read.
- Speak clearly, but not in a very loud or exaggerated way.
- Give the child time to respond.
- Do not use an overly sophisticated general vocabulary.
- Learn and use alternative means of communication if the child cannot communicate through speech, e.g. Irish Sign Language, Lámh or PECS.

USE OF ASSISTIVE TECHNOLOGY

There is a wide range of assistive technology on the market today to help people with communication difficulties communicate more effectively.

Radio hearing aids

Radio hearing aids are used in conjunction with the child's own hearing aid. In schools, the teacher wears a transmitter that is tuned into the child's hearing aid. The teacher's voice is then heard more clearly by the child.

Teacher with radio transmitter to child's hearing aid

Computerised augmentative alternative communication systems

These are sometimes called synthetic speech devices and have become both possible and popular with the development of computers. Perhaps the most famous person using a computerised augmentative alternative communication system is the physicist Stephen Hawking.

These devices originated with the manual PECS system discussed below. Basically, with these devices, the user either spells out what it is he or she wishes to communicate or picks from a range of pictorial or symbolic messages on a display. If the user has the use of his or her hands, then he or she will press the keys manually. If the user is not able to do this, then on some systems a red light moves along from one picture or symbol to the next on the display, and when the correct picture or symbol is arrived at, the user presses down on a large pressure-sensitive button. The device then speaks what the user has indicated.

Augmentative alternative communication system

Text-to-voice and voice-to-text software

To assist students with dyslexia, both text-to-voice and voice-to-text software can be invaluable. Most modern computers have text-to-voice software. If a piece of text is highlighted, then the computer will read it out in a chosen voice. While it does come with some computers, good speech recognition software (speech-to-text) may be bought separately. One software package currently available is Dragon Naturally Speaking 10. Time is spent 'training' the software to recognise the user's voice. Once this is done, the user speaks through a set of headphones and the computer types what he or she says. Other computer facilities such as grammar and spell check are also invaluable.

Voice recognition software

USE OF ALTERNATIVE WAYS OF COMMUNICATING

- Lámh
- Picture exchange communication system (PECS)
- Irish Sign Language

Lámh

Lámh is a manual sign system developed in the early 1980s, used by children and adults with intellectual disabilities and communication needs in Ireland. Some people use Lámh as their main way of communicating, while others use Lámh signs along with speech and other methods of communicating. Lámh signs are based on Irish Sign Language and natural gesture.

With Lámh, only key words in a sentence are signed and signs are always accompanied by speech. This teaches the child to associate various important concepts with speech sounds, and signing and speaking together provides the child with information they can both see and hear (*see* the sign, *hear* the word). Use of manual sign has been shown to support communication skills and can help the child's speech to develop, at which time the child will 'drop' the sign.

An assessment is carried out before deciding whether Lámh is the appropriate type of communication support for the child. Information is gathered from the child's *communication partners,* i.e. family, carers, others. The initial signs chosen will be determined by the signs that are motivating for the child and can be used in their everyday life. Additional signs are chosen when the child begins to understand and to use the signs, and the focus can then move to introducing signs that can be combined to create short sentences, e.g. '(I) (like) (biscuits)', '(Kick) the (ball)', etc.

Irish Sign Language is a natural *sign language (naturally evolving)* and is used by the deaf community in Ireland. Lámh is a manual *sign system* that has been developed for people with intellectual disability and communication needs.

Information about Lámh is available from www.lamh.org or the Lámh Development Office, Innovation Centre, Carlow IT, Kilkenny Rd, Carlow, Ireland; tel.: (059) 913 9657, email: info@lamh.org.

Picture exchange communication system (PECS)

A **picture exchange communication system (PECS)** is a form of augmentative and alternative communication (AAC) that uses pictures instead of words to help children communicate. PECS was designed especially for children with autism who have delays in speech development.

Picture exchange communication system (PECS)

When first learning to use PECS, the child is given a set of pictures of favourite foods or toys. When the child wants one of these items, he or she gives the picture to whoever he or she is communicating with, e.g. parent, sibling, psychologist, teacher or caregiver. They then hand the child the food or toy. This exchange reinforces the concept of communication.

PECS can also be used to make comments about things seen or heard in the environment. For example, a child might see a dog in the garden and hand a picture of a dog to his or her parent. As the child begins to understand the usefulness of communication, the hope is that he or she will then begin to use natural speech. As with Lámh, PECS could be used with young children who have yet to develop expressive speech.

Irish Sign Language

Irish Sign Language (ISL) has been used by the Irish deaf community for at least 150 years in Ireland and Northern Ireland. Like all languages, it is continuously developing with the addition of new words and phrases. Irish Sign Language is like any other language, e.g. English or French, in that it has all the features of language, e.g. grammar (rules about word endings, plurals, etc.) and syntax (rules about word order in a sentence). Like all languages, ISL has its own alphabet. Unlike the British sign alphabet, ISL is signed with just one hand. The alphabet can be used to spell out words but also forms the basis of many of its 4,000 signs.

If you are interested in training in Irish Sign Language, contact Irish Deaf.com, 1st Floor, 386 North Circular Road, Dublin 7. Fax: (01) 484 6449, SMS/text only: (085) 726 3511, email: info@irishdeaf.com, website: www.irishdeaf.com. In addition, many local Education and Training Boards (formerly VECs) offer ISL as a night class.

chapter fifteen

The Special Needs Practitioner

> ### CHAPTER OUTLINE
>
> ▷ Characteristics and values of an effective special needs practitioner
> ▷ Assessment and planning
> ▷ Effective behaviour management
> ▷ Dealing with stressors in the workplace

CHARACTERISTICS AND VALUES OF AN EFFECTIVE SPECIAL NEEDS PRACTITIONER

Since the widespread introduction of SNAs into Irish schools following the Education of Persons with Special Edcuational Needs Act 2004, special needs practitioners have had an enormous impact on the lives of children with special needs in our schools. To be an effective special needs practitioner, certain characteristics and values are very important.

For a special needs practitioner to be effective, they need to build strong, trusting and respectful relationships with the child or children they are working with. Dr William Glasser (1925–), with his *choice theory*, believed that children, like adults, have what he calls a *quality world*. Children, like adults, place all the people, places and things that make them feel good and affirmed into this quality world. People are one of the most important elements in an individual's quality world. Children (and indeed adults) co-operate with and relate much better to people who are in their quality world, as opposed to people who are not. It is therefore vital that the special needs practitioner is firmly situated within the quality world of the child/children they are working with. For this to happen, certain characteristics and values are important. If an SNA possesses these characteristics and holds these values, then they are more likely to have a quality relationship with the child or children they are working with and be part of their quality world.

Caring, friendly and approachable

From time to time, school can be a daunting place for all children. For children with special or additional needs, this can be the case even more so. It is therefore vital that children with special needs have a caring, friendly and approachable adult in the school environment that they can rely on for support and guidance. Smile and use a friendly, upbeat tone of voice and manner. Be attentive, listen and watch carefully for what the child is trying to communicate to you.

Patient

If children feel pressurised in the school environment, it can be very stressful for them. If an adult is becoming impatient with them, all children, including children with special needs, pick up on it very quickly. This can panic, frustrate, anger, upset and worry them. Patience is therefore an absolutely essential attribute or characteristic to have. Children can readily pick up verbal and non-verbal signals of impatience, so practitioners need to be aware of how they sound and how they are acting. Be careful that your tone of voice is calm and unhurried without sounding bored or disinterested. Be careful that your body language is not signalling frustration or impatience, e.g. by sighing or raising your eyes upwards. Speak enthusiastically and encouragingly. Use positive body language, e.g. nodding in agreement, smiling or perhaps giving a short clap or high five if progress or effort is being made. Stay on task with the child for as long as they are able and do not insist on task completion if the child is clearly struggling.

Calm, consistent and fair

From time to time, situations arise in the classroom (or home environment, if this is where you are working) where the child becomes frustrated and distracted, perhaps even becoming angry and aggressive. It is important that as an SNA, you remain calm in these situations. Good systems of behaviour management (see below) help you to remain consistent and fair when challenging situations arise: do not say or do anything to damage the relationship you have developed with the child you are working with. If you are calm, consistent and fair, then even if you have to impose sanctions on the child, it will not have a damaging effect on your relationship. For example, if a child is speaking aggressively to you, you could say, 'Alan, I don't like it when you speak angrily to me. I need you to go to time out. You can come out when you want to talk kindly again.'

Observant

Observation, whether formal or informal, is one of the main ways we learn about how children are developing and progressing. As an SNA, you will need to observe the child/children you arc working with very closely every day. This will become easier to do effectively as you get to know the child/children well. One of the most important skills an SNA can have is the ability to observe a child's body language and non-verbal communication along with his/her verbal communication in order to accurately assess how the child is feeling and whether they understand and are motivated to do what they have been asked to do. When a SNA can effectively do this, they can adjust what they say and how they work with the child. For example, a five-year-old child with ADHD is becoming agitated because he is losing concentration while completing an art activity. With the teacher's OK, the SNA helps him tidy the art activity away for completion at a later date and goes to another area of the room to work on a short computer activity while the other children complete their art. In this example, the teacher and the SNA are observing that because of his special need, the child is not able to cope completely with what the rest of the class is doing. Rather than forcing the child to stick with the activity, probably resulting in the child becoming agitated and upset and possibly aggressive, they observe the child and effectively plan for him. This is not 'giving in' to the child or teaching him bad habits – he has a special need. By observing him and planning effectively for his needs, his concentration and ability to stay on task will improve with time.

Organised

There are a number of areas in which an effective SNA requires good organisational skills.

- A practitioner file needs to be maintained for every child you are working with. Information such as observation notes and records, attendance and records of conversations with the child's teacher, their parents or other professionals working with the child should be kept here.

- A symptom of a significant number of special needs is a difficulty with organisation. Some children require assistance in this area, e.g. taking the correct books home for homework. This issue can become more of a problem as they progress into second level, where the child needs to move from room to room, use a locker and may have up to 11 or 12 different subjects. SNAs can help children with this by coming up with systems to help the child. For example, a child with Asperger's syndrome starting second level finds having the right books and copies for his classes overwhelming. Working together, he and his SNA develop a system whereby all the books and copies for a subject are covered in a specific colour, e.g. all geography-related material is covered in green. This way, the child is able to go to his locker and pick out just the green-covered books for geography. Geography is also colour coded green on his timetable.

- Many SNAs also have classroom assisting duties. This may involve working with the class teacher to prepare materials for use in class. This work requires good organisational skills in that good advance planning is necessary.
- Many children with special needs value and benefit from good care and educational routines. SNAs therefore need to plan and carry out these routines effectively. Good organisational skills are required for this.
- Sometimes SNAs work with a number of different children, perhaps in different classes. This requires the practitioner to divide their time accordingly. The practitioner must organise their time to take account of individual need, times of day where one child may require their assistance in particular, etc. An SNA needs to consult with the class teachers and children they are working with to arrive at a practical and flexible working schedule that best suits the needs of the children in their care.

A good communicator

Being a good communicator is one of the most important characteristics of an effective SNA. There are a number key skills involved in being a good communicator.

- **Be an active listener:** When you are working with any child, including children with special or additional needs, it is important that they know you are listening carefully to them. If they are small or use a wheelchair, get down to their physical level so that you can have full and unstrained eye contact. Show that you are listening to what they are communicating by giving verbal and non-verbal feedback to them, e.g. nodding and saying 'OK', 'that's right', etc. Active listening also involves remembering what the child is saying and referring to it in future conversations. For example, a child with dyslexia tells you she finds it difficult to use a standard pencil, so you get a supply of triangular pencils for her. When you give her the pencil, you say, 'Remember you were saying you found using an ordinary pencil difficult? I got this type of pencil for you to try.'
- **Be clear and concise:** An effective communicator gets what they are trying to say across in a clear and concise manner. Many experienced SNAs and teachers know how to do this very well. When you first start working as an SNA, listen carefully to how other effective practitioners do this. Use short, clear sentences. When giving instructions or directions, do not try to communicate too many at the same time. Break tasks up into manageable chunks.

- **Communication availability:** Children in your care need to know that you are available to communicate with them, that you will listen to them and that you will take what they say on board. However, children must also be aware that you may not always be able to give them your attention exactly when they request it. This is an important balance to strike. Children need to be confident that you will listen to them, but they must also learn the skill of waiting for your attention.

- **Patience:** Some children have difficulty communicating their needs effectively. Others have difficulty following instructions and directions communicated to them. SNAs need to be patient in this regard. For example, you have just asked a child to take out their maths copy. Within a short space of time, she asks you what copy she needs. Rather than saying, 'I told you already – take out your maths copy', the SNA should realise that the child would not ask if they already knew. Instead, simply say, 'Take out your maths copy. Good girl.'

- **Repeat back what you think the child has communicated:** This is a useful method to check whether you are correctly interpreting what the child has said. It is particularly useful for working with children who do not have good verbal communication skills. For example, say, 'You're saying you want to take a break from this and do some computer work?'

- SNAs need to communicate effectively with other people involved with the child. This could include a number of different things, e.g. speaking with parents about the child's day when they come to pick them up or keeping a diary of the child's day for parents who do not pick the child up personally, evaluating the day with the class teacher and planning for the next day, and communicating with other professionals working with the child, e.g. a physiotherapist or speech and language therapist.

Non-judgemental

To be an effective SNA, it is important to be open, non-judgemental and under-standing. When difficult situations arise, always try to consider issues from all perspectives. If a child is displaying challenging behaviour, try not to just focus on the behaviour, but instead what is motivating it. Consider the situation from the child's perspective.

Open to new ideas and ways of doing things

As an effective SNA, it is important to be open to new ideas and ways of doing things. Technology is one area that is being used more and more in special needs education. It is therefore important that you keep up to date with it. The Special Education Support Services (SESS) provides a variety of training programmes and these should be availed of if possible. There is often a wide variety of expertise among school staff, so SNAs should watch how effective class teachers and other SNAs work and learn from this.

Reliable and professional

The SNA is a vital part of a school team and therefore needs to be reliable, dependable and professional at all times.

- Class teachers, parents and the children themselves rely on the SNA to support children with special needs in school. Without SNA support, many children could not attend a mainstream school. It is therefore vital that an SNA is an excellent timekeeper and misses work only if it is absolutely unavoidable.
- In terms of professionalism, it is vital that confidentiality is respected. The child or children the SNA is working with should never be the subject of discussion outside the professional setting.
- An SNA should be professionally presented.

ASSESSMENT AND PLANNING

Individual education plans (IEPs)

Individual education plans (IEPs) are used to tailor the broader overall curriculum, e.g. the primary school curriculum, to the individual child and their specific needs. Sometimes in out-of-school settings, e.g. early years settings, individual education plans are called individual learning plans (ILPs). There is no standard way of presenting IEPs, with variations existing in different settings. This section offers one way, but students are advised that this may be somewhat different from that used in their workplace or placement.

The purpose of IEPs

- Helps the adult focus on the specific needs of the child
- Ensures that children's unique interests and strengths are provided for
- Informs overall curriculum and individual session planning
- Helps to monitor the child's individual progress
- Helps to ensure that equipment and activities are appropriate for the child
- Helps the adult review, evaluate and improve their practice

IEPs are particularly useful in helping staff work effectively with children with additional needs in one or more developmental areas and are required under the Education for Persons with Special Needs Act 2004.

How to create and use an IEP

The best people to create an IEP for a specific child are the people who know the child best and who work with him/her most. In a school setting, this will be the class teacher and SNA. The starting point for creating an IEP for a child is to find out what his/her interests and developmental needs are. This is done in two ways: by observing the child closely in the setting over a period of time and then by consulting with others who know the child well, i.e. parents/guardians and other professionals who have had contact with the child, e.g. speech and language therapists.

IEPs will often have a relatively tight area of focus, e.g. a child's language development, and the plan will set specific goals and targets in this area only. The child's other areas of development may not require the special attention of an IEP and are sufficiently catered for by the general curriculum. Having said this, some children have more complex special needs and their IEP may target more than one area of development. In addition, if other agencies are working with the child, e.g. a physiotherapist, they may have specific recommendations for the setting to include in the child's plan.

Sometimes IEPs are created for children with specific strengths in a particular area, e.g. a child who has already begun to read at preschool. The plan could put in place extension activities for this child so that they remain stimulated in the environment.

It is important to note that IEPs are not only created for children with more severe long-term additional needs. They can be created over short periods of time too, e.g. if a child is going through a difficult time at home and it is causing behavioural problems in the setting. They can also be created for children who have particular strengths that should be built upon.

Devising an IEP

▸ **Identify the child's needs:** In an education setting, most IEPs are initiated as a result of planned assessments, health checks or formal and informal observations carried out with the child. These assessments will be carried out by a variety of professionals, e.g. teachers, educational or clinical psychologists, speech and language therapists and/or physiotherapists. Who exactly will be involved will largely be determined by the individual child's needs.

Set clear aims and goals: Once a child's specific needs have been identified, the next step is to set one or two clear aims for the child together with a small number of clear goals. In this way, all staff working with the child will have a clear understanding of what the priorities are for working with him/her. If a child has complex needs, it is best to concentrate on one area at a time rather than trying to tackle everything at once.

Create the IEP: Once the aim and goals of the IEP are arrived at, the next step is to think about and record the strategies that will be used by the setting to work towards their achievement. Everyone working with the child needs to be made aware of these strategies. The exact format an IEP takes varies from setting to setting; a sample is given here as a guide.

Sample IEP

Name of child: Eoin B   **Age:** 9 years 2 months

Date of plan: 3/10/13   **Date of review:** 4/11/13

SNA: Joan

Aim of plan: To help Eoin use a number of techniques to alleviate the physical symptoms of his anxiety

Goal	Strategies	Comments

To alleviate the physical symptoms of anxiety	1. Observe Eoin closely for signs that he is becoming anxious.
	2. Listen carefully to what Eoin is saying about what is causing him to become anxious.
	3. Realise that Eoin knows all the reasons why he should not be anxious over this particular issue.
	4. Ask Eoin if he has any pains or other uncomfortable feelings.
	5. Ask Eoin if he wants to do any of his relief activities:
	  ◦ Redirection to safe activity, e.g. IPad
	  ◦ Physical energy burn: running in the assembly area or outside
	  ◦ Massage in special needs room
	  ◦ Deep pressure activity: lying under his heavy cushion in the special needs room
	  ◦ Chewing gum to relieve jaw pressure	

This plan has been developed for Eoin B, a nine-year-old boy attending a main-stream primary school. Eoin has Asperger's syndrome, resulting in a number of complex additional needs. This plan is designed to help address one of those needs: to alleviate the physical symptoms of his high anxiety levels (stomach pains, headaches, racing heart, constricted chest and tight muscles).

IEPs are only effective if they are integrated into the overall plans for the setting. If they are not, they become unsustainable. Plans must also be regularly evaluated and reviewed. In addition, if the plan works, the child may no longer need an IEP for this area of development.

It is important that parents/guardians are involved in IEPs. Parents/guardians of children with special needs are usually extremely knowledgeable regarding their children's needs and are often an invaluable source of information. They should be consulted at all stages of the planning process and if appropriate they should carry on the strategies suggested in the plan at home.

EFFECTIVE BEHAVIOUR MANAGEMENT

Characteristics and behaviours associated with emotional disturbance and/or behavioural problems may include aggressive or anti-social behaviour, inattentiveness, distractibility and impulsiveness; impaired social interactions; a general inability to cope with the routine of daily tasks; obsessive and repetitive behaviours; attention-seeking behaviours, such as negative interactions or a poor attitude towards work, peers or teachers; and depressed behaviours, such as withdrawal, anxiety or mood swings (Signposts 2009).

Challenging behaviour can be a characteristic of a number of different special needs. As an SNA, one of your roles will be to deal effectively with challenging behaviour. This may be one of the reasons why you have been employed to work with a particular child. In fact, almost 20 per cent of applications for additional supports made to the Department of Education and Skills cite behavioural and emotional issues as a reason for the application (Department of Education and Skills 2009, as cited in O'Leary 2011). Unlike the class teacher, you will be working with a relatively small number of children with whom you should have a close working relationship. It is therefore vital that you become good at helping children in your care to manage their challenging behaviour. The Special Education Support Services website (www.sess.ie) has a section on behaviour management that you might find useful – look under Resources.

Three-tiered continuum of support for behaviour

The National Educational Psychological Service (NEPS) conceptualises the supports given to children to manage their behaviour in school as a three-tiered continuum of support:

- **Tier 1 – whole school or classroom approaches for all students:** This layer of the continuum involves the school's behavioural policies and procedures, with teachers applying them as necessary, e.g. removing golden time minutes (see below) for breaches of discipline.

- **Tier 2 – small group or individual approaches:** These types of interventions target small groups of students who require more individualised monitoring and more frequent feedback, e.g. students who are on behavioural contract sheets that need to be signed after each subject lesson or each hour/half hour in a primary school setting. Students requiring tier 2 supports will also require those at tier 1.

- **Tier 3 – intensive individualised support:** These students do not respond effectively enough to tier 1 and 2 interventions alone and need individualised support. As an SNA, these are the students that you are likely to be working with. Students requiring tier 3 supports will also require those at tier 1 and 2 and may be involved with other support agencies, e.g. NEPS.

As an SNA, you will be very involved with helping students with behavioural issues manage their behaviour. In this section, a number of different strategies commonly used in the Irish education system are outlined, with key principles underlining all strategies.

Key principles

- **Balance:** The needs of all students in the class must be balanced with the needs of the child with behavioural issues.

- **Focus on positives:** Emphasis should always be put on what the student is doing well. High expectations of behaviour should always be communicated clearly to students.

- **Clarity:** Students should be very clear in relation to classroom rules and expectations regarding behaviour. Some class teachers display a golden rules poster in the classroom.

- **Problem-solving approach:** All behaviour can be changed. Interventions should therefore find out *why* the behaviour is happening; come up with strategies that target the causes of the behaviour as well as the actual behaviour;

involve the child and his/her parents in coming up with possible strategies; be consistently applied; and be evaluated in terms of their effectiveness and changed if they are not working.

- **Quality relationships:** Children and adolescents respond much more effectively to adults they have a strong, trusting relationship with. Adults should take great care that in dealing with incidents of problem behaviour, their relationship with the student is not negatively impacted upon. While penalties and sanctions may have to be applied, *how* they are applied is very important. They should always be applied in a respectful, consistent and fair manner.

Examples of strategies

Golden rules and golden time

This strategy was developed by the educationalist Jenny Mosley to encourage a respectful, hard-working atmosphere in the classroom. Golden rules and golden time are currently used to great effect in many primary schools throughout the country. Basically, golden time is a period of at least half an hour at the end of the week where children get to do activities they love to do – golden time activities. Ideally, a number of activities will be available to the children so that each child can pick something they really like. It is best if golden time is a school-wide concept, as then more variety can be given. For example, there will be someone in the yard to supervise children playing soccer if this is their chosen golden time activity, while other children are inside doing something else. If golden time is confined to the classroom, a variety of activities should be allowed for. Children choose their golden time activity at the beginning of the week.

The golden rules are the key to the whole approach. The overarching concept underlying the rules is that of respect – *respect for myself, respect for others and respect for property.* The golden rules are displayed in classrooms, corridors and throughout the school.

The six golden rules:
Do be gentle – do not hurt anybody.
Do be kind and helpful – do not hurt people's feelings.
Do work hard – do not waste your or other people's time.
Do look after property – do not waste or damage things.
Do listen to people – do not interrupt.
Do be honest – do not cover up the truth.

If a child keeps the golden rules all week, then they have an automatic right to their chosen golden activity during golden time.

If a child breaks a golden rule, they are given a yellow card sanction, which is placed beside them on their desk. They may be asked quietly about which rule was broken. The card is left there until the end of the session (or it may be taken back more quickly if a child has special needs). If a child breaks this same rule or another golden rule while the card is on their desk, they lose 5 minutes of golden time. A student can lose up to 30 minutes of golden time, *but* do make sure they can earn back 15 minutes of this – all students must be allowed 15 minutes of golden time.

During the 15 minutes that the students cannot take part in golden time, they sit and watch – a stopwatch or stand timer is used.

Choice theory

The psychiatrist William Glasser (1925–) believes, like others, that we have a number of basic needs. He also believes that if any of these needs are not being met, then the individual will feel bad and will make efforts to fulfil the need not currently being met. Glasser's choice theory suggests that we have five basic needs:

- Survival
- Love
- Power
- Fun
- Freedom

Choice theory proposes that at any one time, we choose whatever behaviour is most need satisfying at the time, sometimes regardless of the consequences.

Good schools try to ensure that student's five basic needs are being met. This is particularly important for students coming from difficult circumstances, whereby these needs are perhaps not being met at home.

How can schools facilitate students' needs?

Survival

- Provide a warm, clean and inviting environment for students.
- Provide food where necessary, e.g. breakfast club, and have a healthy eating policy.
- Provide other basic essentials if required, e.g. sanitary products, showers.

Love

In this context, love means regard, friendship and caring.

▷ It is vital that students like the teachers and SNAs they work with as people and that staff also like them as people too. Staff must be part of their quality world (see below).

▷ Never use coercion, negative comments, sarcasm or putdowns. They do not work and they damage the student–adult relationship.

▷ Show interest in students as people. Ask about their hobbies, interests and concerns.

▷ Share parts of your own life with students. Share small problems and age-appropriate problems with learners – they can often help you with excellent advice, e.g. what mobile phone package to choose for your teenage son or daughter.

▷ Do not be afraid to let students see that you can make mistakes too.

▷ Be polite and courteous at all times with students. For example, if you want to borrow a pen to write something down, ask for it, don't just lift it off a student's desk.

Power

▷ Allow students to make choices about what and how they learn, e.g. ask them which piece of work they would like to begin with.

▷ Keep rules to an absolute minimum and never use coercion as a means of enforcement. Instead, approach rule breaches in a problem-solving way.

▷ There is nothing to be gained from trying to establish who is at fault in a situation. Instead, concentrate on finding ways to avoid the problem in the future.

▷ Be careful that your own power needs do not affect how you relate to students. If a student is not co-operating, cajole and negotiate rather than coerce.

▷ Classrooms need to be run democratically. Students need to know that their opinions and wishes can initiate real change.

Fun

▷ Make classes as interesting as possible. Help the teacher with class preparation to facilitate this.

▷ It is vital that those working with children have a sense of humour and do not take things too seriously.

▷ Give students choice about what they learn at any particular time so that they enjoy what they are doing.

Freedom

▶ Give students freedom of choice with regards to what and how they learn in so far as is possible. This is more likely to be possible in the classroom situation with the help of an SNA.

▶ All classrooms and the school itself should be run democratically. Students should be aware that they are free to voice their opinions on issues relating to them and that they will be listened to and acted upon.

Quality world

The concept of **quality world** is an important part of Glasser's (1992) theories on classroom management. He believes that every one of us has what he calls a quality world. A person's quality world is filled with pictures of people, things and situations that help satisfy their five basic needs and thus make them feel good. People, things and situations that do not help satisfy a person's five basic needs and therefore do not make them feel good will not be in their quality world. Glasser maintains that while we do not always understand *why* we feel a certain way (that one or more of our five basic needs are not being met), we are always aware of *how* we feel, and that we will always act on how we feel. Glasser believes that the most important pictures in our quality world are pictures of **people**. However, if something or someone is not in a person's quality world, then they will not want to pursue it or co-operate with that person.

Students will therefore not work effectively in school unless the school itself – its management, teachers, SNAs, other students and the work done in the school – is part of their quality world.

When a child first goes to school, school is almost always part of his or her quality world. This has a lot to do with the fact that homes (even if parents have had negative school experiences themselves) are generally **'school supportive'**. It is no coincidence that school attendance rates are highest in the junior cycle of primary school (infants through to the end of second class, ironically at a time when childhood illness rates are actually at their highest). As time goes on though, some children, particularly if they have special learning or emotional needs, begin receiving negative feedback from school and schools begin to become coercive. When this happens, homes start to become **'school unsupportive'** and as a result children begin to remove school, schoolwork and teachers from their quality worlds. This trend continues and peaks during grade 9, according to Glasser (1992) (roughly the American equivalent of our second year of post-primary schooling).

Once students begin removing schooling and teachers from their quality worlds, they will start to become disruptive; be present but not work to their full potential; skip classes; begin 'sicking' (frequently complaining of being sick to avoid taking part in classroom activities); begin 'depressing' (frequently becoming lethargic and appearing depressed and fed up, without any actual depression); or drop out of education altogether. To prevent this from happening, three key elements are important:

1. School staff must be part of students' quality worlds.
2. Students must know what quality work is.
3. School staff must know how to deal effectively with disruption.

School staff must be part of students' quality worlds

Students in schools are often following a set curriculum, such as primary school, Junior Certificate, etc. At times, much of the work for these qualifications is not immediately needs satisfying. However, students are much more likely to endure the sort-term 'pain' of figuring out how to do something if the person teaching or supporting them (SNA) is part of their quality world.

Students must perceive the classroom as a pleasant place to work. Therefore, it must be well lit and well heated. It should be pleasantly decorated, with comfortable tables and chairs at which to work. Students should be allowed to make classrooms more attractive by hanging pictures or displaying work or posters. The atmosphere in the classroom should be calm and friendly.

School staff must show an interest in their students as people. It is important to make an effort to find out about their hobbies and interests. Always smile and be positive and cheerful. Negativity breeds negativity and should *always* be avoided.

School staff should *never*, under any circumstances, use coercion or criticism to try to get learners to co-operate. It does not work and will actually make things worse. Always be positive, even if you don't feel that way.

> To get into the students' quality worlds, the teacher must have a track record of asking the students to do what feels good in the long run and asking them to do it in a way that feels good right away. This means that lead-teachers add kindness, courtesy and humour to whatever they ask students to do. (Glasser 1992, p. 75)

The same rules apply to SNAs. Most SNAs have a very close relationship with the student(s) they support. This is hugely important and means that students often co-operate very well with them in the classroom.

Students must know what quality work is

It is vital that school staff give learners an understanding of what quality work is and that they put the message across to students that they believe and indeed expect that they will be able to produce quality work.

It is very important that students be facilitated to produce at least one piece of quality work early on in the day. What is considered quality work will depend on the child. It need not be anything very elaborate, but it can set the tone for the day. SNAs have an important role here in supporting this process.

Students should *always* be asked to self-evaluate. Teachers/SNAs should never be tempted to jump the gun – they should always ask the student what they think about a piece of work first. If the student is reluctant to comment, use leading questions to encourage self-evaluation – do not be tempted to skip this process.

Example: A student is asked to evaluate a letter of complaint they have written. The teacher asks them what they think of the letter. The learner is quite uncommunicative and says, 'I don't know if it's any good or not.' The teacher does not then start to point out the letter's good and bad points, but instead asks, 'Well, what do you think of the layout? Are the addresses in the right place? Is the date in the right place? Did you use the right greeting?' and so on. SNAs can support this work.

Students should always be allowed to re-do work if they wish to improve its quality, e.g. re-doing assignments or class tests until the learner is happy with their performance. Students should never be forced to do so, however. Low grades or poor-quality work should always be viewed as a temporary difficulty – merely that the student does not know the material or is not quite able to carry out the skill just yet.

School staff must know how to deal effectively with disruption

- It is important to negotiate a small number of sensible, well-thought-out rules with students in the school. See the golden rules above suitable for primary schools.
- Never put yourself in the position of adversary – always take a **problem-solving** approach to breaches of discipline.
- Do not spend time trying to establish who is at fault. This is a waste of time.
- Do spend time finding solutions for the future. For example, if this situation happens again, what will we do?
- School staff should talk to students about their grievances and be open to suggestions.

Time out

Glasser believes that if a student is not able to calm down and discuss a difficulty in a problem-solving way in the classroom, then they must be asked to leave. They should not be asked to 'get out', but rather, the teacher should say something like,

'Since you won't calm down, I have to ask you to leave. I hope we can sort this out together later, but if you are not willing to settle down now, it's better that you leave now.' Students are asked to leave so that the relationship between student and adult is not damaged.

Glasser (1992) suggests that schools should have a time out room overseen by a teacher experienced in dealing with discipline issues in a problem-solving way. The student must stay in the time out room until a working solution to the problem they are experiencing has been found. The main thing is that the time out room is seen as an opportunity to solve a problem rather than as a punishment. The job of the teacher in the time out room is not to find out who was at fault in the situation, but to plan for the future. Thus, if a student claims that the teacher (from whose class he/she has been sent) hates them, the class is boring or is 'no use to me', the time out teacher does not argue with this, but instead concentrates on finding solutions to the actual problems that have arisen. Learners should not be allowed back to class too quickly – it is important that the time out room is not seen as a revolving door. The role of an SNA in this type of structure will be to accompany the student to the time out room. This structure is not very common in the Irish education system. Behavioural units similar to what Glasser recommends were proposed in the past for Irish second-level schools, but these have not become a widespread reality.

Social skills training

Many children who display challenging behaviour, including children with particular special needs such as AS disorders, ADHD, conduct disorder and general or specific learning difficulties, may display deficits in their social behaviours. This often results in the child adopting maladaptive behaviours to meet their social needs, which can lead to eventual rejection by peers. For example, a child with dyslexia who feels uncomfortable at reading time may try to make peers laugh in an effort to halt class progress. If this happens consistently over a period of time, his/her peers may become annoyed by this behaviour and begin rejecting him/her. Social skills training teaches children what to do in situations they find socially demanding. Social skills training is particularly useful for helping children with problems related to anger management. Students talk about and role-play situations that can cause angry feelings. Ways of avoiding angry outbursts are explored and acted out. Sometimes a traffic light system is introduced. As an SNA, you may be asked to help a child implement such a system in class.

Stop
(calm down)

Think
(of a plan)

Act
(wisely)

Functional communication training

Some children with special needs regularly experience communication difficulties, which can negatively influence their relationships within the classroom setting. Children experiencing these difficulties benefit greatly from functional communication training. Essentially, children are taught very directly (usually through the use of role-play, storyboards and social stories) how to communicate their needs effectively. The child then uses what he/she has learned in real-life situations. As an SNA, you will be asked to help the child use what they have learned as part of their functional communication training and provide positive reinforcement as the child uses their skills in the classroom situation.

Example of a social story – getting my teacher's attention in class

My name is Eric and sometimes I need to get my teacher's attention in class. When I want my teacher's attention, I need to do these things:

- First I need to think about what I am going to ask her.
- Then I need to decide if it is relevant to what we are working on now.
- I also need to decide if Alison, my SNA, could help me instead.
- If I still think I need my teacher's attention, I must raise my hand and wait.
- If she does not see me after a minute, I say 'teacher' and wait.
- When my teacher looks at me and says 'yes, Eric', I speak to her.

Student self-directed interventions

Two self-directed strategies (self-management and self-monitoring) have been shown to be successful for pupils with emotional and behavioural disorders (Fitzpatrick and Knowlton 2009).

Self-directed interventions or strategies typically occur in two stages:

- **Stage 1:** Students learn to become aware of internal and external behaviours causing concern. Internal behaviours are within the individual, e.g. having angry thoughts, whereas external behaviours are visible or audible to others, e.g. using abusive language towards the teacher. External methods used to manage these behaviours are paired with internal (self-directed) strategies. Gradually, externally managed strategies are replaced completely by internal strategies.
- **Stage 2:** Students learn to use self-directed strategies with different people, in different situations and in different contexts.

Self-management involves the gradual shifting of 'responsibility' for behavioural management from the teacher (external control) to the student (internal control). Once work has been done on helping the students become aware of the behaviours that are causing concern, they can be helped with developing a set of internal control strategies. For example, a first class student with ADHD has a small colouring book that he uses if he feels that he cannot concentrate any longer in class. Sometimes he just colours a small amount, just enough for him to refocus and rejoin the class.

Self-monitoring involves the student collecting data on their own behaviour (usually positive behaviours) in the classroom. The teacher helps the child identify target behaviours, e.g. they put their hand up to ask a question rather than shouting out. The child then records each incidence of the behaviour (the teacher or SNA may have to remind him/her). This reinforces the positive behaviour. It is best not to have a child monitor and record negative behaviours.

STRESSORS IN THE WORKPLACE

- **Job insecurity:** While some SNAs have permanent positions, many have little job security and are employed on a casual, part-time basis, are not paid for holidays and have no guarantee that they will be reemployed for the following academic year. This is very stressful for SNAs trying to make mortgage repayments and pay other important household bills.

- **Lack of promotional possibilities:** Unlike many other professions, there are few promotional opportunities for SNAs. This can be stressful, as many SNAs are highly skilled and experienced and this is not formally recognised.

- **Lack of clarity about your role:** The actual role of an SNA varies from school to school. Some schools permit SNAs to do very little except look after the physical care needs of specific students. This can mean that much of the day is spent waiting to be called on to carry out a care task, e.g. to help a student with their toileting needs. This can be frustrating for highly motivated SNAs who have a lot more to offer. Other schools involve SNAs in classroom work, seeing them as a valuable support to learning. However, SNAs should never be asked to take full charge of a class, e.g. if a teacher is out sick.

- **No opportunity to use personal talent and ability effectively:** As stated above, some schools restrict the work that SNAs can do. This can be frustrating for people, as they are provided with little opportunity to use their personal talents and abilities.

- **Poor working relationship with teaching staff:** While most teachers welcome the support of having an SNA in their classroom, a minority of teachers resent it and do not like having another adult present in their classroom while they are teaching. This can lead to a difficult working atmosphere. In addition, SNAs may not agree with how some teachers manage their classrooms, which can also cause stress.

- **Feelings of powerlessness:** As stated above, sometimes situations arise whereby an SNA may not agree with how a teacher manages his/her classroom. Because the teacher is considered the most senior member of staff, SNAs may experience feelings of powerlessness, which can be stressful.
- **Slow progress:** Sometimes when you work with a child every day, their progress is difficult to see. It can seem as if you are working hard every day for change that is not happening. This is rarely the case. It is important that class teachers work with SNAs to evaluate progress and give positive feedback.

Dealing with stressors in the workplace

- Establish good care and educational routines.
- Concentrate on developing a strongly positive working relationship with the child or children you are assisting.
- Some schools have a system of staff support to help staff deal with workplace stressors. Staff support is usually provided by school management, although some schools bring in a qualified counsellor. During a staff support session, individuals normally discuss their work, both positive and negative, and any issues that may be of concern to them. Staff support can help people deal positively with workplace stressors.
- Follow the normal guidelines for reducing stress: eat regularly and well, take exercise, get enough sleep and avoid smoking or drinking too much alcohol.

References

Adams, J. and Hitch, G. (1997), 'Working Memory and Children's Mental Addition', *Journal of Experimental Child Psychology*, 67/1, 21–38.

American Psychiatric Association (2000), *Diagnostic and Statistical Manual of Mental Disorders*, <http://psych.org/MainMenu/Research/DSMIV.aspx>.

Aspire (2009), *Development Plan 2007–2010*. Dublin: Aspire – The Asperger Syndrome Association of Ireland.

Asthma Society of Ireland (2003), *Global Burden Report on Asthma*, <http://asthmasociety.ie/images/uploads/file/Asthma-in-Ireland-4-5-12.pdf>.

Betts, G. and Neihart, M. (1988), 'Profiles of the Gifted and Talented', *Gifted Child Quarterly*, Vol. 32. New York: NGC and SAGE publications in NCCA (2007), *Exceptionally Able Students, Draft Guidelines for Teachers*, Dublin.

Commission of Inquiry into the Reformatory and Industrial School System 1934–1936, <http://scotens.org/sen/articles/develofspecialedroi.pdf>.

Commission on the Status of People with Disabilities (2006), *A Strategy for Equality: Report of the Commission on the Status of People with Disabilities*. Dublin: Government Stationery Office.

Council of Europe (2003), *Malaga Ministerial Declaration on People with Disabilities: Progressing Towards Full Participation as Citizens*. Strasbourg: Council of Europe.

Council of Europe (2006), *Action Plan to Promote the Rights and Full Participation of People with Disabilities in Society: Improving the Quality of Life of People with Disabilities in Europe 2006–2015* (adopted by the Committee of Ministers on 5 April 2006). Strasbourg: Council of Europe.

Culliton, G. (2009), 'Explosion of Sickle Cell Disease Could Mean Early Deaths', *Irish Medical Times*, <www.imt.ie>.

Cusack, J. (2007), 'Suicide-killings Take Lives of 10 Children Cross-border Social Services to Tackle "Dangerous Parents"', *Irish Independent*, 18 November.

Department of Children and Youth Affairs (2011), *National Guidance for the Protection and Welfare of Children*. Dublin: Government Publications, <www.dcya.gov.ie/documents/child_welfare_protection/ChildrenFirst.pdf>.

Department of Education and Science (1993), *Report of the Special Education Review Committee*. Dublin: Stationery Office.

Department of Education and Science (1995), *Charting our Education Future*. Dublin: Stationery Office.

Department of Education and Science (1999), *Ready to Learn*. Dublin: Stationery Office.

Department of Education and Science (2002), *Report of the Task Force on Dyslexia*. Dublin: Stationery Office.

Department of Health and Children (1999), *Children First: The National Guidelines for the Protection and Welfare of Children*. Dublin: Brunswick Press Ltd.

Fitzpatrick, M. and Knowlton, E. (2009), 'Bringing Evidence-based Self-directed Intervention Practices to the Trenches for Students with Emotional and Behavioral Disorders', *Preventing School Failure*, 53/4, 253–66.

Frith, U. (1997), 'Brain, Mind and Behaviour in Dyslexia', in C. Hulme and M. Snowling (eds.), *Dyslexia: Biology, Cognition and Intervention*. London: Whurr, 1–19.

Gardner, H. (1983), *Frames of Mind*. London: Fontana Press.

Glasser, W. (1992), *The Quality School*. New York: HarperCollins.

Grigorenko, E. (2001), 'Developmental Dyslexia: An Update on Genes, Brains and Environments', *Journal of Child Psychology and Psychiatry*, 42, 91–125.

Johnson, A. (2002), 'Prevalence and Characteristics of Children with Cerebral Palsy in Europe', *Developmental Medicine and Child Neurology*, 44/9, 633–40.

Joslin Diabetes Center, 'Genetics & Diabetes: What's Your Risk?', <www.joslin.org/info/genetics_and_diabetes.html>.

Knip, M., Veijola, R., Virtanen, S.M., Hyoty, H., Vaarala, O. and Akerblom, H.K. (2005), 'Environmental Triggers and Determinants of Type 1 Diabetes', <http://diabetes.diabetesjournals.org/content/54/suppl_2/S125>.

Leonard, L. (1997), *Children with Specific Language Impairment*. Cambridge, MA: Bradford Books.

Morton, J. and Frith, U. (1995), 'Causal Modelling: A Structural Approach to Developmental Psychopathology', in D. Cicchetti and D. Cohen (eds.), *Manual of Developmental Psychopathology*. New York: John Wiley & Sons, 357–90.

National Council for Special Education (2006), *Guidelines on the Individual Education Plan Process*. Dublin: Stationery Office.

NCCA (2005), *Guidelines on Intercultural Education in the Primary School*. Dublin: NCCA.

NCCA (2007a), *Exceptionally Able Students – Draft Guidelines for Teachers*. Dublin: Stationery Office.

NCCA (2007b), *Guidelines for Teachers of Students with General Learning Disabilities*. Dublin: Stationery Office.

Nicholson, R. (2001), 'The Role of the Cerebellum', in A. Fawcett (ed.), *Dyslexia: Theory and Good Practice*. London: Whurr.

Nicholson, R. and Fawcett, A. (1990), 'Automaticity: A New Framework for Dyslexia Research?', *Cognition*, 35/2, 159–82.

O'Leary, S. (2011), 'Supporting Behaviour Management in School for Students with Behavioural, Emotional and/or Social Difficulties (BESD)', <www.sess.ie>.

Signposts (2009), *Signposts: A Resource Pack for Teachers. Meeting the Learning and Teaching Needs of Pupils with Special Educational Needs*, <www.sess.ie>.

Swan, D. (2000), 'From Exclusion to Inclusion', *Frontline Magazine*.

Todd, J.A. (1990), 'Genetic Control of Autoimmunity in Type 1 Diabetes', <http://omim.org/entry/222100>.

UNESCO and Ministry of Education and Science, Spain (1994), *The Salamanca Statement and Framework for Action on Special Needs Education*, <www.unesco.org/education/pdf/ SALAMA_E.PDF>.

United Nations, Department of Economic and Social Affairs, Division for Social Policy and Development (2006), *International Convention on the Rights of Persons with Disabilities*, <www.un.org/esa/socdev/enable/rights/ahc8adart.htm>.

Wakefield, A., Murch, S. and Anthony, A. (1998), 'Ileal-lymphoid-nodular Hyperplasia, Non-specific Colitis, and Pervasive Developmental Disorder in Children', *Lancet*, 351/9103, 637–41.

World Health Organization (2008), *Report of the WHO Technical Reference Group, Paediatric HIV/ART Care Guideline Group Meeting*, <www.avert.org/hiv-children.htm>.

Young, E. (2002), 'Down's Syndrome Lifespan Doubles', *New Scientist*, <www.newscientist. com/article.ns?id=dn2073>.

WEBSITES

www.aspire-irl.org
www.autismireland.ie
www.dyspraxiafoundation.org.uk
www.hpsc.ie

Index

Page numbers in **bold** indicate figures and diagrams.